Automatic
Process Control

by the author . . . .

AUTOMATIC PROCESS CONTROL
INDUSTRIAL INSTRUMENTATION
PRINCIPLES OF INDUSTRIAL
PROCESS CONTROL

Automatic

New York · London · Sydney . . . .

Process Control

Donald P. Eckman . . . .

*Professor of Instrumentation
Engineering
Case Institute of Technology*

. . . . John Wiley & Sons, Inc.

Preface

This book affords a study of automatic control with particular emphasis, by way of example, on process control. The techniques of analysis are used to the fullest extent, and enough detail is carefully presented so that some of the more difficult problems in automatic process control may be inspected rather closely.

The purpose of this book is to present to the beginning engineer the important principles of automatic control, beginning with process analysis and carrying on into the generalized behavior of closed-loop systems. System problems are given a great deal of study.

The book is intended primarily for the undergraduate in engineering, and a knowledge of the elements of calculus, differential equations, mechanics, thermodynamics, and fluid mechanics is assumed. LaPlace transform is not used except in the last chapter, although its use may be helpful from the beginning.

The teacher may wish to peruse the subjects in the topical order of the book. However, other orders may be used. For a study beginning with measurement and control, the following order of chapters is suggested:

$$1, 5, 3, \text{ and/or } 6, 7, 2, \text{ and } 4.$$

For a study having emphasis on the mathematical approach the following order might be used:

$$1, \text{Appendix}, 4, 9, 10, 5, 7, 8.$$

An attempt has been made to keep the material as independent as possible, but without repetition. Thus, the order may be made flexible and the logic developed to individual requirements.

The material appearing herein that was first published in *Principles of Automatic Process Control* has been completely edited and rewritten and the material up-dated to include all recent advancements and developments in the field of process control.

I wish to acknowledge the many contributions made to the writing of this text by colleagues at Case Institute of Technology and the many students, both graduate and undergraduate, who have suggested topics and problems and criticized not a few. In particular, Dr. Irving Lefkowitz, the author's associate, is to be thanked for many valuable suggestions. Professor Lawrence G. Seigel made many contributions to this work. Professor G. L. Tuve also, through his vast experience, is responsible for improvements in presentation of the laboratory. Mrs. D. P. Eckman is to receive much credit for manuscript and proof preparation.

DONALD P. ECKMAN

Cleveland, Ohio
April, 1958

AUTOMATIC PROCESS CONTROL is based in part on PRINCIPLES OF INDUSTRIAL PROCESS CONTROL by Donald P. Eckman, a book that was written and published while the author was employed by the Brown Instrument Company, now operated as the Brown Instruments Division of the Minneapolis-Honeywell Regulator Company.

Contents

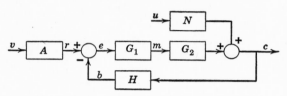

<table>
<tr><th>Variables</th><th>Elements</th></tr>
</table>

	Variables		Elements
v	Set point	A	Input elements
r	Reference input	G_1	Control elements
e	Actuating signal	G_2	System elements
m	Manipulated variable	H	Feedback elements
c	Controlled variable	N	Load elements
b	Feedback variable		
u	Load variable		

chapter 1

The Science
of Automatic Control

Automatic process control is a principal part of the industrial progress during what is now termed the second industrial revolution. The increased use of the science of automatic control has come about through evolution rather than revolution, an evolution that results from the widespread use of the techniques of measurement and control. The universal recognition of the advantages of automatic control has been highlighted through increased study of automation.

Automatic process control is used primarily because it results in economy of operation of industrial processes that more than pays for the expense of the control equipment. In addition, however, there are many intangible gains such as the elimination of work not requiring a worthwhile mental effort and a corresponding demand for work with a much higher skill. Elimination of human error is another positive contribution of use of automatic control.

The principle of automatic control, the employment of a feedback or measurement to actuate a controlling mechanism, is very simple. This may be seen by an inspection of the diagram on the facing page. The same principle of automatic control is used in so many different fields that it would be impossible to name them all—a few of them are: chemical and petroleum process control, control of furnaces in steel manufacture, machine-tool control, and missile guidance.

Understanding of the principle of automatic control is necessary in modern, analytical engineering because its use is as common as the use of the principles of electricity or of thermodynamics and should therefore be a most important part of the span of knowledge of the engineer. The use of analog and digital computing machines has made possible applica-

1

tion of automatic control ideas to physical systems that only a few years ago were impossible to analyze or control.

A clear concept of the principle of automatic control benefits the engineer because, as pointed out by J. Von Neumann, "There is no point in using exact methods where there is no clarity in concepts and the issues to which they are to be applied." Furthermore a need for automatic control has often resulted in a careful and systematic analysis of the physical part of the process.

Automatic control devices employ the principle of feedback within themselves in order to better their performance and are therefore a subject of study. Although this book will discuss automatic control from a general standpoint, most of the examples are selected from process control. Some discussion of the principle of operation of control mechanisms is presented in Chapters 6 and 7.

What Is Automatic Control?

Automatic control is the maintenance of a desired value of a quantity or condition by measuring the existing value, comparing it to the desired value, and employing the difference to initiate action for reducing this difference. Thus automatic control requires a closed loop of action and reaction operating without human aid.

To illustrate the closed-loop action, consider the control of a home-heating system as illustrated by Fig. 1–1. Suppose that it is desired to

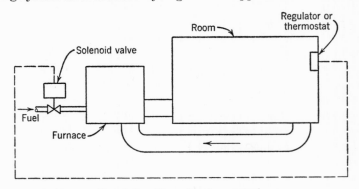

FIG. 1–1.   Home-heating control.

maintain the temperature of the home at 72 F. This temperature is the *desired value or set point*.[1] A thermometer is installed on an inside wall of the home and measures an existing room temperature. This temperature is to be the *controlled variable*. A person watching the

[1] A glossary of automatic control terminology is included in the Appendix.

thermometer notes that the temperature is 69 F. and is therefore less than the desired value. The actuating signal is 3 deg. An action is then taken to reduce this difference by throwing a switch that turns on the fuel gas to the furnace burners. The flow of fuel gas is the *manipulated variable*. As the furnace heats, warm air is delivered to the room, and the temperature will presently increase. In a short time the temperature becomes too high, and the whole sequence must be repeated in the opposite direction. The control action is characterized by the closed loop from controlled variable to deviation to manipulated variable to controlled variable as illustrated in Fig. 1–2.

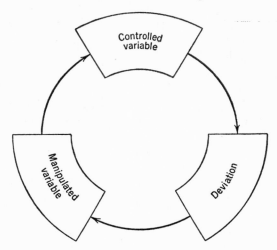

Fig. 1–2.   Action in a closed loop.

Automatic control is accomplished by employing a machine to perform such dull and time-consuming tasks as watching a thermometer and operating switches. The great sociological–economic advantage of automatic control is that it frees human beings from menial tasks. The technological advantage of automatic control is that a machine can perform tasks more rapidly and consistently than a human being can.

The *automatic controller* is the machine employed to maintain the controlled variable at the desired value. In the home-heating control discussed above, a thermostat or thermostatic controller, as shown schematically in Fig. 1–3, would be installed. The desired value of temperature is set on the adjusting knob. The existing temperature is measured by the bimetallic strip, which winds and unwinds slightly with changes in temperature. When the temperature increases above the set point, the bimetallic strip moves its contact to the left and breaks the electric circuit. This action de-energizes the solenoid valve which turns off the gas to the furnace.

The most general type of automatic control system is shown in the frontispiece. A system under control, represented by G_2 and N, is under the action of the controller, represented by A, H, and G_1. The value of the controlled variable c is measured, and the feedback or measuring element transmits a signal to the control elements. The feedback variable b is compared to the reference variable r, and the difference is

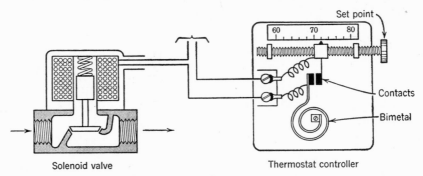

Fig. 1–3.   A simple thermostat controller.

the actuating signal e. The reference variable is provided by the input element and is directly related to the set point v. The controller operates on the system through the manipulated variable m.

There are two general problems in automatic control. The first of these is the control to reduce the effect of load disturbances. Referring again to the frontispiece, the set point is fixed at a desired value and is not a function of time:

$$v = V \tag{1–1}$$

The load variable, however, is changing either continuously or sporadically with some function of time

$$u = f(t) \tag{1–2}$$

The automatic controller must be designed to prevent the load disturbances u from affecting the value of the controlled variable. The control of load disturbances is generally a problem of automatic process control.

Load-disturbance control is best illustrated by a process water heater for which the operational diagram is shown in Fig. 1–4. The outlet temperature of the heater c is measured and operates an automatic controller which adjusts the flow of heat m into the heater. The purpose of the automatic controller is to maintain a constant outlet temperature in spite of variations in the inlet water temperature u.   This kind of automatic control is characterized mainly by a fixed set point but a variable load.

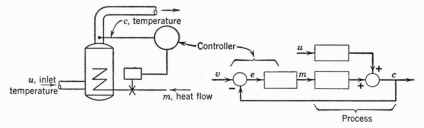

FIG. 1–4.   Automatic control employed for load variation.

The second problem in automatic control is the control of the system variable to follow a desired set point.   In this problem the load variable is usually fixed and is not a function of time:

$$u = U \qquad (1\text{--}3)$$

The set point, on the other hand, is changing in a continuous or discontinuous manner,

$$v = g(t) \qquad (1\text{--}4)$$

The automatic controller must be designed to force the controlled variable to follow the changes in set point as closely as possible.   Following control of this kind is generally a problem of servomechanisms and is not as often encountered in automatic process control.

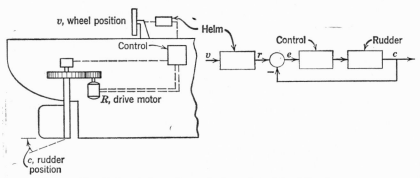

FIG. 1–5.   Automatic control employed for following.

Following control is best illustrated by the ship-steering mechanism of Fig. 1–5.   For a very large ship it would be impossible to operate the rudder by human hands alone. Consequently, a small wheel at the steering station, the position of which is the desired value v of rudder position, transmits a signal r to the steering mechanism. The latter often consists of hydraulic power devices which move the rudder to the desired position. The actual position of the rudder c is compared to the reference value r, and any difference operates the hydraulic control mechanism. This kind of automatic control is characterized mainly by a variable desired value but a fixed load. Following control is employed in automatic process control, for example, when heat-treating furnaces are required to have a temperature raised and lowered according to a certain time schedule.

Automatic Control in Industry

The first use of automatic control seems to have been the flyball governor on Watts's steam engine in about 1775. This device was employed to regulate the speed of the engine by manipulating the steam flow by means of a valve. Thus all the elements of feedback are present.

Earlier in history there does not appear any known reference to the use of automatic control, and it does seem incredible that in the ancient water works of Rome, Greece, or Egypt no recorded use of closed-loop water regulating devices was made. Even if there was, there is no discussion of the philosophy of automatic control.

The first analysis of automatic control is the mathematical discussion of the flyball governor by James Clerk Maxwell in 1868. A set of historical references is provided at the end of the chapter. Further application of the governor techniques to other engines and turbines was made, and in the early 1900's the application to process control began. At the same time regulators and servomechanisms were being studied for their application to steam-power regulators and ship steering.

The first general theory of automatic control was founded by Nyquist in the famous article on "Regeneration Theory." This study provided the basis for the determination of stability of systems without having to solve completely the differential equations. Further developments in electric amplifiers and electric servomechanisms provided the many locus and frequency techniques in use today.

The general applications of process control did not begin until the 1930's. The usefulness of control techniques quickly established their value, so that by the 1940's rather complex control networks were in common use.

Automatic control devices are used in almost every phase of industrial operations. They are commonly employed in

1. Processing industries such as petroleum, chemical, steel, power, and food for the control of temperature, pressure, flow, and similar variables.

2. Goods manufactures such as automobile parts, refrigerators, and radios for the control of assembly operations, work flow, heat treating, and similar operations.

3. Transportation systems such as railway, airplanes, free missiles, and ships.

4. Power machines such as machine tools, compressors and pumps, prime movers, and electric power-supply units for the control of position, speed, and power.

Automatic control devices are used because their application results in economical behavior of the system under control or because they are required for humanitarian purposes. There are many advantages to the widespread use of automatic control. Some of these are:

(a) Increase in quantity or number of products.
(b) Improvement in quality of products.
(c) Improvement in uniformity of products.
(d) Savings in processing materials.
(e) Savings in energy or power requirement.
(f) Savings in plant equipment.
(g) Decrease of human drudgery.

These factors generally lead to an increase in productivity.

The widespread application of automatic control in industry has made necessary the upgrading and education of a large class of semiskilled workers to a higher skill, that of operating and maintaining instrumentation and control equipment.

Cybernetics and Instrumentation

The science of cybernetics or instrumentation is concerned with the phenomena of communication and control whether in nature, in man, or in machines.[1,2] As shown in Fig. 1–6, there are two divisions of work in the field of instrumentation.

1. The study of communication and information theory.
2. The study of control and feedback theory.

The important laws of communication and control deal with information concerning the state and behavior of systems and are not primarily

[1] N. Weiner, *Cybernetics*, John Wiley and Sons, New York, 1948.
[2] H. S. Tsien, *Engineering Cybernetics*, McGraw-Hill Book Company, New York, 1954.

concerned with energy or its transfer to or within a system. The use of energy is only secondary to the main purpose of control or communication.

Communication and information theory[1,2] is based upon the concept that all ideas can be expressed in messages translatable into a common language. The amount of information can be defined and therefore

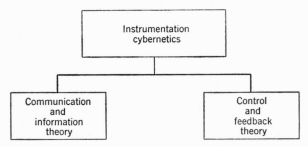

FIG. 1–6. Science of instrumentation.

measured, and, as a consequence, laws governing the transmission of information can be stated. The technology of measurement, telemetering, television, language structure, number systems, and automatic computation employ the basic ideas of information and data handling and processing.

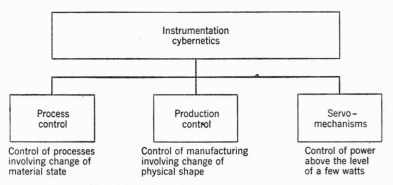

FIG. 1–7. Technology of instrumentation.

The field of automatic control from the subjective viewpoint can be divided into three divisions as shown in Fig. 1–7. These subjects are not mutually exclusive but are found often in industry.

[1] C. E. Shannon "A Mathematical Theory of Communication," *Bell System Tech. J.*, Vol. 27, 1948, pp. 379, 623.
[2] S. Goldman *Information Theory*, Prentice-Hall, New York, 1956.

Information and Energy

Communications and control is primarily concerned with the manipulation of information concerning physical systems. Consider the system shown in Fig. 1–8. The physical diagram is that kind of diagram used in engineering to depict the important features of the system. In thermodynamics it is called a system diagram, in mechanics it is termed a free-body diagram, and in other sciences it is termed differently. The main purpose of such diagrams is to show the flow of material and energy (mass and energy transfer). The physical diagram in Fig. 1–8 shows that there is an inflow m, an outflow q, and fluid is stored in the vessel.

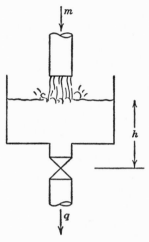

FIG. 1–8. Physical diagram for system analysis.

The block diagram illustrates the behavior of the system by depicting the action of the variables of the system. The circle represents an algebraic function of addition as is seen in Fig. 1–9. The rectangular box represents a dynamic function such that the variable x, called the output, is a function of time and is also a function of the variable y, called the input. Notice that the terms input and output refer to signals and not necessarily to mass or energy flow.

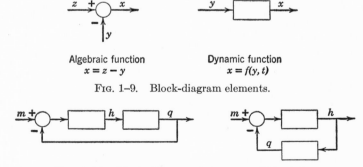

Algebraic function
$$x = z - y$$

Dynamic function
$$x = f(y, t)$$

FIG. 1–9.   Block-diagram elements.

FIG. 1–10.   Block diagrams for process of Fig. 1–8.

The block diagrams of Fig. 1–10 correspond to the system shown in Fig. 1–8. A block diagram is not unique and its arrangement depends upon the viewpoint of the analysis. The diagram on the left is drawn as though the outflow is the important variable being influenced by inflow. The feedback occurs because an increase in outflow feeds back to decrease head h. At the same time an increase in inflow will increase the outflow. Thus, the relationship of variables may be written as

$$q = f(h, t) \tag{1-5}$$

$$h = g(m - q, t) \tag{1-6}$$

Therefore, the overall relationship is

$$q = f\{[g(m - q, t)], t\} \tag{1-7}$$

The important point is that the block diagram illustrates the relation of these variables.

The block diagram on the right in Fig. 1–10 is for the same process but is shown to illustrate that inflow influences the head in the vessel and that the outflow is the secondary variable. This diagram does not relate one to one to the mass flow because the input is flow and the output is head. Recombining equations 1–5 and 1–6, the overall relationship is

$$h = g\{[m - f(h, t)], t\} \tag{1-8}$$

There are only a few rules for the use of block diagrams:

1. Blocks and circles may be rearranged without destroying validity if the system can be described by linear differential equations with constant coefficients.

2. Only one line may enter, and only one line may leave a rectangular block.

3. Only two lines may enter, and only one line may leave a circle. The block diagram is used as an aid in visualizing the behavior of a system and in obtaining a solution of the problems.

HISTORICAL REFERENCES

The following references are selected for the contribution each makes to the knowledge of automatic control. Prior to 1900 there are many articles on governors, but most of them provide consideration of individual detailed problems.

1868   J. C. Maxwell, "On Governors," *Proc. Royal Soc. London*, Vol. 16, p. 270.
1893   A. Stodola, "Uber die Regulierung von Turbinen," *Schweiz. Bauztg.*, Vol. 22, p. 117.
1907   A. M. Liapounov, "Problème général de la stabilité du mouvement," *Ann. fac. sci. univ. Toulouse.*
1911   R. von Mises, "Regulierung des Maschinenganges," *Encyl. der Math. Wiss.*, Band IV, 2 Teilband, p. 254.
1919   W. Trinks, *Governors and the Governing of Prime Movers*, D. Van Nostrand Co., New York.

1921   M. Tolle, *Regelung der Kraftmaschinen*, J. Springer, Berlin.
1922   N. Minorsky, "Directional Stability of Automatically Steered Bodies," *J. Am Soc. Naval Engrs.*, Vol. 34, p. 280.
1926   T. Stein, "Regelung und Ausgleich in Dampfanlagen," J. Springer, Berlin.
1930   G. Wünsch, "Regler fur Druck und Menge," R. Oldenbourg, Munich.
1932   H. Nyquist, "Regeneration Theory," *Bell System Tech. J.*, Vol. 13, p. 1.
1932   M. F. Behar, *Fundamentals of Instrumentation*, Instruments Publishing Co., Pittsburgh.
1933   J. J. Grebe, R. H. Boundy, R. W. Cermak, "The Control of Chemical Processes." *Trans. Am. Soc. Chem. Engrs.*, Vol. 29, p. 211.
1934   H. S. Black, "Stabilized Feedback Amplifiers," *Bell System Tech. J.*, Vol. 13, p. 1.
1934   H. L. Hazen, "Theory of Servomechanisms," *J. Franklin Inst.*, Vol. 218, p. 279.
1934   A. Ivanoff, "Theoretical Foundations of the Automatic Regulation of Temperature." *J. Inst. Fuel*, Vol. 7, p. 117.
1935   S. D. Mitereff, "Principles Underlying the Rational Solution of Automatic Control Problems," *Am. Soc. Mech. Engrs., Trans.*, Vol. 57, p. 159.
1936   A. Callendar, D. R. Hartree, A. Porter, "Time Lag in a Control System—I," *Phil. Trans., Royal Soc. London*, Vol. A235, p. 415.

PROBLEMS

1–1.   Give examples of the use of automatic control devices for (a) reducing the disturbances due to load variables in a system; (b) human safety.

1–2.   Name and describe briefly several automatic control devices found in the home.

1–3.   Name and describe briefly several instruments found in the home.

1–4.   Sketch a block diagram for a man in a boat with an outboard motor performing the operation of steering for a point ashore.

1–5.   Describe a device that could be employed to maintain the constant speed of an automobile.

chapter 2

Process Characteristics

A process, in the science of automatic control, denotes an operation or series of operations on fluid or solid materials during which the materials are placed in a more useful state. The physical or chemical state of the materials is not necessarily altered. In chemical engineering, a unit process involves a change of chemical state. In mechanical engineering, a process usually produces a change in physical state.

Many external and internal conditions affect the performance of a process. These conditions may be expressed in terms of process variables such as temperature, pressure, flow, liquid level, dimension, weight, volume, etc. The process may be controlled by measuring a variable representing the desired state of the product and automatically adjusting one of the other variables of the process. Ambient conditions must always be included in the list of process variables.

Process Variables

The controlled variable of the process should be that variable which most directly indicates the desired form or state of the product. *Direct control* from product quality is most likely to insure proper performance of the process and to produce and maintain the desired quality of product. Consider the water heater in Fig. 2–1. The purpose of the heater is to maintain a supply of heated water. The variable most indicative of this purpose is the temperature of water at the heater outlet, and this is selected as the controlled variable.

Indirect control from a secondary variable of the process may be necessary when direct control is difficult to accomplish. For example, an annealing furnace is designed to produce properly annealed metal parts, and therefore the controlled variable should be the annealed condition of the metal. However, this measurement is very difficult to make with simple equipment, and it is necessary to select furnace temperature as the controlled variable. It is assumed that the annealed condition of the metal is directly related to furnace temperature. Indirect control of a process is usually not as effective as direct control, because a definite and fixed relationship does not always exist between the secondary controlled variable and the form or state of the product.

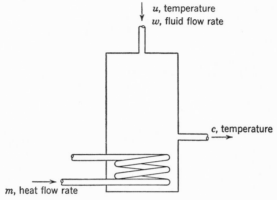

FIG. 2–1.   A water-heating process.

The manipulated variable of the process is that variable which is selected for adjustment by the automatic controller so as to maintain the controlled variable at the desired value. The manipulated variable may be any of the process variables that causes a fast response of the controlled variable and is relatively easy to manipulate. For the water heater of Fig. 2–1, the heat flow m should be manipulated by the controller. It is possible, but not as practical, to manipulate the water throughput rate w or the incoming water temperature u.

The load variables of the process are all other independent variables except the controlled variable and the manipulated variable. For the water heater of Fig. 2–1, the incoming water temperature u is the load variable. It is expected that the automatic controller will correct for fluctuations in load variables and maintain the controlled variable at the desired value.

Process Degree of Freedom

The state of a process or the configuration of a system is determined when each of its degrees of freedom is specified. Consider, for example, a ball placed on a billiard table. In order to specify its position, we would require three coordinates: one north–south coordinate, one east–west coordinate, and the height. However, the height is not arbitrary because it is given by the height of the table surface above a reference plane. Consequently the ball has two degrees of freedom. This result is derived from the following relation:

$$n = n_v - n_e \qquad (2\text{-}1)$$

where n = number of degrees of freedom
$\quad n_v$ = number of variables of the system
$\quad n_e$ = number of defining equations of the system

In the example of the billiard ball there are three variables of position, one defining equation (height = constant), and therefore two degrees of freedom.

Similarly, a process has a finite number of degrees of freedom. Consider the heat exchanger of Fig. 2–1. There are four variables:

$$u = \text{inlet temperature}$$
$$c = \text{outlet temperature}$$
$$w = \text{water flow rate}$$
$$m = \text{heat input rate}$$

and $n_v = 4$. There is one defining equation obtained from conservation of energy (first law of thermodynamics). Therefore, $n_e = 1$. The number of degrees of freedom are

$$n = n_v - n_e = 4 - 1 = 3$$

System variables and system parameters must be carefully distinguished. For example, the weight of water contained in the heater of Fig. 2–1 and the specific heat of water are parameters not variables.

The number of independently acting automatic controllers on a system or process may not exceed the number of degrees of freedom. To illustrate this rule, suppose that three automatic controllers are installed on the heater of Fig. 2–1 so that inlet temperature u is maintained constant, the water flow rate w is maintained constant, and the heat input rate m is maintained constant. Then all three degrees of freedom are specified and outlet temperature c must be constant. More than three automatic controllers cannot be employed because redundancy would exist (only four variables and five equations). However, fewer than three automatic controllers are adequate, and, in fact, only one controller is usually employed.

For chemical processes involving separation, distillation, or fractionation where heterogeneous equilibrium exists and where each component is present in each phase, a modification of the rule of equation 2–1 may be derived. It is known as Gibbs's phase rule,

$$n = n_c - n_p + 2 \qquad (2\text{–}2)$$

where n = number of chemical degrees of freedom
$\quad n_c$ = number of components
$\quad n_p$ = number of phases

This applies only to the chemical states of the process, and the number 2 in the equation above represents temperature and pressure. For an isothermal process

$$n = n_c - n_p + 1 \qquad (2\text{–}3)$$

and for a constant-pressure process

$$n = n_c - n_p + 1 \qquad (2\text{–}4)$$

For example, consider a steam boiler producing *saturated* steam. The number of components is one (water), and the number of phases are two (liquid and gas). Therefore, the number of degrees of freedom are

$$n = 1 - 2 + 2 = 1$$

and either temperature or pressure (but not both) may be selected as the independent variable. For a boiler producing superheated steam the number of degrees of freedom are two, and both temperature and pressure must be controlled.

Example 2–1. For the liquid-to-liquid heat exchanger shown in the figure, the following variables are given below the diagram:

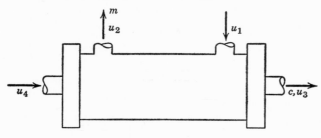

c = heated fluid outlet temperature
m = heating fluid flow rate
u_1 = heating fluid inlet temperature
u_2 = heating fluid outlet temperature
u_3 = heated fluid flow rate
u_4 = heated fluid inlet temperature

Calculate the maximum number of independent controllers that could be used.

There are six variables:
$$n_v = 6$$
There is one equation (conservation of energy):
$$n_e = 1$$
The number of degrees of freedom are, assuming no boiling of liquids,
$$n = 6 - 1 = 5$$
and no more than five automatic controllers may be used.

Example 2–2. A binary mixture (benzene and toluene) is to be distilled at atmospheric pressure (figure at left). The variables are:

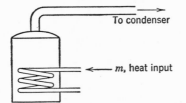

q = overhead flow
c = overhead temperature
m = heat input rate

Calculate the degrees of freedom. For the distillation at constant pressure
$$n = n_c - n_p + 1$$

The number of components are two, and the number of phases are two. Therefore
$$n = 2 - 2 + 1 = 1 \text{ (temperature } c\text{)}$$

For the process, the number of variables are three (q, c, and m), and the defining relations are two (conservation of energy and mass), therefore the number of degrees of freedom is
$$n = n_v - n_e = 3 - 2 = 1$$

Thus, no more than one automatic controller may be employed.

Example 2–3. A binary mixture is to be distilled by the continuous process (fractionation) which is shown in the figure below. The variables are related to the supply of material and energy and are listed below:

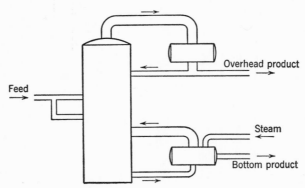

c_1 = overhead temperature u_4 = bottom flow rate
c_2 = overhead pressure u_5 = feed temperature
c_3 = overhead composition u_6 = feed pressure
c_4 = overhead flow rate u_7 = feed composition
u_1 = bottom temperature u_8 = feed per cent vapor
u_2 = bottom pressure u_9 = feed flow rate
u_3 = bottom composition m = steam flow rate (heat input)

Note that the process may contain internal heat exchange or any other arrangement of equipment. Also the pressures c_2, u_2, and u_6 are generally the same. Calculate the number of degrees of freedom. What are the maximum number of automatic controllers that may be used?

Employing Gibbs's phase rule at the overhead there are two components and two phases:

$$n = 2 - 2 + 2 = 2$$

so that any two of the three variables (c_1, c_2, c_3) are independent. The same is true at the bottom where any two of the three variables (u_1, u_2, u_3) are independent. For the feed also any two of the three variables (u_5, u_6, u_7) are independent.

The degrees of freedom may now be calculated. The number of variables are eleven:

Overhead—any two of c_1, c_2, c_3; and c_4
Bottom—any two of u_1, u_2, u_3; and u_4
Heat input—m
Feed—any two of u_5, u_6, u_7; and u_8, u_9

The number of equations are three (conservation of each mass or continuity, and conservation of energy). Then

$$n = 11 - 3 = 8 \text{ deg of freedom}$$

No more than eight automatic controllers may be used.

Characteristics of Physical Systems

The basic concepts for system analysis in automatic control are the fundamental laws relating the behavior of the system. Statical or steady-state behavior is important, but even more important in automatic control is the dynamic behavior of mechanical, fluid, thermal, and electric systems. The important characteristics of fluid and thermal processes are their resistance and capacitance.

Electric systems composed of pure resistance elements and pure capacitance elements in various combinations have many characteristics in common with fluid and thermal processes. Consequently a study of electric systems serves to clarify many similar ideas in fluid and thermal systems.

The *flow law* for electric conductors (Fig. 2–2) having resistance but no inductance or capacitance is Ohm's Law,

$$e_1 - e_2 = iR \tag{2–5}$$

where e = electric potential, volts
    i = current in amperes = coulombs/sec
    R = resistance, ohms

Electric resistance is, therefore,

$$R = \frac{de}{di} \text{ ohms} \qquad (2\text{-}6)$$

For common industrial values of voltage and current, the resistance does not depend upon voltage or current.

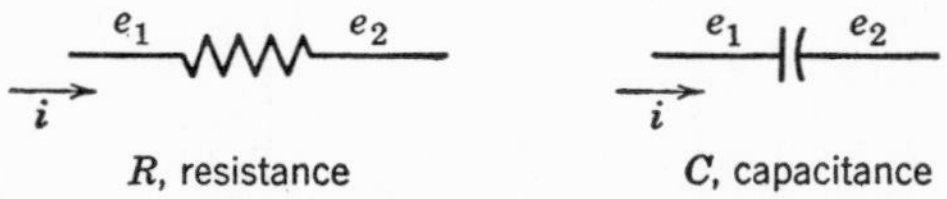

R, resistance   C, capacitance

Fig. 2–2.   Electrical resistance and capacitance.

The *charging law* for electric capacitors having no resistance or inductance (Fig. 2–2) is

$$C \frac{de}{dt} = i \qquad (2\text{-}7)$$

where C = electric capacitance, farads
    e = potential, volts
    t = time, sec
    i = current, amperes

Electric capacitance is defined by

$$C = \frac{dv}{de} \text{ farads} \qquad (2\text{-}8)$$

where v = electric charge, coulombs.   Electric capacitance in the usual range of voltage and charge does not depend upon the voltage or charge.

Electric systems of resistance and capacitance may be analyzed by employing these two laws.

Liquid systems composed of liquid-filled tanks or vessels and connected through pipes, tubes, orifices, valves, and other flow-restricting devices may be analyzed by using the fundamental laws governing the flow of fluids.   Liquid tanks are considered to have a free surface of liquid.   Connecting pipes are assumed to be full of liquid.   In liquid-filled systems it is also assumed that fluid accelerations are small, that is, steady flow or nearly steady flow persists.

The *flow laws* for liquid-conducting elements as in Fig. 2–3 are of two different types: turbulent flow for which the Reynolds number is greater than about 4000, and laminar flow for which the Reynolds number is less than about 2000. In turbulent flow through pipes, orifices, valves,

R, resistance C, capacitance

FIG. 2–3.   Fluid (liquid) resistance and capacitance.

and other flow-restricting devices in general, the flow is found from Bernoulli's law and may be reduced to

$$q = KA\sqrt{2g(h_1 - h_2)} \qquad (2-9)$$

where q = liquid flow rate, ft^3/sec
K = a flow coefficient (usually about 0.6)[1]
A = area of restriction, ft^2
g = acceleration due to gravity, ft/sec^2
h = head of liquid, ft

This law may be compared to Ohm's law for electric conductors equation 2–5, the basic difference being that it involves the square root of the head or potential.

The *turbulent resistance* is found from

$$R = \frac{dh}{dq} = \frac{q}{gK^2A^2} = \frac{2(h_1 - h_2)}{q} \text{ sec/ft}^2 \qquad (2-10)$$

if the flow coefficient K is considered constant. Therefore the turbulent resistance is not constant but depends upon the flow rate and head differential existing at any time. Consequently it is necessary to define a turbulent resistance at a particular value of flow and head and to employ this value of resistance over a narrow operating range. For every new operating range, a new value of resistance is required. In many instances the values of the flow coefficient or area are not known. The resistance may be determined graphically by plotting head against flow and calculating the slope.

[1] For pipe flow the pipe-friction formula is usually employed where $K = 1/\sqrt{FL/D}$, F is the friction factor, L is the equivalent pipe length, and D is the internal diameter of the pipe.

Example 2–4. The flow versus differential head for a 1-in. orifice is plotted in the adjacent figure. The orifice coefficient is assumed to be constant at 0.6 except for very low flow where the Reynolds number is small.

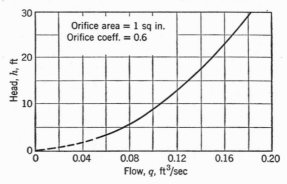

The resistance may be calculated at any particular head and flow and will vary directly with flow. The resistance at any head may be calculated from

$$R = \frac{2}{KA} \left(\frac{h}{2g}\right)^{\frac{1}{2}} \text{ sec/ft}^2$$

The resistance for different heads is shown in the following table:

Head, ft	Resistance, sec/ft^2
16	306
18	324
20	342
22	358
24	374

If the differential head averages about 20 ft, the resistance changes only plus 10 to minus 10 per cent for a 4-ft variation in head.

For laminar flow in general, the flow in circular tubes or pipes is found from the Poiseuille–Hagen law:

$$h_1 - h_2 = \frac{128\mu L}{\pi\gamma D^4} q = \frac{128\nu L}{g\pi D^4} q$$

where h = head, ft
 ν = kinematic viscosity, ft^2/sec
 L = length of tube or pipe, ft
 D = inside diameter of pipe, ft   (2–11)
 q = liquid flow rate, ft^3/sec
 μ = absolute viscosity, lb-sec/ft^2 = $\gamma\nu/g$
 γ = fluid density, lb/ft^3

The laminar flow law is directly comparable to Ohm's law because the flow (current) is directly proportional to the head (potential).

Unfortunately, laminar flow is not often encountered in industrial practice.

The *laminar resistance* is found by

$$R = \frac{dh}{dq} = \frac{128\nu L}{g\pi D^4} \text{ sec/ft}^2 \tag{2-12}$$

Laminar resistance is constant and is directly analogous to electric resistance.

The *continuity law* or law of conservation of mass for a tank containing liquid, as in Fig. 2–3, is

$$A\frac{dh}{dt} = q \tag{2-13}$$

where A = cross-section area of tank at liquid surface, ft^2
$\quad h$ = head, ft
$\quad t$ = time, sec
$\quad q$ = flow rate into tank, ft^3/sec

This law should be compared to the charging law for electric capacitors (equation 2–7).

Liquid capacitance is defined by

$$C = \frac{dv}{dh} \text{ ft}^2 \tag{2-14}$$

where v = volume of liquid in tank, ft^3. Liquid capacitance of a tank is therefore equal to the cross-section area of the tank A taken at the liquid surface. If the tank has a constant cross-section area, the liquid capacitance is constant for any head.

Gas systems consisting of pressure vessels or chambers and various connecting pipes, valves, etc. may be analyzed by using the fundamental laws for the flow of compressible gases. For systems in which the pressure differentials are less than about 5 per cent of the static pressure, the compressibility is not usually important and they may be treated as liquid systems. Ventilating and other air-transport systems where changes of air density are small may be treated as incompressible flow systems. Generally, however, the pressure differentials are substantial in most industrial problems.

The *flow laws* for gas in conducting elements (Fig. 2–4) must also be given for turbulent and laminar flow. For turbulent flow through pipes, orifices, and valves, the steady-flow energy equation (first law of thermodynamics) for adiabatic flow of ideal gases is

$$w = KAY\sqrt{2g(p_1 - p_2)\gamma} \tag{2-15}$$

where w = gas flow rate, lb/sec
 K = a flow coefficient
 A = area of restriction, ft^2 .
 Y = rational expansion factor
 γ = gas density, lb/ft^3
 p = pressure lb/ft^2

Turbulent gas-flow resistance is, therefore,

$$R = \frac{dp}{dw} \text{ sec/ft}^2 \qquad (2\text{–}16)$$

This resistance is not easily calculated because the expansion factor Y depends considerably upon pressure. In this case it is easier to determine

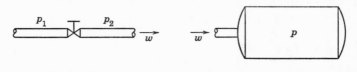

R, resistance   C, capacitance

Fig. 2–4.   Fluid (gas) resistance and capacitance.

resistance from a plot of pressure against flow for any particular device. Laminar gas-flow resistance of tubes and pipes can be calculated from the Poiseuille–Hagen law (equation 2–11).

A special case of gas flow occurs when the pressure differential is larger than a critical value. In such instances, critical or "sonic" flow is obtained when the velocity in the orifice is acoustic velocity and downstream pressure waves cannot propagate upstream. The flow rate, therefore, depends only upon upstream pressure and temperature $w = (K_a A/\sqrt{T_1})p$, where the coefficient K_a is different for each gas and orifice. Temperature T_1 is the upstream temperature and pressure p is the upstream pressure.

The *continuity law* for a pressure vessel (Fig. 2–4) may be written

$$C \frac{dp}{dt} = w \qquad (2\text{–}17)$$

where C = gas capacitance, ft^2
 p = pressure, lb/ft^2
 t = time, sec
 w = flow rate, lb/sec

It is assumed that the volume of the vessel is constant.

Gas capacitance is defined by

$$C = \frac{dv}{dp} \qquad (2\text{--}18)$$

where v = weight of gas in vessel, lb. The capacitance of a pressure vessel must be calculated from thermodynamic relations because the gas expands from a region of high pressure into the vessel at lower pressure, or expands from the vessel into a region of lower pressure. A polytropic expansion process is assumed so that the change of state of the gas lies along some path between an isothermal and adiabatic path,

$$\frac{p}{\rho^n} = \text{constant} \qquad (2\text{--}19)$$

where ρ = gas density, lb/ft^3
$\quad n$ = polytropic exponent ($n = 1.0$ for isothermal expansion and n = ratio of specific heats for adiabatic expansion)

The gas capacitance can now be calculated by employing the ideal gas law:

$$C = \frac{dv}{dp} = V\frac{d\rho}{dp} = \frac{V}{nRT}\text{ft}^2 \qquad (2\text{--}20)$$

where V = volume of vessel, ft^3
$\quad R$ = gas constant for a specific gas, ft/deg
$\quad T$ = temperature of gas, deg

Numerous tests show that the polytropic exponent n is approximately 1.0 to 1.2 for uninsulated metal vessels at common pressures and temperatures. Therefore the gas capacitance of a vessel is constant and is analogous to electric capacitance.

Example 2–5. Calculate the gas capacitance of a 20-gal pressure vessel containing air at 200 F.

$$C = \frac{V}{nRT} = \frac{20 \times 0.134}{1 \times 53.3 \times 660} = \underline{0.000076 \text{ ft}^2}$$

Employing moles and the universal gas constant R,

$$pV_1 = \frac{v}{M}RT$$

where $\ p$ = pressure, lb/ft^2
$\quad V_1$ = volume, ft^3
$\quad v$ = weight, lb
$\quad M$ = molecular weight of gas, lb/mole
$\quad R$ = universal gas constant, lb-ft/mole deg R^{-1} = 1546
$\quad T$ = temperature, deg R

Then

$$C = \frac{dv}{dp} = \frac{MV_1}{RT}$$

$$C = \frac{29 \times 20 \times 0.134}{1546 \times 660} = \underline{0.000076 \text{ ft}^2}$$

Thermal systems involving heat transfer from one substance to another are also characterized by resistance and capacitance. In thermal systems it will be assumed that substances characterized by resistance to heat flow have negligible storage of heat (as a very thin air film), and substances characterized by heat storage have negligible resistance to heat flow (as a block of copper or aluminum).

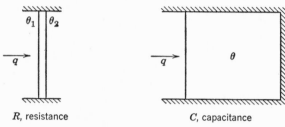

R, resistance   C, capacitance

Fig. 2–5.   Thermal resistance and capacitance.

The *flow laws* for heat conductors (Fig. 2–5) are of two different types corresponding to conduction or convection, and radiation. For conduction of heat through a specific conductor, the heat flow is given by the Fourier law which reduces to

$$q = \frac{KA}{\Delta X} (\theta_1 - \theta_2) \tag{2–21}$$

where q = heat flow, Btu/sec
K = thermal conductivity, Btu/ft sec^{-1} deg^{-1}
A = area normal to heat flow, ft^2
ΔX = thickness of conductor, ft
θ = temperature, deg

For convection heat transfer,

$$q = HA (\theta_1 - \theta_2) \tag{2–22}$$

where H = convection coefficient, Btu/ft^2 sec^{-1} deg^{-1}

The *thermal resistance* is, therefore,

$$R = \frac{d\theta}{dq} = \frac{\Delta X}{KA} \text{ deg sec/Btu} \quad \text{(conduction)} \tag{2–23}$$

or

$$R = \frac{d\theta}{dq} = \frac{1}{HA} \text{ deg sec/Btu} \quad \text{(convection)} \qquad (2\text{--}24)$$

Thus, the thermal resistance is constant if thermal conductivity K is constant or if the convection coefficient H is constant. Generally these factors are nearly constant and thermal resistance is directly analogous to electric resistance.

Example 2–6. A steady heat flow occurs through a $\frac{1}{8}$-in. thick carbon steel plate with an area of 2.0 sq ft. The temperature drop is from 330 F to 180 F. Calculate the resistance. The thermal conductivity is 29. Btu/ft deg^{-1} hr^{-1}. For steady-state heat conduction,

$$R = \frac{d(\Delta\theta)}{dq} = \frac{(\Delta X)}{KA} = \frac{0.125}{12} \times \frac{3600}{29 \times 2} = \underline{0.65 \text{ deg sec/Btu}}$$

For radiation heat transfer, the flow is given by the Stefan–Boltzmann law for a surface receiving radiation from a black body:

$$q = KAE(\theta_1^4 - \theta_2^4) \qquad (2\text{--}25)$$

where q = heat flow, Btu/sec
  K = a constant = 47.4×10^{-14} Btu/ft^2 sec^{-1} deg^{-4}
  E = emissivity
  A = surface area, ft^2
  θ = temperature, deg R

This is a fourth-power law as compared to a square-root relation for turbulent fluid flow, and a linear law for electric current.

The *radiation resistance* is

$$R = \frac{d\theta}{dq} = \frac{1}{4KAE\theta_a^3} \text{ deg sec/Btu} \qquad (2\text{--}26)$$

where θ_a = average of radiator and receiver temperatures. Radiation resistance varies inversely as the cube of temperature and must be employed for a small range of temperature. Actually, the resistance calculated above is not seriously in error even when the source and receiver temperatures differ by a factor of two.

Example 2–7. A steady flow of heat occurs in an electrically heating furnace with walls at 1800 F to a large steel casting at 1400 F. The surface area is 1.0 sq ft. Calculate the resistance. Assume emissivity is one.

$$R = \frac{d\theta}{dq} = \frac{1}{4KAE\theta_a^3} = \frac{10^{14}}{4 \times 47.4 \times 1.0 \times 2060^3}$$

$$R = \underline{60 \text{ deg sec/Btu}}$$

The *temperature change law* is a consequence of the first law of thermo-dynamics relating heat and internal energy. For the metal block of Fig. 2–5, heat into the system raises the internal energy and for a given system,

$$C \frac{d\theta}{dt} = q \tag{2-27}$$

where C = thermal capacitance, Btu/deg
$\quad\quad t$ = time, sec

The *thermal capacitance* is, therefore,

$$C = WC_p \tag{2-28}$$

where W = weight of block, lb
$\quad\quad C_p$ = specific heat at constant pressure, Btu/deg lb^{-1}

Thermal capacitance is directly analogous to electric capacitance.

Example 2–8. Calculate the thermal capacitance of a 30-gal water tank. From equation 2–28

$$C = WC_p = 30 \times 8.3 \times 1 = 249 \text{ Btu/deg}$$

Note: It is sometimes necessary to include the capacitance of the vessel walls.

Thermal systems do not always have isolated resistance and capacitance. A thick stone wall, for example, has resistance to flow of heat by virtue of finite thermal conductivity and capacitance because of the specific heat of the material. Such systems are said to have distributed capacitance and resistance and the equations above do not strictly apply. Fortunately there are many physical problems in which thermal resistances and capacitors are sufficiently isolated so that some calculations of characteristics can be made.

Electrical, thermal, liquid, and gas characteristics are summarized in Table 2–1.

Table 2–1.   Dimensions of Process Characteristics

	Electrical	Thermal	Liquid	Gas
Quantity	coulomb	Btu	ft^3	lb
Potential	volt	deg	ft	lb/ft^2
Time	sec	sec	sec	sec
Flow	$\dfrac{\text{Coul.}}{\text{sec}}$ = amp	Btu/sec	ft^3/sec	lb/sec
Capacitance	$\dfrac{\text{Coul.}}{\text{volt}}$ = farad	Btu/deg	$\dfrac{\text{ft}^3}{\text{ft}}$ = ft^2	ft^2
Resistance	$\dfrac{\text{volt}}{\text{amp}}$ = ohm	deg-sec/Btu	sec/ft^2	sec/ft^2

Mechanical systems may be composed of various masses connected by members providing damping effects and spring effects. Although some systems are analogous to electric systems, the analog comparison may be made in many ways. Consequently, it is better to consider mechanical systems on their own merits.

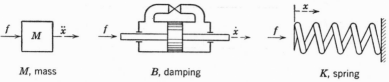

M, mass   B, damping   K, spring

FIG. 2-6.   Characteristics of mechanical systems.

Newton's second law of motion defines the relation between a mass, its acceleration, and an applied force. As in Fig. 2-6,

$$f = \frac{d}{dt}\left(M\frac{dx}{dt}\right) = M\frac{d^2x}{dt^2} \qquad (2\text{-}29)$$

where f = force, lb
    t = time, sec
   M = mass, lb-sec^2/ft
    x = displacement, ft

The mass is considered constant.

Damping is provided by piston dashpots as in Fig. 2-6 and by well-lubricated surfaces moving over one another. For an oil-filled dashpot the force resisting a velocity of motion arises from the pressure differential at the piston required to cause laminar flow through the capillary fluid resistance. A damping law is given by

$$f = B\frac{dx}{dt} \qquad (2\text{-}30)$$

where B = damping coefficient, lb sec/ft. Damping is also provided by the shear forces of viscous fluids acting against a moving surface.

Spring action as in the coil spring of Fig. 2-6 and for cantilever and pinned-end beams may be described by a form of Hooke's law,

$$f = Kx \qquad (2\text{-}31)$$

where K = spring gradient or modulus, lb/ft. Basically, a spring action results from compressive, tensile, or shear stresses below the elastic limit.

Elements of Process Dynamics

Dynamic analysis is necessary in automatic control because automatic control is based upon dynamic action. Whereas dynamic or transient analysis is commonplace for mechanical and electrical systems, it is relatively new for fluid and thermal systems.

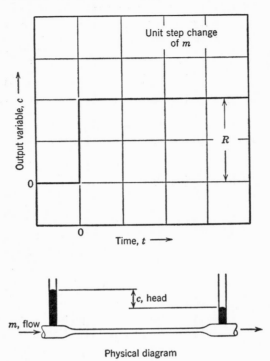

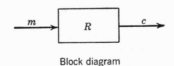

Block diagram

FIG. 2–7.   The proportional element.

Analysis of processes is made easier through a study of the elements of process dynamics.   These elements are

1. Proportional element.
2. Capacitance element.
3. Time-constant element.
4. Oscillatory element.

These are the "building blocks" of processes and almost all industrial processes are described by arrangements of numbers of these elements in various series and parallel arrangements.

The *proportional element* is described in Fig. 2–7. Consider, for example, the capillary shown in the physical diagram. The flow rate of liquid m through the capillary is regarded as the variable being changed and thus is termed the input variable. The head c is the result of the variable flow rate and is regarded as the output variable. A capillary constitutes a laminar resistance and the flow-head equation may be written

$$c = Rm \qquad (2\text{--}32)$$

where c = output variable (head)
R = resistance
m = input variable (flow)

This relation may be considered in the following form:

$$\text{Output} = (\text{system function})(\text{input}) \qquad (2\text{--}33)$$

Thus, the output is determined from the product of the system function and the input. In the example of the capillary the system function is the resistance of the capillary. Note that the system function is a characteristic of the system and is given in terms of the physical characteristics.

Other proportional elements are electrical resistance, gas flow resistance, thermal resistance, and the mechanical spring.

The response of a proportional element is also shown in Fig. 2–7. For a unit step change of input flow m, the output repeats this step at the same time but with magnitude R.

The *capacitance* element is illustrated in Fig. 2–8. As one example of a capacitance element, consider the liquid tank shown in the physical diagram. The flow into or out of the tank m is considered the input variable and the head of liquid in the tank c is the output variable. For a capacitance element,

$$C\frac{dc}{dt} = m \qquad (2\text{--}34)$$

where C = capacitance
c = output variable (head)
t = time
m = input variable (flow)

In order to obtain the system function the operational notation of differential equations must be used:

$$s = \frac{d}{dt} \qquad (2\text{--}35)$$

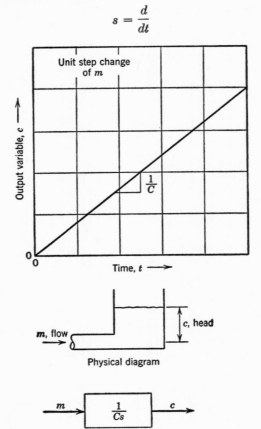

FIG. 2–8.   The capacitance element.

where s = differential operator.[1]   Then equation 2–34 may be written

$$(Cs)c = m \qquad (2\text{--}36)$$

or

$$c = \left(\frac{1}{Cs}\right) m \qquad (2\text{--}37)$$

[1] The differential operator is sometimes given the symbol D. At this particular time there is no relation other than intentional coincidence between the differential operator s and the LaPlace transform complex variable s.

The system function is therefore $1/Cs$ and describes symbolically the capacitance element. Again the product of system function and input variable gives the output variable. Other capacitance elements are

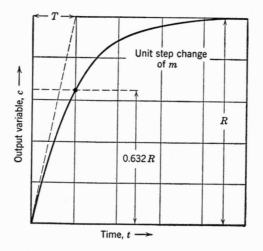

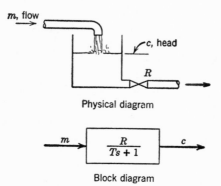

Physical diagram

Block diagram

FIG. 2–9. The time-constant element.

illustrated by electric capacitance, gas capacitance, and thermal capacitance and are characterized by storage. The response of a capacitance element is found by integrating equation 2–34. For a constant inflow M and with the tank initially empty,

$$c = \frac{1}{C} \int_0^t M \, dt = \left(\frac{M}{C}\right) t \qquad (2\text{–}38)$$

This equation is plotted in Fig. 2–8. For a step change of input flow M, the output variable increases linearly with time with a rate of change inversely proportional to capacitance.

The *time-constant* element is shown in Fig. 2–9 and is exemplified by the liquid tank and resistance. The input variable is the inflow rate m and the output variable is the tank head c. For the tank capacitance C,

$$C \frac{dc}{dt} = m - q \qquad (2\text{–}39)$$

where q is the outflow. For the fluid resistance R,

$$q = \frac{c}{R} \qquad (2\text{–}40)$$

Combining equations 2–39 and 2–40 to eliminate outflow q,

$$RC \frac{dc}{dt} + c = Rm \qquad (2\text{–}41)$$

The product of resistance and capacitance RC is a time which will be designated as T. Then the operational equation is

$$c = \left(\frac{R}{Ts + 1} \right) m \qquad (2\text{–}42)$$

This system function is characteristic of the time-constant element. Any series arrangement of capacitance and resistance in which the rate of change of potential at the capacitance is decreased by increasing outflow through a resistance produces a time-constant element. Combinations of electrical, liquid, gas, and thermal resistance and capacitance may produce a time constant element.

The response of the time-constant element is found by solving equation 2–41 for a step change of inflow M with the tank initially empty.[1]

$$c = RM(1 - e^{-t/T}) \qquad (2\text{–}43)$$

This equation is plotted in Fig. 2–9.

[1] The solution to any differential equation of the form

$$A \frac{dx}{dt} + x = By$$

is given by the sum of the particular integral and complementary function. The particular integral is

$$x = By$$

if y is a constant. The complementary function is the solution of

$$A \frac{dx}{dt} + x = 0$$

The time $(T = RC)$ is the time constant of the element and is found experimentally when $t = T$,

$$c = RM\left(1 - \frac{1}{e}\right) = RM(1 - 0.368) = 0.632RM$$

Therefore the time constant is the time required to reach 63.2 per cent of the final value. Times for other magnitudes of change are found from tables of e^{-x}:

Per cent response	Units of T
50.0	0.69
63.2	1.00
95.0	3.00
98.0	3.90
99.0	4.60

There are other important characteristics of the exponential response of the time constant element. As shown in Fig. 2–9, the final value for a unit step change is proportional to the resistance R. The time constant is the intersection time of the initial slope at the final value and the initial slope is inversely proportional to the time constant.

The *oscillatory element* is shown in Fig. 2–10. Although it is not encountered in ordinary liquid, gas, and thermal processes, it is typical of many measuring instruments such as the Bourdon-tube pressure gage. Consider the mass spring and damping system of Fig. 2–10. Newton's second law of motion gives

$$M\frac{d^2c}{dt^2} = -B\frac{dc}{dt} - Kc + m \qquad (2\text{–}44)$$

where the force m is regarded as the input variable and the displacement of the mass is considered the output variable. Rewriting equation 2–44

---

and is always

$$x = Ce^{-\lambda t}$$

Substituting in the equation immediately above,

$$-AC\lambda e^{-\lambda t} + Ce^{-\lambda t} = 0$$

and solving for λ,

$$\lambda = 1/A$$

The complete solution is therefore

$$x = By + Ce^{-t/A}$$

The arbitrary constant C is found from initial conditions.

in operational form,

$$c = \left(\frac{1}{Ms^2 + Bs + K}\right) m \qquad (2\text{-}45)$$

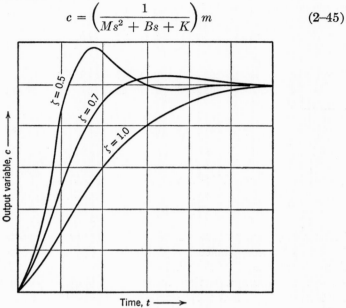

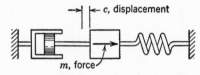

Physical diagram

Block diagram

Fig. 2–10.   The oscillatory element.

For convenience the following definitions are often employed:

$$T = \sqrt{\frac{M}{K}} \qquad \text{characteristic time} \qquad (2\text{-}46)$$

$$\zeta = \sqrt{\frac{B^2}{4KM}} \quad \text{damping ratio} \qquad (2\text{-}47)$$

Combining the last three equations, there results

$$c = \left(\frac{1/K}{T^2 s^2 + 2\zeta T s + 1} \right) m \qquad (2\text{-}48)$$

The system function is typical of oscillatory elements when the damping ratio ζ is less than one (underdamped).

The response of an oscillatory element is shown in Fig. 2–10 for a unit step change of input variable. Solving equation 2–48, under the conditions that the system is initially at rest,[1]

$$c = \frac{M}{K} \left[1 - \frac{\zeta e^{-\zeta t/T}}{\sqrt{1 - \zeta^2}} \sin \sqrt{1 - \zeta^2} \, \frac{t}{T} - e^{-\zeta t/T} \cos \sqrt{1 - \zeta^2} \, \frac{t}{T} \right] \qquad (2\text{-}49)$$

[1] The solution to any differential equation of the form

$$A \frac{d^2 x}{dt^2} + B \frac{dx}{dt} + x = Cy$$

is given by the sum of the particular integral and complementary function. The particular integral is

$$x = Cy$$

if y is constant. The complementary function is the solution of

$$A \frac{d^2 x}{dt^2} + B \frac{dx}{dt} + x = 0$$

and is found by substituting

$$x = Ke^{-\lambda t}$$

in the equation above,

$$AK\lambda^2 e^{-\lambda t} - BK\lambda e^{-\lambda t} + Ke^{-\lambda t} = 0$$

Solving for λ from

$$A\lambda^2 - B\lambda + 1 = 0$$

there results from the quadratic formula

$$\lambda_1, \lambda_2 = \frac{+B \pm \sqrt{B^2 - 4A}}{2A}$$

The form of the complementary function depends upon whether $B^2 > 4A$, $B^2 = 4A$, or $B^2 < 4A$. In the latter case the roots λ are complex and the complete solution is

$$x = Cy + K_1 e^{-\lambda_1 t} + K_2 e^{-\lambda_2 t}$$

Employing Euler's relation,

$$e^{\pm i\lambda t} = \cos \lambda t \pm i \sin \lambda t$$

the solution may be placed in the form

$$x = Cy + e^{-Bt/2A} \left[K_3 \sin \sqrt{\frac{1}{A} - \frac{B^2}{4A^2}} \, t + K_4 \cos \sqrt{\frac{1}{A} - \frac{B^2}{4A^2}} \, t \right]$$

where K_3 and K_4 are arbitrary constants which must be evaluated from initial conditions.

The period of oscillation may be determined from the characteristic time and damping ratio:

$$P = \frac{2\pi T}{\sqrt{1 - \zeta^2}} \qquad (2\text{--}50)$$

For damping ratios ζ of one half and less, the square-root term approaches unity. The frequency of oscillation is the inverse of the period in cycles per second.

When the damping ratio in equation 2–48 is equal to or greater than one or, if $B^2 > 4KM$ in equation 2–45, the system is no longer an oscillatory element. That is, for a unit step change of the input variable, the response does not overshoot the final value but changes smoothly from initial to final value. Under this condition the system function of equation 2–45 may be factored:

$$\frac{1}{Ms^2 + Bs + K} = \frac{1/K}{(T_1 s + 1)(T_2 s + 1)} \qquad (2\text{--}51)$$

where the time constants are given by

$$\frac{1}{T_1}, \frac{1}{T_2} = \frac{B}{2M}\left(1 \pm \sqrt{1 - \frac{4KM}{B^2}}\right) \qquad (2\text{--}52)$$

Therefore a second-order system with overdamped action ($B^2 > 4KM$) may be factored into two time-constant elements. If the system is critically damped, these two time-constants are equal.

The response of an oscillatory element always overshoots the final value and comes to rest practically at a time dependent upon the amount of damping and the characteristic time. The amount of overshoot is also greatly dependent upon the damping. The frequency of oscillation depends primarily upon the characteristic time T.

Liquid Processes

Processes involving the flow of liquids through connected pipes and vessels are common examples of industrial processes and are often employed for demonstrating the operation of many different kinds of processes.

The single-vessel process of Fig. 2–11 has a constant outflow u but a variable inflow m. The inflow m is assumed to be the manipulated variable, and the vessel head is assumed to be the variable to be controlled, c. The continuity relation for the vessel is

$$C\dot{c} = m - u \qquad (2\text{--}53)$$

where C is the vessel capacitance. The system equation is

$$c = \left(\frac{1}{Cs}\right) m - \left(\frac{1}{Cs}\right) u \qquad (2\text{–}54)$$

The system function is $1/Cs$ and the process is identified as a capacitance element. The outflow u is the load variable. The operational equation indicates that the action of the load variable u is identical but opposite in sign to the action of the manipulated variable. A step increase of the manipulated variable m made while holding outflow u

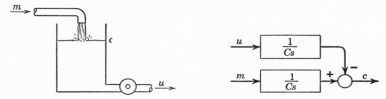

FIG. 2–11. Capacitance-type liquid-level process.

fixed produces a linear increase of head c with time as identified in Fig. 2–8. A step increase of load u made while holding inflow m fixed produces a linear decrease of head c with time.

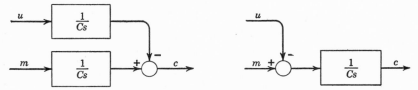

FIG. 2–12. Equivalent block diagrams.

The block diagram for the process of Fig. 2–11 may be drawn in two ways as shown in Fig. 2–12. These two diagrams produce identical relationships between the variables of the system.

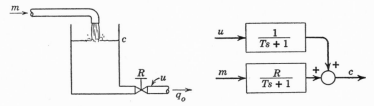

FIG. 2–13. Time-constant-type liquid-level process.

The single vessel of Fig. 2–13 in which the outflow is through a liquid-flow resistance is identified as a time-constant element. The inflow m

is considered the manipulated variable, the vessel head c is assumed to be the variable to be controlled, and the downstream head u is the load variable. The continuity relation for the vessel is,

$$C\dot{c} = m - q_o \qquad (2\text{-}55)$$

where C = vessel capacitance
q_o = outflow

The outflow resistance is assumed to be laminar so that outflow depends upon head differential:

$$q_o = \frac{1}{R}(c - u) \qquad (2\text{-}56)$$

where R = valve resistance. Combining these two equations to eliminate outflow q_o there results

$$T\dot{c} + c = Rm + u \qquad (2\text{-}57)$$

where $T = RC$ is the time constant of the process. The system equation is

$$c = \left(\frac{R}{Ts+1}\right)m + \left(\frac{1}{Ts+1}\right)u \qquad (2\text{-}58)$$

Thus the process is identified as a time-constant element. Its response to a step change of inflow m (head u fixed) is the typical exponential response of Fig. 2–9. Note also that a steady-state change of inflow m results ultimately in R units of change in head. A step increase of head u results also in the typical exponential response of head but the magnitude of steady-state change is the same for both head u and vessel head c (unit sensitivity or gain).

The process of Fig. 2–14 consists of two vessels in series or "cascade" and, although it is not a common industrial process, the general arrangement is often found in thermal processes. The inflow m will be considered the manipulated variable and the head c in the lower tank will be considered the variable to be controlled. Inflows u_1 and u_2 will be considered load variables. Downstream head at the lower vessel is considered constant.

The continuity relation for the upper vessel is

$$C_2\dot{h}_2 = m + u_2 - q_r \qquad (2\text{-}59)$$

where C_2 = capacitance (area) of upper vessel
h_2 = head in upper vessel
q_r = outflow at upper vessel

The outflow is assumed to be directly proportional to head (laminar resistance):

$$h_2 = q_r R_2 \qquad (2\text{--}60)$$

where R_2 is the outlet valve resistance. Combining these equations,

$$T_2 \dot{h}_2 + h_2 = R_2 m + R_2 u_2 \qquad (2\text{--}61)$$

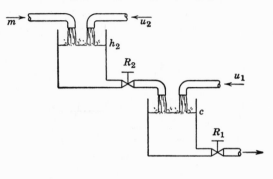

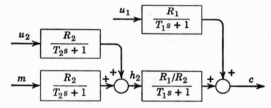

FIG. 2–14. Two time-constants in series.

where $T_2 = R_2 C_2$ and is the time constant of the upper vessel. The latter equation may be placed in operational form

$$h_2 = \left(\frac{R_2}{T_2 s + 1}\right) m + \left(\frac{R_2}{T_2 s + 1}\right) u_2 \qquad (2\text{--}62)$$

The block diagram is shown by the lower left-hand rectangular blocks and circle of Fig. 2–14.

The continuity relation for the lower vessel is

$$C_1 \dot{c} = q_r + u_1 - q_o \qquad (2\text{--}63)$$

where C_1 = capacitance (area) of lower vessel
      q_o = outflow, ft^3/sec

The outflow is assumed to be directly proportional to head (laminar flow),

$$c = q_o R_1 \qquad (2\text{--}64)$$

where R_1 is the outlet valve resistance. Combining these last two equations,

$$T_1\dot{c} + c = \frac{R_1}{R_2} h_2 + R_1 u_1 \qquad (2\text{-}65)$$

where $T_1 = R_1 C_1$ and is the time constant of the lower vessel. The latter equation may be placed in operational form:

$$c = \frac{R_1}{R_2}\left(\frac{1}{T_1 s + 1}\right) h_2 + \left(\frac{R_1}{T_1 s + 1}\right) u_1 \qquad (2\text{-}66)$$

The block diagram representing this equation is shown in Fig. 2–14 by the right-hand set of two blocks and circle. The process is thus seen

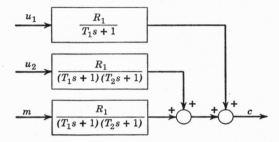

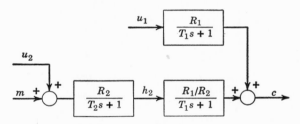

Fig. 2–15.   Equivalent block diagrams.

to be two time-constant elements in series. Combining equations 2–62 and 2–66 to eliminate head h_2 gives

$$c = \frac{R_1}{(T_1 s + 1)(T_2 s + 1)} m + \frac{R_1}{(T_1 s + 1)(T_2 s + 1)} u_2 + \frac{R_1}{(T_1 s + 1)} u_1 \qquad (2\text{-}67)$$

and the operational equation for the overall system is obtained. The block diagram for the overall system is shown in Fig. 2–15 where comparison may be made to the previous block diagram.

For two time-constant elements in series, the response is found by solving the differential equation for the overall system. If the load variables u_1 and u_2 are zero (flows turned off), equation 2–67 becomes

$$T_1 T_2 \ddot{c} + (T_1 + T_2) \dot{c} + c = R_1 m \qquad (2\text{–}68)$$

This is a linear second-order differential equation and is typical of many industrial processes. The process response can be obtained by allowing a step change of inflow m. The solution is

$$\frac{c - c_o}{c_f - c_o} = 1 + \frac{T_1}{T_2 - T_1} e^{-t/T_1} - \frac{T_2}{T_2 - T_1} e^{-t/T_2} \quad \text{if} \quad T_1 \neq T_2 \quad (2\text{–}69)$$

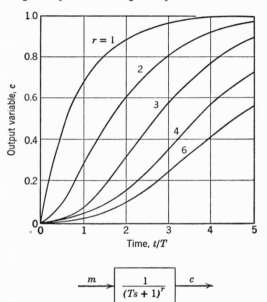

FIG. 2–16. Response of processes with several equal time constants in series.

where $c_f = R_1 m$ is the final steady value of head in the lower vessel, and c_o is the initial value of head in the lower tank. Another solution is

$$\frac{c - c_o}{c_f - c_o} = 1 - e^{-t/T_1} - \frac{t}{T_1} e^{-t/T_1} \quad \text{if} \quad T_1 = T_2 \qquad (2\text{–}70)$$

This equation is plotted in Fig. 2–16, together with the response of a single time-constant process. Notice that the addition of the second time-constant produces the typical S-shaped curve and serves to retard the initial response.

Liquid processes, and in fact many other kinds of processes, may involve more than two time constants in series. Sometimes three, four, or many more capacitances are connected in series. The response of such processes is shown in Fig. 2–16. The response is always of the typical S-shape but is more pronounced as the number of time constants becomes larger. It is much easier to define such processes by their individual time constants $T_1, T_2, T_3 \ldots T_n$ than by the response that is produced by the overall system.

Example 2–9. A single capacitance process like that of Fig. 2–13 has a normal operating head of 4 ft and a normal value of outflow of 0.125 cu ft per sec. The cross-section area of the vessel is 6 sq ft. Calculate the time constant.

If the resistance to flow is parabolic, the resistance is given by

$$R = \left(\frac{2h}{q}\right)_{\text{normal}} = \frac{2 \times 4}{1/8} = 64 \text{ sec/ft}^2$$

$$C = 6 \text{ ft}^2$$

$$T = RC = 64 \times 6 = \underline{384 \text{ sec}}$$

Example 2–10. Show that the time constant of a single vessel as shown in Fig. 2–13 is proportional to the time required to change the fluid in the vessel.

The capacitance is the area of the vessel and the resistance of the outlet valve depends upon head and flow. For turbulent resistance,

$$T = RC = \frac{2h}{q_o}\bigg|_{\text{av.}} \times A = 2\frac{hA}{q_o}\bigg|_{\text{av.}} = 2\,\frac{\text{volume of fluid}}{\text{outflow}}$$

For laminar resistance

$$T = RC = \frac{h}{q_o}\bigg|_{\text{av.}} \times A = \frac{hA}{q_o}\bigg|_{\text{av.}} = \frac{\text{volume of fluid}}{\text{outflow}}$$

Example 2–11. The two-capacitance process shown in the figure consists of two vessels in series (not cascaded). Derive the process differential equation and define the two system time constants.

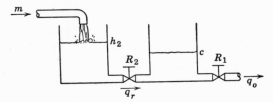

For the left-hand vessel

$$C_2 \dot{h}_2 = m - q_r$$

and for linear resistance R_2

$$h_2 - c = q_r R_2$$

For the right-hand vessel

$$C_1 \dot{c} = q_r - q_o$$

and for linear resistance R_1,

$$c = q_o R_1$$

where C_2 = capacitance of left-hand vessel
R_2 = resistance between vessels
C_1 = capacitance of right-hand vessel

Combining the four equations to eliminate head h_2 and flow q_r,

$$T_1 T_2 \ddot{c} + (T_1 + T_2 + R_1 C_2)\dot{c} + c = R_1 m$$

where $T_1 = R_1 C_1$ and $T_2 = R_2 C_2$. Comparing this result to equation 2–68, the difference is that the factor $R_1 C_2$ is added to the second term of the equation. Employing the quadratic solution we may define two new time constants T_a and T_b so that

$$\frac{1}{T_a}, \frac{1}{T_b} = + \frac{(T_1 + T_2 + R_1 C_2) \pm \sqrt{(T_1 + T_2 + R_1 C_2)^2 - 4T_1 T_2}}{2T_1 T_2}$$

and write the above equation in the new form:

$$T_a T_b \ddot{c} + (T_a + T_b)\dot{c} + c = R_1 m$$

Thus the two process time constants are T_a and T_b.

Gas Processes

Processes involving the flow of gas through connected pipe lines and pressure vessels are common in industrial practice.

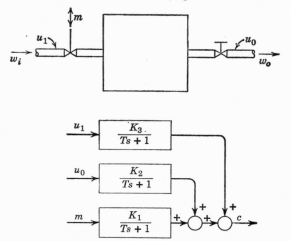

Fig. 2–17.   Single time-constant-type gas process.

As an example consider the pressure vessel of Fig. 2–17. Pressure c in the vessel is the variable to be controlled. The stem position or opening m of the inlet valve, not the inflow w_i must be taken as the manipulated variable, because the characteristics of the throttling valve enter into the response of the process. The continuity relation for the vessel is

$$C\dot{c} = w_i - w_o \qquad (2\text{--}71)$$

where C = gas capacitance of vessel
    w_i = inflow
    w_o = outflow

The vessel outflow w_o is a function of two variables if the pressure differential is not large, so that acoustic velocity is not obtained:

$$w_o = f(c, u_0) \qquad (2\text{--}72)$$

where u_0 is the downstream pressure. The total differential for a function of two variables is

$$dw_o = \left(\frac{\partial w_o}{\partial c}\right)_{u_0} dc + \left(\frac{\partial w_o}{\partial u_0}\right)_c du_0 \qquad (2\text{--}73)$$

This situation is illustrated by Fig. 2–18 in which the flow rate is plotted for an actual valve, first with downstream pressure u_0 constant, and second, with upstream pressure c constant. The partial derivatives of equation 2–73 are shown as slopes of the pressure-flow curve. Because the right-hand partial derivative is negative, a negative sign is used in equation 2–73. If the pressure ratio is less than critical (0.53 critical pressure ratio for air), the flow rate does not depend upon downstream pressure and the second term of equation 2–73 is zero. We will assume that the outlet valve is operated near the horizontal and vertical dotted lines of Fig. 2–18. In a small operating region, the slopes may be considered constant and equation 2–73 may be integrated:

$$w_o = \left(\frac{1}{R_a}\right)c + \left(\frac{1}{R_0}\right)u_0 + M_0 \qquad (2\text{--}74)$$

where M_0 is a constant of integration.

The inflow (w_i) is a function of three variables, the stem position m of the inlet valve, the upstream pressure u_1, and the vessel pressure c, so that

$$w_i = f(m, u_1, c) \qquad (2\text{--}75)$$

The total differential is

$$dw_i = \left(\frac{\partial w_i}{\partial m}\right) dm + \left(\frac{\partial w_i}{\partial u_1}\right) du_1 + \left(\frac{\partial w_i}{\partial c}\right) dc \qquad (2\text{--}76)$$

The partial derivatives may be evaluated as for the outlet valve with the addition of one more plot of flow rate against valve stem position at constant pressure differential. The slope of the latter curve is the first partial derivative above and is termed the valve sensitivity K_v.

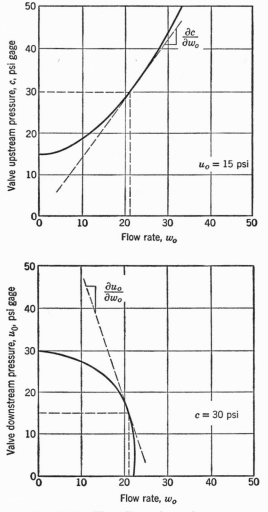

FIG. 2–18. Throttling-valve resistances.

Considering these slopes constant in the operating region,

$$w_i = K_v m + \left(\frac{1}{R_1}\right) u_1 + \left(\frac{1}{R_b}\right) c + M_0 \qquad (2\text{–}77)$$

where M_0 is a constant of integration.

Combining the equations 2–71, 2–74, and 2–77 the *process equation* is

$$T\dot{c} + c = K_1 m + K_2 u_0 + K_3 u_1 \qquad (2\text{–}78)$$

or in operational form

$$c = \left(\frac{K_1}{Ts + 1}\right) m + \left(\frac{K_2}{Ts + 1}\right) u_0 + \left(\frac{K_3}{Ts + 1}\right) u_1 \qquad (2\text{–}79)$$

where

$$T = \frac{C}{1/R_a + 1/R_b}, \qquad\qquad K_1 = \frac{K_v}{1/R_a + 1/R_b}$$

$$K_2 = \frac{1}{R_0/R_a + R_0/R_b}, \qquad\qquad K_3 = \frac{1}{R_1/R_a + R_1/R_b}$$

The block diagram is shown in Fig. 2–17. The process response is first order with a time constant T. Compare the response of this process to the response of the liquid-level process in Fig. 2–13.

Example 2–12. A pressure vessel connected as in Fig. 2–17 has a supply pressure u_1 of 45 psig, a vessel pressure of 15 psig, and an air exhaust to atmosphere. The average flow rate is 1.0 lb per minute and the vessel volume is 10 cu ft. Calculate the system function.

First, the critical pressure ratios give:

$$\frac{14.7}{0.53} = 27.8, \qquad \frac{29.7}{0.53} = 56.0$$

Since $27.8 - 14.7 = 13.1$ psi < 15 psig vessel pressure the outlet valve has critical (acoustic) flow. Also because $56.0 - 14.7 = 41.3 < 45$ psig, the inlet valve has critical flow. Therefore $R_0 \rightarrow \infty$ and $R_b \rightarrow \infty$, and thereby $K_2 = 0$ in equation 2–79. The time constant is

$$T = R_a C = \frac{15 \times 144}{1.0} \times \frac{10}{1.0 \times 53.3 \times 530} = 0.76 \text{ min}$$

$$K_1 = R_a K_v$$

$$K_3 = \frac{R_a}{R_1} = 2.0$$

The system function is, therefore,

$$c = \left(\frac{R_a K_v}{0.76s + 1}\right) m + \left(\frac{2}{0.76s + 1}\right) u_1$$

Example 2–13. The single capacitance pressure process shown in the figure is supplied with a constant flow u lb per sec. The controlled variable is the vessel pressure c psi gage. The stem position of the outlet valve m is the manipulated variable. The outlet valve downstream pressure is less than critical. Derive the process equation.

The continuity relation is

$$C\dot{c} = u - w_o$$

The outflow does not depend upon downstream pressure, so

$$w_o = \left(\frac{\partial w_o}{\partial m}\right) m + \left(\frac{\partial w_o}{\partial c}\right) c$$

or

$$w_o = K_v m + \left(\frac{1}{R}\right) c + M_0$$

The process equation is

$$T\dot{c} + c = -RK_v m + Ru - RM_0$$

and the operational equation is

$$(c + RM_0) = -\left(\frac{RK_v}{Ts + 1}\right) m + \left(\frac{R}{Ts + 1}\right) u$$

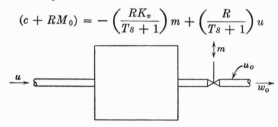

where $T = RC$. The resistance R of the outlet valve is the slope of the upstream pressure versus flow curve at constant valve stem position and is usually obtained by test. In drawing the block diagram, constants (such as RM_0) are usually omitted because they do not directly influence process dynamics.

Flow Processes

The automatic control of fluid flow in pipelines would at first appear to be a simple problem of manipulating a throttling valve so as to maintain the flow rate at the desired value. In practice, the analysis involves a large number of factors related to flow characteristics, and a separate consideration of flow-rate processes is necessary. The analysis of flow-rate processes will be made by assuming no effect due to inertia of flowing fluid. This assumption is quite close to reality, because in practical applications the changes in variables occur relatively slowly. In addition it is assumed that the capacitance of pipelines is negligible. Liquid-flow problems will be discussed first, and then gas-flow problems will be reviewed.

Liquid flow rate is assumed to be measured by some type of metering device such as an orifice, nozzle, or Venturi as shown in Fig. 2–19. The flow rate through the metering device is given by

$$c = J_1 A_1 \sqrt{2g(u_0 - u_1)} \qquad (2\text{–}80)$$

where c = liquid flow rate

$\quad J_1$ = flow coefficient (including velocity-of-approach factor)

$\quad A_1$ = area of restriction

$\quad u_0$ = upstream head

$\quad u_1$ = downstream head

$\quad g$ = gravitational constant, ft/sec^2

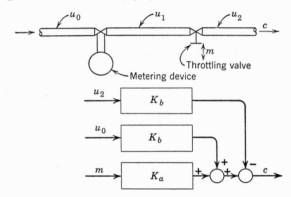

Fig. 2–19.   A flow-rate process.

The coefficients J_1 and area A_1 may be considered constant in some operating region of flow and head differential.   Then, since flow is a function of two variables (u_0 and u_1), the total differential is defined as

$$dc = \left(\frac{\partial c}{\partial u_0}\right) du_0 + \left(\frac{\partial c}{\partial u_1}\right) du_1 \qquad (2\text{--}81)$$

The partial derivatives are equal, so

$$K_1 = \frac{\partial c}{\partial u_0} = -\frac{\partial c}{\partial u_1} = \frac{J_1 A_1}{2}\left(\frac{2g}{u_0 - u_1}\right)^{1/2} = \frac{c}{2(u_0 - u_1)} \qquad (2\text{--}82)$$

Equation 2–81 may be integrated provided the flow is approximately constant:

$$c = K_1(u_0 - u_1) + M_1 \qquad (2\text{--}83)$$

where M_1 is the constant of integration.   The flow also passes through the throttling valve and the flow rate is given by

$$c = J_2 A_2 m \sqrt{2g(u_1 - u_2)} \qquad (2\text{--}84)$$

where J_2 = flow coefficient

$\quad A_2$ = maximum valve port area

$\quad m$ = fraction of valve port opening

$\quad u_2$ = downstream head

The coefficient J_1 and the area A_2 may be considered constant in some operating region of flow rate, head, and valve opening. Then, since flow is a function of three variables (m, u_1, u_2), the total differential is defined as

$$dc = \left(\frac{\partial c}{\partial m}\right) dm + \left(\frac{\partial c}{\partial u_1}\right) du_1 + \left(\frac{\partial c}{\partial u_2}\right) du_2 \qquad (2\text{-}85)$$

The partial derivatives may be calculated from equation 2–84:

$$K_v = \frac{\partial c}{\partial m} = J_2 A_2 \sqrt{2g(u_1 - u_2)} = \frac{c}{m} \qquad (2\text{-}86)$$

where K_v is the valve sensitivity. Also,

$$K_2 = \frac{\partial c}{\partial u_1} = -\frac{\partial c}{\partial u_2} = \frac{J_2 A_2 m}{2}\left(\frac{2g}{u_1 - u_2}\right)^{\frac{1}{2}} = \frac{c}{2(u_1 - u_2)} \qquad (2\text{-}87)$$

The throttling-valve flow equation is now written

$$c = K_v m + K_2(u_1 - u_2) + M_2 \qquad (2\text{-}88)$$

by integrating equation 2–85 with M_2 as a constant of integration.

The "process equation" can be found by eliminating variable u_1 between equations 2–83 and 2–88:

$$c = \left(\frac{K_1 K_v}{K_1 + K_2}\right) m + \left(\frac{K_1 K_2}{K_1 + K_2}\right)(u_0 - u_2) + M_3 \qquad (2\text{-}89)$$

where M_3 is a constant. Simplifying,

$$c = (K_a)m + (K_b)u_0 - (K_b)u_2 + M_3 \qquad (2\text{-}90)$$

where $K_a = \dfrac{K_1 K_v}{K_1 + K_2} = \left(\dfrac{c}{m}\right)\left(\dfrac{u_1 - u_2}{u_0 - u_2}\right)$

$K_b = \dfrac{K_1 K_2}{K_1 + K_2} = \dfrac{c}{2(u_0 - u_2)}$

Thus the "process" is a simple algebraic one and constitutes a proportional element as shown in Fig. 2–19. The response of the process is direct; that is, any change in the position of the throttling valve m results immediately in the same change in flow rate modified by the process sensitivity K_a. Changes in upstream head (u_0) and downstream head (u_2) act similarly.

Gas flow-rate processes may be analyzed by the same procedure as that employed for liquid flow-rate processes. However, the flow rate depends upon three variables rather than two because the weight flow of gas through a restriction depends upon upstream temperature, upstream pressure, and downstream pressure. Also, the flow through the throttling valve depends upon similar variables. In order to eliminate two of the variables, the energy equation (first law of thermodynamics) must be employed. Thus the analysis becomes rather complex even when simplifying assumptions are made. Consequently, we rely upon the previous analysis to write

$$c = (K_a)m + (K_0)u_0 + (K_1)u_1 - (K_2)u_2 + M \qquad (2\text{-}91)$$

where c = gas flow rate $-$ lb/sec

K_a = constant, lb/sec

m = position of throttling valve

K_0 = constant, lb/sec $(\deg R)^{-1}$

u_0 = upstream temperature, deg R

K_1 = constant, ft^2/sec

u_1 = upstream pressure, lb/ft^2

K_2 = constant, ft^2/sec

u_2 = valve downstream pressure, lb/ft^2

M = constant of integration

The constant coefficients (K's) must be evaluated from graphs of flow rate c versus the four variables m, u_0, u_1, and u_2. If the pressure ratio at the throttling valve is greater than critical, the flow does not depend upon downstream pressure u_2 and the factor K_2 is zero.

Thermal Processes

All thermal processes possess characteristics attributed to capacitance (specific heat and weight) and resistance. Thermal processes, however, are clearly distinguished from fluid processes, because the resistance and capacitance are usually distributed throughout heat transfer paths. Fortunately there are a number of thermal-process elements that are characterized mainly by capacitance (agitated fluids) and by resistance (insulation).

The air-heating process of Fig. 2–20 is an example of a simple thermal process. Heat flow m into the system is provided by an electrical heater (usually rated in watts electrical input). Since all of the electrical energy must be transferred to the air,

$$C\dot{c} = m + QPu - QPc \qquad (2\text{-}92)$$

where C = thermal capacitance = WP, Btu/deg

W = weight of air contained in heater, lb

c = heater outlet temperature, deg

m = heat input, Btu/sec

Q = weight flow of air through heater, lb/sec

P = specific heat of air, Btu/lb deg^{-1}

u = inlet air temperature, deg

The heat losses and the capacitance of metal parts in the heater are assumed to be negligible. Rewriting equation 2–92, the process equation is obtained:

$$c = \left(\frac{1}{QP}\right)\left(\frac{1}{Ts+1}\right) m + \left(\frac{1}{Ts+1}\right) u \qquad (2\text{–}93)$$

where $T = C/QP = W/Q$ is the time constant of the process. The block diagram is shown in Fig. 2–20. The process represents a time-

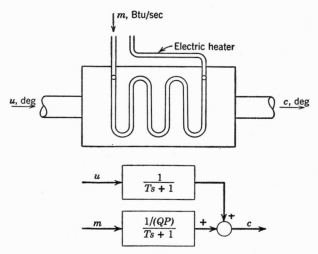

FIG. 2–20. Time-constant-type thermal process.

constant element with time constant T. It is interesting to note that the dynamic characteristics of this process are the same as for the liquid-vessel process of Fig. 2–13 and the gas process of Fig. 2–17, because they are all time-constant elements characterized by a single time constant.

The thermal time constant of most simple thermal processes is given by the storage and throughput rate. Thus, the time constant is calculated from

$$T = \frac{W}{Q} = \frac{\text{weight of fluid contained}}{\text{weight rate of throughput}}$$

This time is the inverse of the rate at which the fluid substance is changed.

The thermal process of Fig. 2–21 consists of a heating furnace such as might be used in continuous heat treating. A gas–air mixture is burned in the furnace and represents a specified rate of heat addition, m. We shall suppose that the main heating load is the metal boxes containing metallic parts. These boxes are carried continuously through the furnace by the conveyor. Heat losses occur at the furnace walls

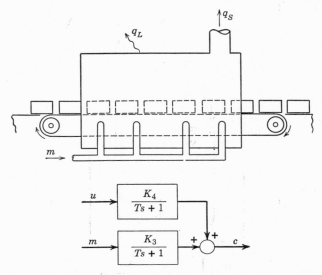

FIG. 2–21. Time-constant-type thermal process.

and at the stack. The controlled variable c is to be the temperature of the boxes and parts. For conservation of energy

$$(PKL)\dot{c} = m - (PKV)c - UA(c - u) - q_s \qquad (2\text{–}94)$$

where P = specific heat of boxes and parts, Btu/lb deg^{-1}

K = material on conveyor, lb/ft

L = length of furnace, ft

V = velocity of conveyor, ft/sec

U = heat loss coefficient Btu/ft^2 deg^{-1} sec^{-1}

A = heat loss area, ft^2

u = ambient temperature, deg

q_s = stack heat loss, Btu/sec

The stack losses are assumed to be a function of the heat input and the furnace temperature.

$$q_s = f(m, c) \qquad (2\text{–}95)$$

Then, the relation of differential changes is

$$dq_s = \left(\frac{\partial q_s}{\partial m}\right) dm + \left(\frac{\partial q_s}{\partial c}\right) dc \qquad (2\text{–}96)$$

For reasonably small fluctuation in heat input and furnace temperature, the above partial derivatives are nearly constant, and

$$q_s = K_1 m + K_2 c + M \qquad (2\text{--}97)$$

Substituting equation 2–97 in equation 2–94, there results after some rearranging of terms

$$c = \left(\frac{K_3}{Ts + 1}\right) m + \left(\frac{K_4}{Ts + 1}\right) u \qquad (2\text{--}98)$$

where $T = \dfrac{PKL}{PKV + UA + K_2}$

$K_3 = \dfrac{1 - K_1}{PKV + UA + K_2}$

$K_4 = \dfrac{UA}{PKV + UA + K_2}$

The process thus turns out to be the single time-constant type. Notice that the amount of material on the conveyor K alters the time constant of the process. Control of thermal processes often involves variable parameters in this manner.

Heat-exchanger processes of the fluid-to-fluid type require a depth of analysis beyond the scope of this text. These processes are usually not describable by linear differential equations with constant coefficients, although any given heat exchanger may be tested experimentally and its dynamic characteristics determined. Sometimes, simple approximations of time constants may be made from experimental data.

Example 2–14. For the air-heating process of Fig. 2–20, the normal air inlet flow is 300 cu ft per min at atmospheric pressure. The inlet temperature is 80 F. The volume of the heater is 500 cu ft. Calculate the time constant of the process.

$$T = \frac{W}{Q} = \frac{500 \times 0.072 \times 60}{300 \times 0.072} = \underline{100 \text{ sec}}$$

Dead Time

Dead time is defined as any definite delay between two related actions. Dead time is illustrated in Fig. 2–22. When the temperature-measuring element is installed at a distance downstream of a heat exchanger a pure time delay occurs before the heated fluid passes from the heater outlet to the point of location of the temperature measuring element. For example, if the fluid flows at 10 ft per sec and the distance is 10 ft, the dead time is one second.

Dead time may be encountered in processes involving pressure. For example if pressure is measured at the end of a long pipe or tube a dead time occurs because of the time for transmission of the first pressure wave down the length of the pipe. For air, the wave velocity is roughly 1000 ft per sec and appreciable dead time would occur for a pipe more than a few hundred feet long. For liquids, the wave velocity is much faster, and the dead time is usually negligible. Dead time may also be found in processes involving chemical reactions when a finite time must elapse before a reaction begins to occur.

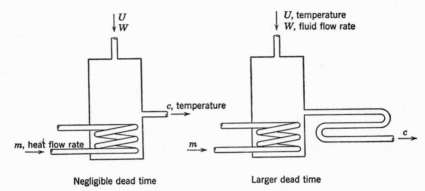

Negligible dead time   Larger dead time

Fig. 2–22.   Water-heating process with and without dead time.

The response of process elements with dead time is shown in Fig. 2–23. The response is simply delayed by a time equal to the dead time L. Therefore if the input to the element is $f(t)$, the output is given by,

$$f(t - L) \tag{2–99}$$

The latter function may be expanded in a Taylor series:

$$f(t-L)=f(t) -f'(t)L+f''(t)\,\frac{L^2}{2!} -f'''(t)\,\frac{L^3}{3!} +f''''(t)\,\frac{L^4}{4!} + \cdots \tag{2–100}$$

where the primes denote the derivative with respect to time. Employing the operator s

$$f(t - L) = f(t)\left[1 - Ls + \frac{(Ls)^2}{2!} - \frac{(Ls)^3}{3!} + \frac{(Ls)^4}{4!} + \cdots \right] \tag{2–101}$$

The power series in the above equation is that for the exponential. Therefore

$$f(t - L) = e^{-Ls} f(t) \tag{2–102}$$

The equation is in the form of output equals system function times input.   Consequently the system function for dead time is

$$G = e^{-Ls} \qquad (2\text{--}103)$$

This function will be dealt with more later on.

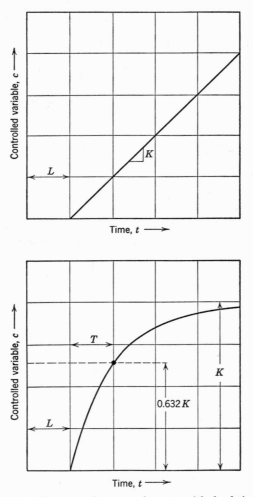

Fig. 2–23.   Response of process elements with dead time, **L**.

PROBLEMS

2–1.   Name the variables of a liquid-heating tank heated by electric current in an electric heater.

2–2. A dam in a small stream stores water and the outlet is adjustable by a weir. Name the variables.

2–3. A room is heated by a gas heater. Name some of the system variables.

2–4. A triangular weir has the equation

$$q = C_v \sqrt{2gh^5}$$

Calculate the resistance.

2–5. A flow-head device has the equation

$$q = h^n$$

Calculate the resistance.

2–6. A liquid storage vessel is spherical in shape. Calculate the capacitance as a function of head.

2–7. If the outflow at a vessel is proportional to the square root of head, what shape vessel results in a steady change of head?

2–8. If the outflow at a vessel is proportional to the square root of head, what shape vessel results in a rate of change of head proportional to the head?

2–9. Name five flow laws relating to fluids, heat, and electricity.

2–10. Calculate the gas capacitance of a 10-cu ft vessel containing air at room temperature.

2–11. Calculate the resistance of 1-sq ft area of a brick wall, 2.5 in. thickness.

2–12. Calculate the thermal capacitance of 1 gal of water.

2–13. Calculate the thermal capacitance of 1 cu in. of copper.

2–14. Which of the following five gases causes the greatest and which the least capacitance in the same vessel at the same temperature: air, ammonia, carbon dioxide, hydrogen, steam.

2–15. A system known to have a time-constant response requires 5 minutes to indicate 98 per cent of response. What is the time constant?

2–16. A tank operating at 10 ft head and 5 gpm outflow through a valve has a cross-section area of 10 sq ft. Calculate the time constant.

2–17. Show that the time constant of a liquid vessel with turbulent resistance is $T = 2HA/Q$.

2–18. If the greatest degree of slowness of action is required of a liquid-storage vessel, would a long cylinder be placed vertical or horizontal.

2–19. For a rectangular-shaped vessel of dimensions A_1, B_1, and L ft, calculate a number of capacitances.

2–20. An oscillatory element has a mass of 2000 lb, damping ratio D of one half, and a natural frequency oscillation of one cycle per minute. Calculate the spring constant K and damping rate D.

2–21. Heat conduction in a cylindrical element is governed by the Fourier Law:

$$q = KA \frac{\partial u}{\partial r}$$

Calculate the thermal resistance of a tube of length L, inside diameter D_i, and outside diameter D_o.

For the following problems, derive the system function relating the variables of the system:

2–22.

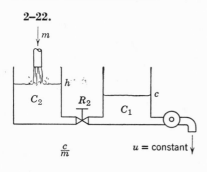

$\frac{c}{m}$ $u = \text{constant}$

2–23.

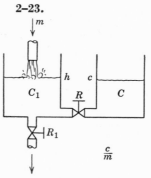

$\frac{c}{m}$

2–24.

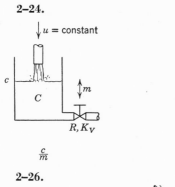

$\frac{c}{m}$

2–25.

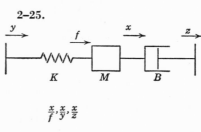

$\frac{x}{f}, \frac{x}{y}, \frac{x}{z}$

2–26.

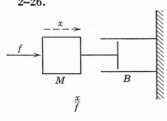

$\frac{x}{f}$

2–27.

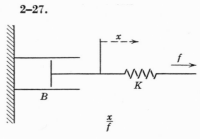

$\frac{x}{f}$

2–28.

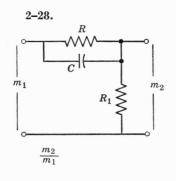

$\frac{m_2}{m_1}$

2–29.

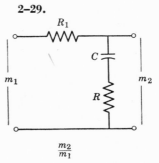

$\frac{m_2}{m_1}$

2–30.

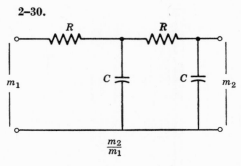

$$\frac{m_2}{m_1}$$

2–31.

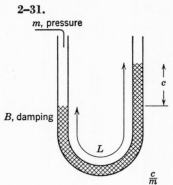

$$\frac{c}{m}$$

2–32.

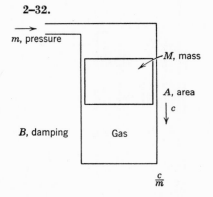

$$\frac{c}{m}$$

2–33.

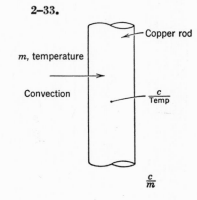

$$\frac{c}{m}$$

Controller Characteristics

The automatic controller, including its measuring means, determines the value of the controlled variable, compares the actual value to the desired value, determines the deviation, and produces the counteraction necessary to maintain the smallest possible deviation. The method by which the automatic controller produces the counteraction is called the mode of control or control action.

In analyzing a specific control problem a choice based on economic factors must be made among the various control actions. Generally speaking, the more difficult the control problem, the more complicated the controlling means become. This does not at all mean that a complicated automatic controller is necessary to produce good automatic control; on the contrary, the simplest control devices are often capable of providing a high quality of control.

The control actions discussed in this chapter may operate through either mechanical, pneumatic, hydraulic, or electric means. The various mechanisms of automatic controllers are discussed in Chapter 6.

The Automatic Controller

An automatic controller, Fig. 3–1, consists of a measuring means $(c \rightarrow b)$, an input means $(v \rightarrow r)$, an actuating signal means $(r, b, \rightarrow e)$, and a controlling means $(e \rightarrow m)$, where

$$c = \text{controlled variable}$$
$$b = \text{feedback variable}$$
$$v = \text{set point}$$
$$r = \text{reference input}$$
$$e = \text{actuating signal}$$
$$m = \text{manipulated variable}$$

59

The *measuring means* converts the controlled variable (temperature, pressure, etc.) into an indicated variable (usually a displacement, pressure, or electrical signal). The *input means* converts the set point

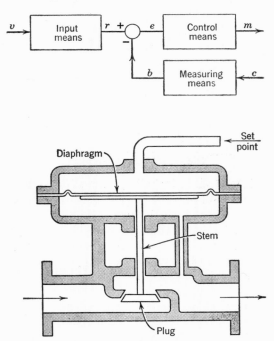

FIG. 3–1. Automatic controller diagrams.

(temperature, pressure, etc.) into a reference input of the same units as the feedback variable. The *actuating means* is simply a subtracting device following the law

$$e = r - b \qquad\qquad (3\text{–}1)$$

The *controlling means* alters the actuating signal by amplifying, differentiating, integrating, etc. to produce a controller output which operates a final control element for changing the magnitude of the manipulated variable m.

The remote-set pressure regulator of Fig. 3–1 contains all of these means. The measuring means is the diaphragm and lower chamber which converts the downstream pressure (the controlled variable c) into an upward force. The upward force is the feedback variable b. The input means is the diaphragm and upper chamber which converts the desired value of pressure (set point v) into a downward force. The downward force is the reference input r. The actuating means is the diaphragm which subtracts the reference input r and the feedback variable b to obtain the difference as the actuating signal e. The controlling means is the stem and plug which convert the actuating signal into a variation of flow of fluid through the regulator. The flow rate is the manipulated variable m.

The study of controlling means and the modes of control is made easier if some simplifications of these details are made. First, industrial automatic controllers usually involve a steady value of the set point. Consequently, the input means is usually a simple mechanical device and the set point is identical to the reference input expressed in the same units as the controlled variable. Thus, throughout this chapter we shall take

$$v \equiv r$$

Second, the measuring lag will be assumed negligible, so

$$c \equiv b$$

Therefore, the actuating signal e is termed the deviation, and

$$e = v - c = r - b$$

Deviation is the difference between controlled variable and set point expressed in units of the controlled variable c. The arrangement in Fig. 3-2 indicates these simplifications.

The controlling means includes the final control element which is usually some type of fluid-control valve. Throughout this chapter it is assumed that the final control element is a linear element such that the controller output (often a pneumatic pressure or

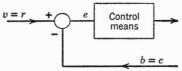

Fig. 3-2. Block diagram for an ideal automatic controller.

an electrical signal) produces a proportional change in fluid flow which is the manipulated variable m. Final control elements are discussed in more detail in Chapter 7.

Proportional Control

Proportional action is a mode of controller action in which there is a continuous linear relation between values of the deviation and manipulated variable. Thus the action of the controlled variable is repeated and amplified in the action of the final control element. For purposes of flexibility, an adjustment of the control action is provided and is termed proportional sensitivity.

Proportional control is illustrated by the liquid-level control of Fig. 3–3. The float lever is directly connected to the stem of the control valve. A set-point mechanism has been omitted from the figure. The controlled variable is the vessel head c and the manipulated variable is

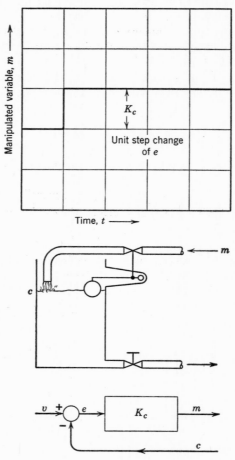

FIG. 3–3.   Proportional control action.

the vessel inflow m. The action of the controller is such that a rise of level c in the vessel rotates the valve operating lever clockwise thereby closing the valve a proportionate amount. This reduces the inflow to the vessel and tends to prevent the level from rising. If the distance from float bearing to connecting link is large, a small change in level produces a large change of flow into the vessel. If this distance is small, a large change in level results in a small change of flow into the vessel. Thus, proportional control follows the law

$$m = K_c e + M \qquad (3\text{--}2)$$

where m = manipulated variable
K_c = proportional sensitivity
M = a constant
e = deviation

The proportional sensitivity K_c is the change of manipulated variable caused by unit change of deviation. In the proportional controller of Fig. 3–3 the units of proportional sensitivity are cubic feet per foot-second. The proportional band is equivalent to the inverse of proportional sensitivity and is defined as the change in level necessary to operate the valve through full stroke. If the controller has a scale showing values of the controlled variable, the proportional band is the percentage of full scale change of the controlled variable required to operate the valve through full stroke.

The constant M in equation 3–2 may be termed the manual-reset constant because the selection of a value for M determines the normal (zero deviation) value of the manipulated variable. On most proportional controllers there is an adjusting knob or other mechanism for selecting the value of the constant.

The operation of proportional control action is illustrated in Fig. 3–3. For a step (sudden) change in deviation

$$e = 0 \qquad t < 0$$

$$e = E \qquad t \geqq 0 \qquad (3\text{--}3)$$

where E is a constant. Substituting in equation 3–2,

$$m - M = K_c E \qquad (3\text{--}4)$$

The change in manipulated variable corresponds exactly to the change in deviation with a degree of amplification depending upon the setting of proportional sensitivity K_c. Thus a proportional controller is simply an amplifier with adjustable gain.

Example 3–1. For the proportional controller of Fig. 3–3, the float arm is 14 in. long, the link to bearing distance is 2 in. and the valve stroke is 1 in. The valve passes 10 gal per minute when full open. What is the controller sensitivity?

$$K_c = \frac{\Delta m}{\Delta e} = \frac{\Delta q_i}{\Delta h} = \frac{0.134}{60} \times \frac{(10 - 0)}{(14/2 \times 1 - 0)1/12} = \underline{0.038 \text{ ft}^2/\text{sec}}$$

Example 3–2. A proportional controller has an output m changing linearly from 0 to 15 psi when the deviation e changes from -100 to 0 to 100 degrees. Calculate the controller sensitivity.

$$K_c = \frac{\Delta m}{\Delta e} = \frac{15 - 0}{100 - (-100)} = \underline{0.075 \text{ psi/deg}}$$

Integral Control

Integral action is a mode of control action in which the value of the manipulated variable m is changed at a rate proportional to the deviation. Thus if the deviation is doubled over a previous value, the final control element is moved twice as fast. When the controlled variable is at the set point (zero deviation), the final control element remains stationary.

Integral control is illustrated in Fig. 3–4. A set-point mechanism is omitted in the drawing. A variable ratio speed reducer, consisting of two parallel disks with a friction drive roller between, operates a control valve through gears. The left-hand disk is driven at constant speed by an electric or other motor. The position of the friction drive roller is set by the float and arm. The controller action is as follows: A rise in level in the tank causes the drive roller to move up from the neutral (zero speed) point. The speed of motion of the valve stem is proportional to the change in head. A fall of level moves the drive roller below the neutral point and the valve is moved at a proportionate speed in the opposite direction.

Integral control follows the law

$$\dot{m} = \frac{1}{T_i} e \tag{3-5}$$

or, in integrated form

$$m = \frac{1}{T_i} \int e \, dt + M \tag{3-6}$$

where m = manipulated variable
   T_i = integral time
   e = deviation
   M = constant of integration

The operational form of the equation is

$$m = \frac{1}{T_i s} e \tag{3-7}$$

and is indicated in Fig. 3–4.

The integral time T_i is defined as the time of change of manipulated variable caused by a unit change of deviation. In the example of Fig.

3–4, the units of integral time are seconds squared per square foot.   A
connection of the roller link in Fig. 3–4 closer to the float produces a
small integral time, and a connection closer to the float bearing produces
a large integral time.

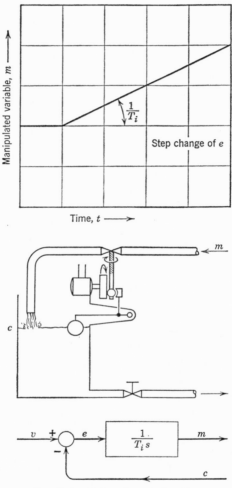

FIG. 3–4.   Integral control action.

Integral control action is shown in Fig. 3–4.   For a step change of
deviation

$$e = 0 \qquad t < 0$$
$$e = E \qquad t \geqq 0$$

(3–8)

where E is a constant. Substituting in equation 3–6 and integrating,

$$m - M = \frac{Et}{T_i} \tag{3–9}$$

Thus, the manipulated variable changes linearly with time and "integrates" the area under the deviation function. For a unit step change of deviation ($E = 1.0$), the slope of the line is inverse of the integral time.

Example 3–3. A hydraulic integral controller has an integral time of $\frac{1}{10}$ sec in. per in. When the deviation e is zero, the piston is at the middle of a 20-in. stroke. Calculate the rate of piston motion if the deviation changes suddenly by (a) 2 in., (b) −4 in.

Employing equation 3–5, (a) $\dot{m} = 10 \times 2 = 20$ in. per sec; (b) $\dot{m} = 10 \times (-4) = -40$ in. per sec.

A negative sign indicates that the piston moves in an arbitrarily negative direction.

Example 3–4. In a certain integral controller the deviation changes sinusoidally with time. Show that the phase of the manipulated variable m is always 90 degrees behind the deviation.

The deviation is taken to be

$$e = \sin \omega t$$

Then, from equation 3–6

$$m = \int \frac{1}{T_i} \sin \omega t \, dt + M$$

and

$$m = - \frac{1}{\omega T_i} \cos \omega t + M$$

Since the manipulated variable m is given by a negative cosine function, the phase lag is seen to be $\pi/2$ or 90 deg.

Proportional-Integral Control

Integral control action is often combined additively with proportional control action. The combination is termed proportional-integral action and is used for the purpose of obtaining certain advantages of both control actions.

Proportional-integral control action is defined by the following differential equation:

$$\dot{m} = \underbrace{\frac{K_c}{T_i} e}_{\text{integral}} + \underbrace{K_c \dot{e}}_{\text{proportional}} \tag{3–10}$$

or, in integrated form,

$$m = \underbrace{\frac{K_c}{T_i} \int e \, dt}_{\text{integral}} + \underbrace{K_c e}_{\text{proportional}} + M \tag{3–11}$$

where m = manipulated variable
$\quad K_c$ = proportional sensitivity
$\quad T_i$ = integral time
$\quad e$ = deviation
$\quad t$ = time
$\quad M$ = constant of integration

These equations illustrate the simple addition of proportional and integral control actions. In operational form

$$m = K_c \left(\frac{1}{T_i s} + 1 \right) e \qquad (3\text{--}12)$$

where the system function $K_c/(T_i s)$ identifies the integral action and the system function K_c identifies the proportional action.

Proportional-integral control action has two adjustment parameters, K_c and T_i, as indicated in equations 3–10, 3–11, or 3–12. The proportional sensitivity is defined the same as for the proportional control action: With the integral response turned off ($T_i \to \infty$), the proportional sensitivity is the number of units change in manipulated variable m per unit change of deviation e. Note in equation 3–12 that the proportional sensitivity K_c affects both the proportional and integral parts of the action.

The integral action adjustment is the integral time. For a step change of deviation e, the integral time is the time required to add an increment of response equal to the original step change of response as indicated in Fig. 3–5. Reset rate is defined as the number of times per minute that the proportional part of the response is duplicated. Reset rate is therefore called "repeats per minute" and is the inverse of integral time.

Proportional-integral control action is shown in Fig. 3–5. For a step change of deviation

$$e = 0 \qquad t < 0$$
$$\qquad \qquad \qquad \qquad \qquad (3\text{--}13)$$
$$e = E \qquad t \geqq 0$$

where E is a constant. Substituting in equation 3–11

$$m - M = K_c E \left(\frac{t}{T_i} + 1 \right) \qquad (3\text{--}14)$$

This is the equation for a straight line. The first term, t/T_i, is the integral response, and the second term is the proportional response. The latter is indicated by the dotted line of Fig. 3–5. Notice that the response of proportional-integral action in Fig. 3–5 is the simple addition of the proportional control action of Fig. 3–3 and the integral control action of Fig. 3–4.

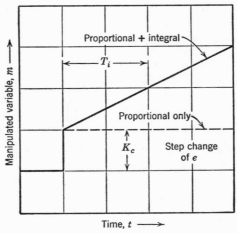

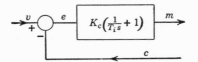

FIG. 3–5.   Proportional-reset control action.

Example 3–5.   A liquid-level controller has an output (proportional to the manipulated variable) given in psi pressure. A test of its action is made as follows: zero deviation is found by holding the float lever in a position to give zero rate of change of output. The float lever is then moved suddenly by 2.0 in. from the zero position. The output changes rapidly by 4 psi and then changes at the rate of 6 psi per minute. What is the controller sensitivity, and integral time?

$$\text{Sensitivity} = \underline{2 \text{ psi/in.}}$$

$$\text{Integral time} = \frac{4 \text{ psi}}{6 \text{ psi/min}} = \underline{0.67 \text{ min}}$$

Example 3–6.   The deviation e of a proportional-integral controller is sinusoidal. Calculate the phase lag of the output m and prove that the phase lag depends upon integral time.

Assume

$$e = \sin \omega t$$

Substituting in equation 3–11,

$$m = \frac{K_c}{T_i} \int \sin \omega t \, dt + K_c \sin \omega t + M$$

Integrating,

$$\frac{m - M}{K_c} = \frac{-1}{\omega T_i} \cos \omega t + \sin \omega t$$

Manipulating into a function of a double angle,

$$\frac{m - M}{K_c} = \sqrt{1 + \left(\frac{1}{\omega T_i}\right)^2} \sin \left(\omega t - \tan^{-1} \frac{1}{\omega T_i}\right)$$

The phase is the second term of the angle:

$$\text{Phase} = \tan^{-1}\left(-\frac{1}{\omega T_i}\right)$$

The phase lag depends inversely upon integral time T_i: for large integral time, the phase lag is small; for small integral time, the phase lag is large.

Proportional-Derivative Control

A derivative control action may be added to proportional control action and the combination termed a proportional-derivative control action. Other terms for derivative response are rate response and lead component. Derivative control action may be defined as a control action in which the magnitude of the manipulated variable is proportional to the rate of change of deviation.

A proportional-derivative control action is defined by

$$m = \underbrace{K_c e}_{\text{proportional}} + \underbrace{K_c T_d \dot{e}}_{\text{derivative}} + M \tag{3-15}$$

where m = manipulated variable
K_c = proportional sensitivity
e = deviation
T_d = derivative time
M = a constant

and is the simple addition of proportional controller action and rate controller action as shown by the operational equation

$$m - M = K_c(1 + T_d s)e \tag{3-16}$$

Proportional-derivative action is not adequately described by employing a step change of deviation because the time derivative of a step change is infinite at the time of the change. Consequently, a linear change of deviation must be used:

$$e = Et \tag{3-17}$$

where E = a constant
t = time

Substituting in equation 3–16

$$m - M = K_c E(t + T_d) \qquad (3\text{–}18)$$

The deviation is defined at time t, whereas the manipulated variable is defined at time $t + T_d$, and the net effect is to shift the manipulated variable *ahead* by a time T_d, the derivative time. In other words as shown in Fig. 3–6, the controller response now *leads* the time change of

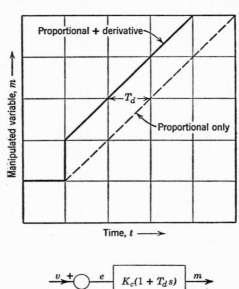

FIG. 3–6.   Proportional-derivative control action.

deviation. To this extent a derivative response "anticipates." Of course, a derivative response can never anticipate an action that has not yet taken place.

Derivative time is defined as the amount of lead, expressed in units of time, that the control action is given. In other words, derivative time is the time interval by which the rate action advances the effect of the proportional control action.

Example 3–7. A proportional-derivative controller has the following relation for the proportional action only:

deviation e, −5 to 5 in.
manipulated variable m, 0 to 1 volt

If the derivative time T_d is 5 seconds and the deviation e changes at a rate of $+2$ in. per minute, how much voltage output is added by the derivative action?

The proportional sensitivity is

$$K_c = \frac{\Delta m}{\Delta e} = \frac{1 - 0}{5 - (-5)} = 0.1 \text{ volt/in.}$$

From equation 3–18

$$m \text{ increment} = E(0.1)T_d$$
$$= \tfrac{2}{60}(0.1)5 = \underline{0.017 \text{ volt}}$$

Example 3–8. A proportional-derivative controller has a sensitivity K_c of 1.0, and a derivative time (T_d) of 1.0 min. If the deviation is sinusoidal, calculate the phase of oscillation of the manipulated variable.

The deviation may be given by

$$e = \sin \omega t$$

Substituting in equation 3–15,

$$m = K_c \sin \omega t + K_c T_d \omega \cos \omega t$$

and, writing as a function of a double angle,

$$m = K_c \sqrt{1 + (\omega T_d)^2} \sin (\omega t + \tan^{-1} \omega T_d)$$

The phase leads:

$$\text{Phase} = \tan^{-1} \omega T_d$$

which depends upon derivative time.

Proportional-Integral Derivative Action

The additive combination of proportional action, integral action, and derivative action is termed proportional-integral-derivative action. It is defined by the differential equation

$$\dot{m} = \frac{K_c}{T_i} e + K_c \dot{e} + K_c T_d \ddot{e} \tag{3–19}$$

or

$$m = \frac{K_c}{T_i} \int e \, dt + K_c e + K_c T_d \dot{e} + M \tag{3–20}$$

where m = manipulated variable
K_c = proportional sensitivity
T_i = integral time
e = deviation
T_d = derivative time
M = a constant

The operational equation is

$$m = K_c \left(\frac{1}{T_i s} + 1 + T_d s \right) e \qquad (3\text{--}21)$$

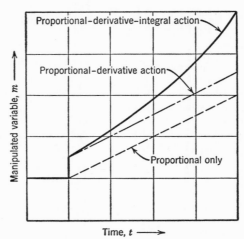

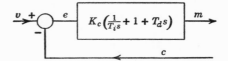

FIG. 3–7. Proportional-reset-derivative control action.

Proportional-integral-derivative control action is illustrated in Fig. 3–7 by plotting the change in manipulated variable for a linear time change of deviation. Assuming the deviation to be given by

$$e = Et \qquad (3\text{--}22)$$

where E = a constant
  t = time

and substituting in equation 3–20

$$m - M = K_c E \left[\frac{1}{T_i} \int t \, dt + t + T_d \right] \qquad (3\text{--}23)$$

Integrating the first term

$$m - M = K_c E \left[\frac{t^2}{2T_i} + t + T_d \right] \qquad (3\text{--}24)$$

The proportional part of the control action repeats the change of deviation (lower straight line). The derivative part of the control action adds an increment of manipulated variable so that the proportional plus derivative action is shifted ahead in time (middle straight line). The integral part of the control action adds a further increment of manipulated variable proportional to the area under the deviation line and, as Fig. 3–7 shows, the increment increases because the area increases at an increasing rate. The combination of proportional, integral, and derivative actions may be made in any sequence, because these actions are described by linear differential equations.

The three adjustment parameters, proportional sensitivity K_c, integral time T_i, and derivative time T_d are defined the same as for proportional-integral and proportional-derivative control actions.

Two-Position Control

The two-position control action, or on–off control, is undoubtedly the most widely used type of control for both industrial and domestic service. It is the kind of control generally employed on home-heating systems and domestic water heaters.

Two-position control is a position type of controller action in which the manipulated variable is quickly changed to either a maximum or minimum value depending upon whether the controlled variable is greater or less than the set point. The minimum value of the manipulated variable is usually zero (off). This mode of control is illustrated by the electric-level control in Fig. 3–8. A float in the vessel operates

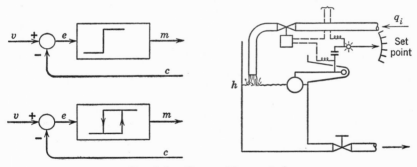

FIG. 3–8. Two-position control.

an electric switch which controls power to a solenoid valve. When the liquid level rises, the switch contacts are closed, the solenoid valve closes, and the inflow is cut off. When the liquid level falls, the switch contacts are opened, the solenoid valve opens, and the inflow resumes. If the float lever has no bearing friction and the electrical contacts draw no arc, the action is sharp or "knife-edge" as shown in Fig. 3–9.

The equations for two-position control are

$$m = M_1 \qquad \text{when} \quad e > 0$$
$$m = M_0 \qquad \text{when} \quad e < 0 \tag{3-25}$$

where m = manipulated variable
M_1 = maximum value of manipulated variable (on)
M_0 = minimum value of manipulated variable (off)
e = deviation

Thus two-position control must be described by two equations, each applying in a certain region of deviation.

A *differential gap* in two-position control causes the manipulated variable to maintain its previous value until the controlled variable has moved slightly beyond the set point. In actual operation it is the same as hysteresis, as may be seen from Fig. 3–9.

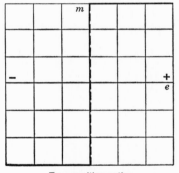

Two-position action

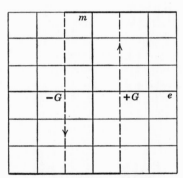

Two-position action
with differential-gap

FIG. 3–9. Two-position control with and without differential gap.

A differential gap is caused in the two-position controller of Fig. 3–8 if small static friction exists at the bearing on the float arm. The liquid level must then rise slightly above the desired value to create sufficient buoyant force to overcome friction when the level is rising. Also, the liquid level must fall slightly below the desired value when the level is falling so that the weight force may overcome the friction. This kind of differential gap may be caused by unintentional friction and lost motion.

A differential gap may be intentional, as when a magnet is installed on the float arm in Fig. 3–8, causing a hysteresis in float-arm action.

Similar arrangements are common in domestic thermostats and are employed for the purpose of preventing rapid operation of switches and solenoid valves and for reducing arcing of electrical contacts.

The three-position mode of control is one in which the manipulated variable takes one of three values: high, medium, or low, depending upon whether the deviation is large positively, close to zero, or large negatively. Similarly, four- and five-position control may be used.

Single-Speed Floating Control

In the single-speed floating mode of control the manipulated variable changes at a constant rate in one direction when the deviation is positive and in the opposite direction at a constant rate when the deviation is negative. This action may be visualized from Fig. 3–8 if the solenoid is replaced by a reversible motor with gear reducer to move the control

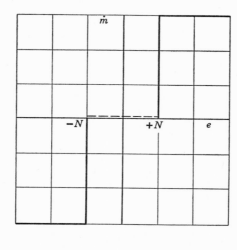

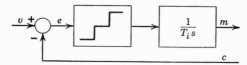

Fig. 3–10.   Single-speed floating control.

valve stem. When the level rises, the switch contact is made, and the motor-reducer slowly closes the control valve. As soon as the level falls, the switch contact is broken and the motor-reducer reverses its direction of rotation and opens the control valve. (A double-throw electrical relay may be required.)

A neutral zone is used in single-speed floating control so that the motor remains stationary when the deviation is small, as indicated in Fig. 3–10. The equations for single-speed floating control with neutral zone are

$$\dot{m} = M_1 \qquad \text{when} \quad e > +N$$
$$\dot{m} = 0 \qquad \text{when} \quad +N > e > -N \qquad (3\text{–}26)$$
$$\dot{m} = -M_0 \qquad \text{when} \quad e < -N$$

where N is the neutral zone in units of deviation.

Multispeed floating control is sometimes used in which several rates of change of the manipulated variable correspond to several magnitudes of deviation.

PROBLEMS

3–1.   Prove that the sum of a sine wave and a cosine wave is another sine wave of different amplitude and phase.

$$A \sin \omega t + B \cos \omega t = \sqrt{A^2 + B^2} \sin \left(\omega t + \tan^{-1} \frac{B}{A} \right)$$

Use Euler's relation $e^{ix} = \cos x + i \sin x$ or employ vectors in the proof.

3–2.   A controller has the function $m = (1 + T_1 s + T_2{}^2 s^2)e$ which includes an effect of the second derivative.   Plot the steady-state response m if $e = \sin \omega t$.   Use $T_1 = T_2 = 1/\omega$.

3–3.   A controller has the function

$$m = \frac{1}{T^2} \int \int e \, dt \, dt + M$$

Prove that the phase of the output lags 180 degrees behind the input.

3–4.   A controller has the following functions in series: $(T_1 s + 1)$, $(T_2 s + 1)$, $1/Ts$.   What parameters determine derivative time, proportional sensitivity, and integral time?

For the problems below, determine what control actions are present and state the parameters derivative time, proportional sensitivity, and integral time if they exist.

3–5.   **3–6.**

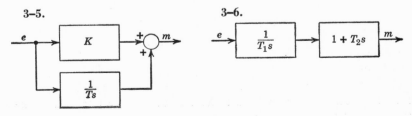

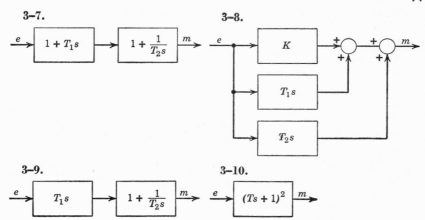

3-7.

$e \rightarrow \boxed{1 + T_1 s} \rightarrow \boxed{1 + \dfrac{1}{T_2 s}} \xrightarrow{m}$

3-8.

3-9.

$e \rightarrow \boxed{T_1 s} \rightarrow \boxed{1 + \dfrac{1}{T_2 s}} \xrightarrow{m}$

3-10.

$e \rightarrow \boxed{(Ts + 1)^2} \xrightarrow{m}$

chapter 4

Closed Loop
in Automatic Control

The problem of process control originates with the necessity for minimizing the effect of changes in load variables. The process and the automatic controller, acting together, comprise the controlled system, and the characteristics of the process as well as the characteristics of the controller affect the performance of the complete system.

Closing the Loop

The closed-loop system is obtained by connecting the process and the automatic controller as shown by the operational diagram of Fig. 4–1. Feedback is denoted in the diagram by the lower line acting to the left.

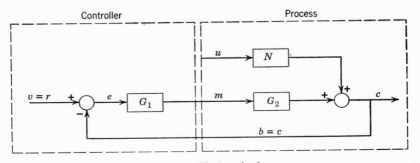

FIG. 4–1. Closing the loop.

This feedback is negative, so that an increase in the controlled variable c effects a reduction of the manipulated variable m, which in turn acts to reduce the amount of change of the controlled variable. Thus the alternate name for automatic control is negative feedback control, or just feedback control.   Feedback is physically embodied in the measuring element of the automatic controller.

The study of automatic control throughout this chapter is made under the following assumptions:

1. The measuring lag of the controller is zero so that the controlled variable is the feedback variable: $b = c$.

2. The controller lag is zero so that the control actions are those described in the previous chapter.

The analysis of the action of the controlled system requires the use of the differential equations describing the action of each element of the system: the process equation as developed in Chapter 2, the controller equation, and the deviation equation as developed in Chapter 3.

The *process equation* in general operational form is, from Fig. 4–1

$$c = G_2 m + \sum_{i=1}^{n} N_i u_i \tag{4-1}$$

where G_2 = process system function
N_i = process load function

It is assumed that there are n load variables at the process, whereas only one load is indicated in Fig. 4–1.

The *controller equation* in general operational form is

$$m = G_1 e \tag{4-2}$$

where G_1 = controller system function

The deviation equation is

$$e = v - c \tag{4-3}$$

The study of controlled system behavior is usually made in steps beginning with the calculation of open-loop performance.   That is, if there were no feedback in Fig. 4–1, the response of the controlled variable to changes in deviation or to changes in load variable would be given by the combination of the controller equation 4–2 and the process equation 4–1:

$$c = G_1 G_2 e + \sum_{i=1}^{n} N_i u_i \tag{4-4}$$

This equation represents the open-loop response and is often found by testing the particular system under study.

The closed-loop performance is found by combining equations 4–1, 4–2, and 4–3 to eliminate variables m and e:

$$c = \left(\frac{G_1 G_2}{1 + G_1 G_2}\right) v + \sum_{i=1}^{n} \left(\frac{N_i}{1 + G_1 G_2}\right) u_i \qquad (4\text{–}5)$$

This equation relates the magnitude of the controlled variable to the magnitude of the set point v and magnitude of load variables u_i.

The closed-loop performance is also found from the same equations by eliminating variables m and c:

$$e = \left(\frac{1}{1 + G_1 G_2}\right) v - \sum_{i=1}^{n} \left(\frac{N_i}{1 + G_1 G_2}\right) u_i \qquad (4\text{–}6)$$

The deviation is the same as the actuating signal e because the measuring lag is zero (thus $b = c$), and because the set point v is the same as reference input r.

The closed-loop equations 4–5 and 4–6 illustrate that there are two direct sources of deviation:

(a) variation of load variables, u_i
(b) variation of set point, v

These sources are regarded as the "disturbances," the effect of which the automatic controller is expected to minimize.

From the standpoint of industrial process control we are generally interested in that part of the deviation due to changes in load variable. For a constant set point, the deviation caused by any one of the load variables u is

$$e_u = -\left(\frac{N_i}{1 + G_1 G_2}\right) u_i \qquad (4\text{–}7)$$

From the standpoint of "following" changes of set-point v, but with all load variables u constant, the deviation is

$$e_v = \left(\frac{1}{1 + G_1 G_2}\right) v \qquad (4\text{–}8)$$

The deviation resulting from a variation of set point is sometimes employed to establish stability of performance of the system.

Proportional Control

One of the simplest closed loops in automatic control is the proportional control of the single-capacitance process shown in Fig. 4–2. On the physical diagram a circle symbol indicates that an automatic controller controls a variable of the process (*LC* indicates a level control in this example). The controller operates a control (throttling) valve at the inflow line.

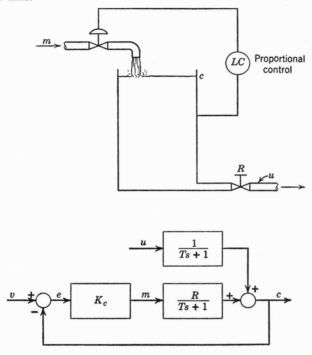

FIG. 4–2. Proportional control of a single-capacitance process.

The process equation is written under the assumptions that the upstream head at the control valve is constant:

$$c = \left(\frac{R}{Ts + 1}\right) m + \left(\frac{1}{Ts + 1}\right) u \qquad (4\text{–}9)$$

where c = controlled variable = vessel head
 R = resistance of outlet valve
 $T = RA$ = vessel time constant
 A = vessel capacitance = area
 m = manipulated variable = inflow
 u = load variable = downstream head

The control equation for proportional control is[1]

$$m = K_c e = K_c(v - c) \tag{4-10}$$

where K_c = proportional sensitivity

The system operational equation is obtained by combining equations 4–9 and 4–10 to eliminate variables m and c:

$$e = \left(\frac{1}{RK_c + 1}\right)\left(\frac{Ts + 1}{T_1 s + 1}\right) v - \left(\frac{1}{RK_c + 1}\right)\left(\frac{1}{T_1 s + 1}\right) u \tag{4-11}$$

where $T_1 = T/(RK_c + 1)$. For a constant value of set point v and for a step change of the load variable u, the deviation is

$$e = -\left(\frac{U}{RK_c + 1}\right)\left(\frac{1}{T_1 s + 1}\right) \tag{4-12}$$

where U = magnitude of step change in load. The differential equation is found by inverting the operational equation 4–12:

$$T_1 \dot{e} + e = \frac{-U}{RK_c + 1} \tag{4-13}$$

A particular solution of equation 4–12 is plotted in Fig. 4–3 for several values of the parameter RK_c. A value of the parameter $RK_c = 0$ represents the response of the process without automatic control. There can be no doubt that the use of proportional control has considerably reduced the effect of variation of load variable u in two ways:

1. Smaller offset: Offset E_o is a steady deviation resulting from a step change in load variable and is characteristic of proportional control. Without automatic control the offset is U and is equal to the change in

[1] Ordinarily the proportional control equation is written

$$m = K_c e + M$$

where M is the value of inflow when deviation e is zero. The constant M is suppressed by writing

$$(m - M) = K_c e$$

and measuring the value of inflow m from the zero-deviation value M so that

$$m = K_c e$$

This procedure is followed in all equations in this chapter by measuring values of the variables c, e, m, and u from the "normal" value existing when the deviation is zero. This procedure makes it unnecessary to carry all the constants through each step of manipulation of the equations.

outlet-valve downstream head. With proportional control the offset is

$$E_o = \frac{-U}{RK_c + 1} \qquad (4\text{--}14)$$

Thus as the proportional sensitivity K_c is increased, the offset is reduced. The offset characteristic of proportional control is caused by the definite proportional relationship that must exist between deviation and manipulated variable.

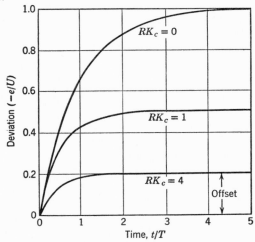

FIG. 4–3. Response of proportional control of a single-capacitance process.

2. Faster stabilization: With proportional control the time to reach 98 per cent of the final value is about four time constants or

$$\text{Stabilizing time} = \frac{4RA}{RK_c + 1} \qquad (4\text{--}15)$$

Thus, as the proportional sensitivity K_c is increased, the stabilizing time is considerably reduced.

A high value of proportional sensitivity K_c reduces offset and decreases stabilizing time, and, in this case, an extremely high proportional sensitivity could theoretically be used. In an actual application, there is an upper limit of proportional sensitivity that cannot be exceeded because excessive oscillation would result. The oscillation would be caused by any existing measuring lag and controlling lag that were not included in this analysis.

Example 4–1. Calculate the offset and stabilization time for the level control system shown in the figure.

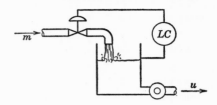

Given u = 2.0 cfs
$\qquad U$ = 0.1 cfs step increase
$\qquad K_c$ = 2 cfs/ft
$\qquad A$ = 10 sq ft

The process equation is (if outflow u does not depend on head)

$$c = \left(\frac{1}{As}\right) m - \left(\frac{1}{As}\right) u$$

The controller equation is, for proportional control,

$$m = (K_c)e = (K_c)(v - c)$$

The system equation is

$$e = \left(\frac{Ts}{Ts + 1}\right) v + \left(\frac{1/K_c}{Ts + 1}\right) u$$

where T = system time constant = A/K_c

For a step increase in the load variable only

$$T\dot{e} + e = \frac{U}{K_c}$$

The offset is

$$E_o = \frac{U}{K_c} = \frac{0.1}{2} = 0.05 \text{ ft decrease of head}$$

The stabilizing time is about four times the time constant:

$$\text{Stabilizing time} = 4\,\frac{A}{K_c} = \frac{40}{2} = \underline{20 \text{ sec}}$$

Proportional control of a two-capacitance process, as in Fig. 4–4, is a more practical example of automatic control. The process equation is

$$c = \frac{R_1}{(T_1s + 1)\,(T_2s + 1)}\, m + \frac{R_1}{T_1s + 1}\, u \qquad (4\text{--}16)$$

where $\quad c$ = controlled variable = head in lower vessel
$\qquad R_1$ = resistance of lower outlet valve
$\qquad T_1$ = time constant of lower vessel = R_1A_1
$\qquad T_2$ = time constant of upper vessel = R_2A_2
$\qquad m$ = manipulated variable = inflow to upper vessel
$\qquad u$ = load variable = inflow to lower vessel

Combining equations 4–16 and the proportional control equation to eliminate the controlled variable c, the relation between deviation, set point, and load variable is

$$e = \frac{(T_1s + 1)(T_2s + 1)}{(T_1s + 1)(T_2s + 1) + R_1K_c} v - \frac{R_1(T_2s + 1)}{(T_1s + 1)(T_2s + 1) + R_1K_c} u$$

$$(4\text{-}17)$$

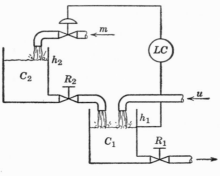

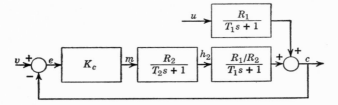

Fig. 4-4. Proportional control of a two-capacitance process (see Fig. 2-14).

This equation can be placed in a more convenient form:

$$e = \left(\frac{1}{R_1K_c + 1}\right) \frac{(T_1s + 1)(T_2s + 1)}{T^2s^2 + 2\zeta Ts + 1} v -$$

$$\left(\frac{R_1}{R_1K_c + 1}\right) \frac{(T_2s + 1)}{T^2s^2 + 2\zeta Ts + 1} u \quad (4\text{-}18)$$

where $T = \sqrt{\dfrac{T_1T_2}{R_1K_c + 1}}$ = characteristic time $\qquad (4\text{-}19)$

$$\zeta = \sqrt{\frac{(T_1 + T_2)^2}{4T_1T_2(R_1K_c + 1)}} = \text{damping ratio} \qquad (4\text{-}20)$$

The response of the controlled system to a change of load variable u and with the set point v fixed may be found by returning equation 4-18 to differential form:

$$T^2\ddot{e} + 2\zeta T\dot{e} + e = -\left(\frac{R_1}{R_1K_c + 1}\right)(T_2\dot{u} + u) \qquad (4\text{-}21)$$

For a step change of load variable u, equation 4–21 becomes by substituting $u = U$

$$T^2 \ddot{e} + 2\zeta T \dot{e} + e = E_o \qquad (4\text{--}22)$$

and

$$E_o = - \frac{R_1 U}{R_1 K_c + 1} = \text{offset} \qquad (4\text{--}23)$$

Equation 4–22 is a second-order linear differential equation and its solution depends upon the characteristic time T and the damping ratio ζ. The solutions may be classified according to damping.

(a) Underdamped or oscillatory, $\zeta < 1.0$.
(b) Critically damped $\zeta = 1.0$.
(c) Overdamped $\zeta > 1.0$.

Several solutions are plotted in Fig. 4–5. A control parameter $R_1 K_c$ of zero represents the response of the process without automatic control. The effect of proportional control is to reduce considerably the deviation.

The choice of a value of proportional sensitivity K_c determines the damping ratio ζ of the system. As proportional sensitivity K_c is made smaller, the response is made more stable, but the offset is larger. A compromise value of proportional sensitivity giving a damping ratio ζ of about 0.33 is generally considered satisfactory. Then from equation 4–20 above

$$R_1 K_c = \frac{1}{4\zeta^2} \left(\frac{T_2}{T_1} + \frac{T_1}{T_2} + 2 \right) - 1 \qquad (4\text{--}24)$$

The "best" proportional sensitivity may be calculated by equation 4–24 for this particular process.

The frequency of oscillation in cycles per unit time is given by

$$f = \frac{1}{4\pi} \left(\frac{T_1 + T_2}{T_1 T_2} \right) \sqrt{(1/\zeta^2) - 1} \qquad (4\text{--}25)$$

It is interesting to note that from the standpoint of stability there is no difference whether the first vessel or the second vessel is the larger of the two, because the damping ratio ζ and frequency of oscillation have the same value when the time constants are interchanged.

The effect of dead time in proportional control is shown by the test results of Fig. 4–5. The proportional sensitivity must be greatly reduced (proportional band increased) in order to maintain stability. Thus, the offset is large, and the stabilization is slow. It is readily observed that a small dead time causes serious consequences in proportional control.

The characteristics of proportional control are summarized in the magnitude of offset accompanying a change in one of the load variables of the process. If changes in load variables are small, proportional con-

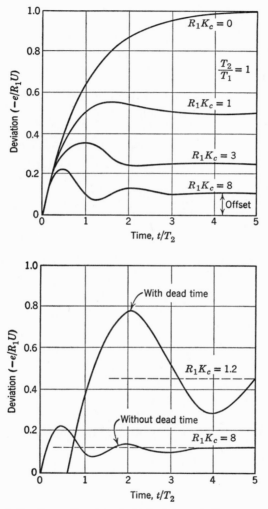

FIG. 4–5. Proportional control of a two-capacitance process.

trol is almost always effective. Furthermore, if all the time constants (lags) of the controlled system except one are small, the proportional sensitivity may be made large and the offset is small under any conditions.

Example 4–2. A process (Fig. 4–4) has time constants of $T_1 = 10$ sec, and $T_2 = 20$ sec. The outlet resistance (R_1) is 10 sec per sq ft. Calculate the proportional sensitivity for a damping ratio of one third. Calculate the offset for a change of downstream head of 1 ft.

From equation 4–24

$$K_c = \tfrac{1}{10}[(2 + \tfrac{1}{2} + 2)\tfrac{9}{4} - 1] = \underline{0.91 \text{ sq ft/sec}}$$

From equation 4–23

$$-E_o = \frac{10 \times 1}{9.1 + 1} = \underline{0.99 \text{ ft}}$$

Example 4–3. A process can be designed so that two vessels as in Fig. 4–4 have the characteristics:

(a) $T_1 = T_2 = 60$ sec, and $R = 1/8$ sec per sq ft or (b) $T_1 = 30$ sec, $T_2 = 120$ sec, and $R = 1/8$ sec per sq ft. Which design provides the least offset? Which design provides the fastest response (frequency)?

(a) $$K_c = 8 \times [(1 + 1 + 2)\tfrac{9}{4} - 1] = 64.0 \text{ cfs/ft}$$

$$-\frac{E_o}{U} = \frac{1}{8}\left(\frac{1}{8+1}\right) = \underline{0.013 \text{ ft per unit of } U}$$

$$f = \frac{1}{4\pi}\left(\frac{60 + 60}{60 \times 60}\right)\sqrt{1/\zeta^2 - 1} = \underline{0.0075 \text{ cps}}$$

(b) $$K_c = 8[(4 + \tfrac{1}{4} + 2)\tfrac{9}{4} - 1] = 104 \text{ cfs/ft}$$

$$-\frac{E_o}{U} = \frac{1}{8}\left[\frac{1}{13.1 + 1}\right] = \underline{0.009 \text{ ft per unit of } U}$$

$$f = \frac{1}{4\pi}\left(\frac{30 + 120}{30 \times 120}\right)\sqrt{1/\zeta^2 - 1} = \underline{0.0094 \text{ cps}}$$

This example illustrates the rule that all lags in the system except one should be small. The process above with the small tank and the large tank provides less offset and faster response.

Integral Control

Integral control is often employed for control of fluid flow, liquid level, and pressure. Consider integral control of the single-capacitance process of Fig. 4–6. The process equation is

$$c = \frac{R}{Ts + 1}\, m + \frac{1}{Ts + 1}\, u \qquad (4\text{–}26)$$

where c = controlled variable = vessel head
  T = vessel time constant = RC
  R = resistance of outlet valve
  C = vessel capacitance = A = area
  m = manipulated variable = inflow
  u = load variable = downstream head

The control equation is

$$m = \frac{1}{T_i s} e = \frac{1}{T_i s} (v - c) \qquad (4\text{-}27)$$

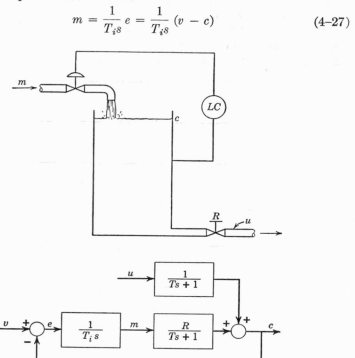

FIG. 4–6.   Integral control of a single-capacitance process.

where T_i = integral time of integral controller.   The system equation
is obtained by eliminating m and c between equations 4–26 and 4–27.

$$e = \frac{T_i s}{R}\left(\frac{Ts + 1}{T_c^2 s^2 + 2\zeta T_c s + 1}\right) v - \frac{T_i s}{R}\left(\frac{1}{T_c^2 s^2 + 2\zeta T_c s + 1}\right) u \qquad (4\text{-}28)$$

where $T_c = \sqrt{\dfrac{TT_i}{R}}$ = characteristic time

$$\zeta = \sqrt{\frac{T_i}{4RT}} = \text{damping ratio}$$

Reverting to differential form for a step change in the load variable
$(u = U)$,

$$T_c^2 \ddot{e} + 2\zeta T_c \dot{e} + e = 0 \qquad (4\text{-}29)$$

GULF COAST TECHNICAL INSTITUTE

This is a second-order linear differential equation and its solution depends upon the damping ratio.

Several solutions are plotted in Fig. 4–7. The offset is zero as predicted by the system equation, because the integral control action forces a complete return to the set point when there is a change in load.

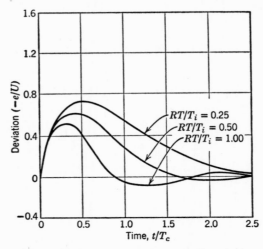

FIG. 4–7. Response of integral control of a single-capacitance process.

The integral time T_i of the controller must be selected to provide proper damping. Since there is no offset, a moderate damping ratio may be chosen and a value of about one third is usually satisfactory. Then, the integral time can be computed from

$$T_i = 4\zeta^2 RT \tag{4-30}$$

With this value of integral time a minimum deviation is obtained without encountering excessive oscillation.

Instability is possible with integral control when the process does not have self-regulation. The arrangement of Fig. 4–8 illustrates this. The process equation is (if the outflow does not depend upon head)

$$c = \frac{1}{Cs}m - \frac{1}{Cs}u \tag{4-31}$$

where c = controlled variable = head in vessel
C = capacitance of vessel = area
m = manipulated variable = inflow
u = load variable = outflow

Employing the control equation and the deviation equation as in the example above, the system equation becomes

$$CT_i\ddot{e} + e = CT_i\ddot{v} + T_i\dot{u} \qquad (4\text{-}32)$$

The transient solution to this second-order differential equation is a sinusoidal function without damping. Therefore, this system arrange-

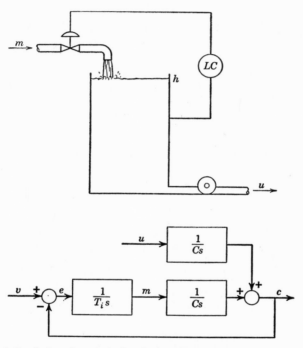

FIG. 4–8. Integral control of a single-capacitance process (unstable).

ment produces a continuous oscillation of the controlled variable. Fortunately most industrial processes have self-regulation and this difficulty is usually avoided.

Integral control may be employed for control of fluid-flow rate as shown in Fig. 4–9. The flow controller FC adjusts a throttling valve in series with the metering device so as to maintain a constant differential head $u_0 - h_1$ across the metering device. The "process" equation is (see Chapter 2)

$$c = K_a m + K_b (u_0 - u_2) \qquad (4\text{-}33)$$

where c = controlled variable = liquid flow rate

$\quad K_a$ = a constant

$\quad K_b$ = a constant

$\quad m$ = position of throttling valve

Equation 4–33 is valid only in the operating region of flow rate where the partial derivative factors involved in the K's are nearly constant.

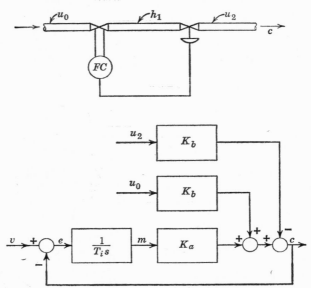

FIG. 4–9.   Integral control of liquid-flow rate.

Employing the same control equation and error equation as in the examples above, the system equation is

$$e = \frac{Ts}{Ts+1}\,v - \frac{K_bTsu_0}{Ts+1} + \frac{K_bTs}{Ts+1}\,u_2 \qquad (4\text{–}34)$$

where T = time constant = T_i/K_a. For a step change of load variable u_2, with upstream head u_0 and set point v constant, the differential equation becomes

$$T\dot{e} + e = 0 \qquad (4\text{–}35)$$

The solution to this equation is plotted in Fig. 4–10.

For a step change in load variable there is no offset. The response to changes in upstream head u_0 is the same as for changes in downstream head u_2 but in the opposite direction. The maximum initial deviation depends upon the magnitude of change in load variable and the ratio of partial derivatives (K's). The controller cannot reduce the maximum initial deviation because the change in upstream or downstream head immediately affects the flow rate before the controller is able to act. The time constant of the controlled system response T is reduced by decreasing the controller integral time. However, the integral time cannot be made extremely small because of other lags (time constants) that usually exist in the system.

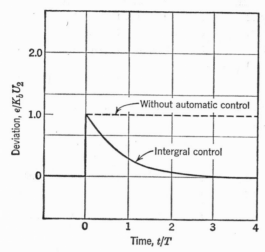

FIG. 4–10. Response of integral control of liquid-flow rate.

The characteristics of integral control contribute to the reduction or elimination of offset. Furthermore, integral control is effective only when there are few energy-storage elements in the process. Although it has not been demonstrated here, a few actual tests will show that a small dead time makes a system with integral control uncontrollable (steady or increasing oscillation).

Example 4–4. A process has a capacitance of 60 Btu per deg F and a resistance of 1.0 deg F per Btu per second. Calculate the integral time and the period of oscillation for integral control.

From equation 4–30, and with a damping ratio of $\frac{1}{3}$,

$$T_i = \frac{4RT}{9} = \frac{4 \times 1 \times 60}{9} = \underline{26.7 \text{ F sec}^2/\text{Btu}}$$

The period of oscillation is found from the characteristic time (T_c),

$$P = \frac{2\pi T_c}{\sqrt{1 - \zeta^2}} = 2\pi \sqrt{\frac{60 \times 26.7}{1(1 - \frac{1}{9})}} = \underline{84.0 \text{ sec}}$$

This example illustrates the point that integral control of processes with large time constants is slow; that is, the period of oscillation is long.

Proportional-Integral Control

Proportional control and integral control are often combined in order to obtain the advantages of inherent stability of proportional control and of elimination of offset by integral control. Proportional-integral control is the most generally useful of all types of control. We will consider examples of this type of control, first, for processes without storage elements, and second, for single-capacitance processes.

Proportional-integral control of fluid-flow rate is shown in Fig. 4–9. The process equation is,

$$c = K_a m + K_b(u_0 - u_2) \qquad (4\text{--}36)$$

where the quantities are defined as for equation 4–33. For proportional-integral control,

$$m = K_c \left(1 + \frac{1}{T_i s} \right) e \qquad (4\text{--}37)$$

where K_c = proportional sensitivity (inverse of proportional band)
T_i = integral time (inverse of reset rate)

Employing the deviation equation to eliminate c and m from the above two equations, the system equation is

$$e = \frac{1}{K_a K_c} \left(\frac{T_i s}{T s + 1} \right) v + \frac{K_b}{K_a K_c} \left(\frac{T_i s}{T s + 1} \right) (u_2 - u_0) \qquad (4\text{--}38)$$

where $T = T_i \dfrac{K_a K_c + 1}{K_a K_c}$

The response of the system to a step change in either load variable may be found from equation 4–38. For a step change in downstream head (u_2),

$$T\dot{e} + e = 0 \qquad (4\text{--}39)$$

The solution to this equation is plotted in Fig. 4–11 for representative values of K_a and K_b. Comparing this response to that of Fig. 4–10 for integral control only, it is seen that the effect of proportional control is to reduce the initial deviation. Naturally the offset is zero because of the integral action of the controller. Although the curves of Fig. 4–11 would indicate that the proportional sensitivity could be increased to a very high value, and the integral time decreased, in a practical application the existence of other lags in the controlled system prevents using high controller sensitivity and small integral time.

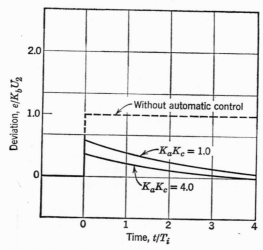

Fig. 4–11. Response of proportional-integral control of liquid-flow rate.

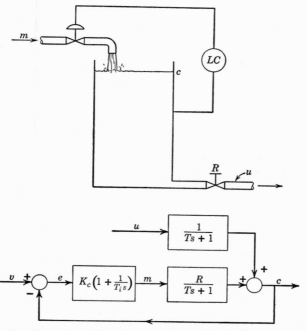

Fig. 4–12. Proportional-integral control of a single-capacitance process.

Another example of proportional-integral control is illustrated in Fig. 4–12. The level in the tank is controlled by adjusting the throttling valve at the tank inlet. The process equation is

$$c = \frac{R}{Ts + 1} m + \frac{1}{Ts + 1} u \qquad (4\text{--}40)$$

where c = controlled variable = h = vessel head
     R = resistance of outlet valve
     T = vessel time constant = RC
     C = vessel capacitance = A = vessel area
     m = manipulated variable = inflow
     u = load variable = downstream head

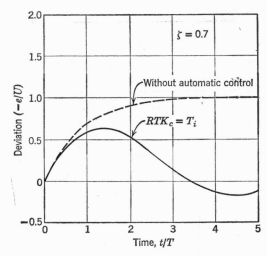

FIG. 4–13. Response of proportional-integral control of a single-capacitance process.

Combining the process equation 4–40 with the control equation 4–37 to eliminate m, and the deviation equation to eliminate c, there results

$$e = \frac{T_i s(Ts + 1)}{T_i s(Ts + 1) + RK_c(T_i s + 1)} v - \frac{T_i s}{T_i s(Ts + 1) + RK_c(T_i s + 1)} u$$
$$(4\text{--}41)$$

This equation may be placed in the more convenient form

$$RK_c e = \frac{T_i s(Ts + 1)}{T_c^2 s^2 + 2\zeta T_c s + 1} v - \frac{T_i s}{T_c^2 s^2 + 2\zeta T_c s + 1} u \qquad (4\text{--}42)$$

where $T_c = \sqrt{T_i T / R K_c}$ = characteristic time

$$\zeta = \sqrt{\frac{(RK_c + 1)^2 T_i}{4RK_c T}} = \text{damping ratio}$$

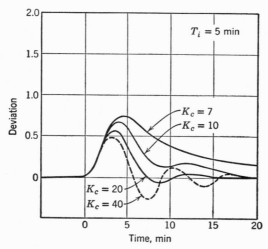

Changing proportional sensitivity

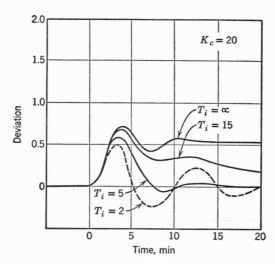

Changing integral time

FIG. 4–14. Adjustment of controller sensitivity and integral time for proportional-integral control.

The response of the system to a step change in load variable u but with constant set point v is found from equation 4–42. Rewriting the equation to differential form

$$T_c{}^2\ddot{e} + 2\zeta T_c\dot{e} + e = 0 \qquad (4\text{–}43)$$

The particular solution for given initial conditions is shown in Fig. 4–13. The damping ratio ζ in Fig. 4–13 is maintained constant at 0.707, a value that produces moderate oscillation. The character of the response depends upon the ratio of controller sensitivity and integral time. The results show that better response is obtained if large controller sensitivity and short integral time are used.

Proper values for controller sensitivity K_c and integral time T_i may be selected for any controlled system, but their calculation is complicated except for simple processes. The effect of these adjustments is illustrated in Fig. 4–14. The overall effect is relatively small in view of the wide range of variation of the control parameters. A proportional sensitivity between 20 and 40 is approximately optimum for this example. A higher proportional sensitivity produces greater oscillation and might actually result in an ever-increasing oscillation until some limit is reached. Referring to the bottom figure, infinite integral time (zero reset rate) allows the usual offset. An integral time of approximately 5 min is optimum. A further decrease of integral time usually results in excessive oscillation and may actually produce an increasing amplitude of cycle. The frequency of oscillation due to excessive integral action is much smaller than the frequency of oscillation caused by excessive proportional action.

Proportional-integral control may be employed for any process having characteristics amenable to the use of either response used separately. The limitations of proportional-reset control are due only to the excessive stabilization time required when the process has many energy storage elements or dead time.

Example 4–5. For proportional-integral control of process shown in the figure, calculate the relation between proportional sensitivity and integral time for a damping ratio of one-third. The process equation is

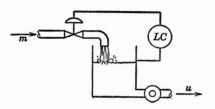

$$c = \frac{1}{Cs} m - \frac{1}{Cs} u$$

where C = process capacitance. The controller equation is

$$m = K_c \left(1 + \frac{1}{T_i s}\right) e + M$$

Combining to eliminate m and adding the deviation equation to eliminate c, and with outflow $u = M$, we have

$$e = \frac{CT_i s^2}{CT_i s^2 + K_c(T_i s + 1)} v$$

or

$$\frac{e}{v} = \frac{\dfrac{C}{K_c} T_i s^2}{T_c{}^2 s^2 + 2\zeta T_c s + 1}$$

where $T_c = \left(\dfrac{CT_i}{K_c}\right)^{\frac{1}{2}}$, $\zeta = \left(\dfrac{K_c T_i}{4C}\right)^{\frac{1}{2}}$

For a damping ratio of one-third

$$K_c T_i = \frac{4C}{9}$$

Use of Derivative Control

Derivative control action is useful for control of systems having a very large number of storage elements and for control of systems having dead time. As an example, consider the control of head in the lower vessel of Fig. 4–15. The process equation is

$$c = \frac{R}{T_1 s(T_2 s + 1)} m - \frac{1}{C_1 s} u \qquad (4\text{–}44)$$

where c = controlled variable = head in lower vessel
  C_1 = capacitance = A_1 = area of lower vessel
  T_1 = time constant = RC_1
  T_2 = upper vessel time constant = RC_2
  C_2 = capacitance = A_2 = area of upper vessel
  R = resistance of upper outlet valve
  m = manipulated variable = upper vessel inflow
  u = load variable = lower vessel outflow

For proportional derivative control the equation is

$$m = K_c(T_d s + 1)e \qquad (4\text{–}45)$$

where K_c = proportional sensitivity
  T_d = derivative time

Employing the usual deviation equation, the system equation is obtained by eliminating variables m and c,

$$e = \frac{T_1 s(T_2 s + 1)}{T_1 s(T_2 s + 1) + RK_c(T_d s + 1)} v +$$
$$\frac{R(T_2 s + 1)}{T_1 s(T_2 s + 1) + RK_c(T_d s + 1)} u \qquad (4\text{–}46)$$

This equation may be placed in more convenient form

$$e = \frac{1}{RK_c} \frac{T_1 s (T_2 s + 1)}{T_c^2 s^2 + 2\zeta T_c s + 1} v + \left(\frac{1}{K_c}\right) \frac{(T_2 s + 1)}{T_c^2 s^2 + 2\zeta T_c s + 1} u \quad (4\text{--}47)$$

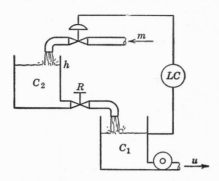

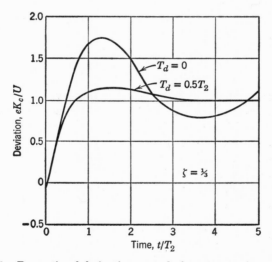

FIG. 4–15.   Proportional-derivative control of a two-capacitance process.

where $T_c = \sqrt{T_1 T_2 / RK_c}$ = characteristic time

$$\zeta = \sqrt{\frac{(T_1 + RK_c T_d)^2}{4RK_c T_1 T_2}} = \text{damping ratio}$$

The response of the system to a step change in load variable u may be found using the system equation 4–47 so that

$$T_c^2 \ddot{e} + 2\zeta T_c \dot{e} + e = U/K_c \quad (4\text{--}48)$$

where U is the change of load variable u. The particular solution is plotted in Fig. 4–15 for a damping ratio of one-third. Then, as derivative

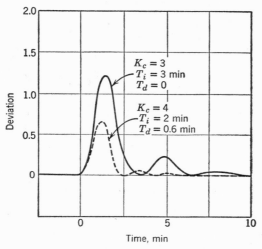

$K_c = 3$
$T_i = 3$ min
$T_d = 0$

$K_c = 4$
$T_i = 2$ min
$T_d = 0.6$ min

Time, min

(*A*) System with five storage elements

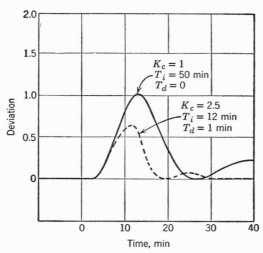

$K_c = 1$
$T_i = 50$ min
$T_d = 0$

$K_c = 2.5$
$T_i = 12$ min
$T_d = 1$ min

Time, min

(*B*) System with dead time

FIG. 4–16.   Use of derivative control.

action is added to the controller $(T_d = 0.5T_2)$, the increased damping becomes readily apparent. The advantage of derivative action is that the proportional sensitivity may now be made larger without producing excessive oscillation. This, in turn, reduces offset. It is sometimes possible through the use of proportional derivative control to reduce offset to such a small value that a integral control action would not be required.

Proportional-integral-derivative control is more effective for control of processes with many energy-storage elements than the proportional-integral control action used alone. The response of controlled systems with many energy-storage elements is difficult to calculate, so we rely upon the results of tests of an actual system as shown in Fig. 4–16. For controlled systems with many energy storage elements (Fig. 4–16(A)), the addition of derivative control action considerably reduces the maximum deviation and the time to stabilize at the set point. With derivative control, the proportional sensitivity may be increased and the integral time reduced. For controlled systems with dead time (Fig. 4–16(B)) similar results are obtained.

Comparison of Proportional, Integral, and Derivative Control

Each of the modes of control is applicable to processes having certain characteristics, and the importance of designing the controlled system must not be overlooked. If all processes consisted only of one capacitance without dead time, there would be no necessity for any complex control actions. The difficulty is that few if any industrial processes are so simple in dynamic structure.

The effectiveness of the various modes of control may be illustrated by comparing the responses to a load change on a given process. The process used for comparison is that of Fig. 4–4:

$$c = \frac{R_1}{(T_1 s + 1)(T_2 s + 1)} m + \frac{R_1}{(T_1 s + 1)} u \qquad (4\text{–}49)$$

where the vessel time constants are equal, $T = 20$ sec. As shown in Fig. 4–17, a change of inflow to the lower vessel may result in appreciable deviation for several minutes. The following comments apply to each type of control. The numbers correspond to the numbered curves of Fig. 4–17.

1. Proportional-derivative control provides the smallest maximum error because the derivative part of the response allows the proportional sensitivity to be increased to a high value. The stabilization time is the smallest because of the derivative action. Offset is allowed but is only half that experienced without derivative action.

2. Proportional-integral-derivative control has the next smallest maximum deviation and offset is eliminated because of the integral

action. Notice, however, that the addition of integral action markedly increases the stabilization time.

Curve	Mode of Control	Prop Sensitivity, RK_c	Integral Time, T_i, sec	Deriv Time, T_d, sec	Period of Cycle, sec	Damping $e^{-t/T}$ T, sec	Max Error units	Offset units
1	Proportional derivative	16	—	0.9	32	15	0.18	0.06
2	Prop int deriv	10	22	2.0	44	20	0.21	0
3	Proportional	8	—	—	45	20	0.29	0.11
4	Proportional integral	4	3	—	66	30	0.37	0
5	Integral	—	35	—	210	100	0.69	0

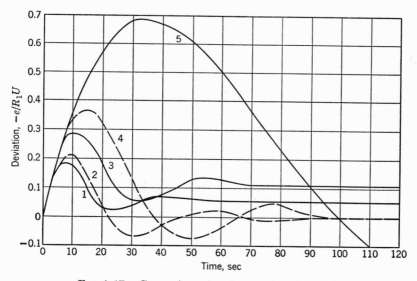

FIG. 4–17. Comparison of various modes of control.

3. Proportional control has a larger maximum deviation than controllers with derivative action because of the absence of this stabilizing influence. Offset is also larger.

4. Proportional-integral control has no offset because of the integral action. The unstabilizing influence of integral response is reflected in the large maximum deviation and the persisting deviation.

5. Integral control is best suited for the control of processes having little or no energy storage and the results of the comparison are not representative of all integral control. However, on this process, the results indicate a large maximum deviation and a long stabilization time.

With the results of this comparison in mind, it is logical to ask why proportional-integral-derivative control action is not universally employed. The answer is generally based on economic reasons, because each additional control action usually requires an additional piece of equipment that must be purchased, installed, and maintained. In addition, each control action may require adjustment of a parameter such as proportional sensitivity, integral time, or derivative time. This often requires considerable installation and maintenance time in order to obtain the proper adjustment of parameters. Consequently, the simplest mode providing adequate control is usually the most desirable.

Static Error, Offset, and Velocity Error

Deviation that results from a changing load or set point may be calculated directly without recourse to the complete solution of the system equations. For steady or steadily changing disturbances the particular integral of the differential equation provides the steady-state solution.

Static error results if, when the set point is changed from one value to another value, the controlled variable does not follow exactly. In other words a steady deviation results. A step change of set point is given by

$$v(t) = 0 \qquad t < 0$$
$$v(t) = V \qquad t \geq 0 \tag{4-50}$$

Thus V is the magnitude of change of the set point. Employing equation 4–8 for the set point deviation

$$e_v = \frac{V}{1 + G_1 G_2} \tag{4-51}$$

This equation represents the deviation as a function of time since G_1 and G_2 generally contain the operator s. For steady-state behavior all derivatives are zero, thereby implying that the operator s can be replaced by zero. The static error can therefore be calculated from the relation

$$E_s = \lim_{s \to 0} \left[\frac{V}{1 + G_1 G_2} \right] \tag{4-52}$$

In order to evaluate the static error it is only necessary to know the individual system functions G_1 and G_2.

Offset may result when the load on the system changes, thereby causing a steady deviation. For a step change in load u,

$$u(t) = 0 \qquad t < 0$$
$$u(t) = U \qquad t \geq 0 \tag{4-53}$$

where U is the magnitude of change of the load. Employing equation 4–7 for the load deviation, there results

$$e_u = \frac{-NU}{1 + G_1 G_2} \tag{4-54}$$

This equation represents the deviation as a function of time. For steady-state behavior we again replace s by zero and the offset is given by

$$E_o = \lim_{s \to 0} \left[-\frac{NU}{1 + G_1 G_2} \right] \tag{4-55}$$

The offset or load-static error as it is sometimes called may be calculated when the system functions N, G_1 and G_2 are known.

Velocity error results when the set point is a steadily changing quantity, and the controlled variable, in attempting to follow the steadily changing input, "lags" behind with a steady deviation. For a set-point change described by

$$\frac{dv}{dt} = A, \qquad t \geq 0 \tag{4-56}$$

where A = rate of change of the set point. In operational form,

$$sv = A \tag{4-57}$$

Substituting the latter equation in the deviation equation 4–8, there results

$$e_v = \frac{1}{s} \left(\frac{A}{1 + G_1 G_2} \right) \tag{4-58}$$

This equation represents the deviation as a function of time. For steady-state behavior all derivatives are zero so that the steady-state velocity error is given by[1]

$$E_v = \lim_{s \to 0} \left[\frac{1}{s} \frac{A}{1 + G_1 G_2} \right] \tag{4-59}$$

In order to evaluate the velocity error it is only necessary to know the system functions G_1 and G_2.

[1] The proof of this relationship is best found by employing the final value theorem of the La Place transform.

Example 4–6. Calculate the static error for the system in Fig. 4–4

$$E_s = \lim_{s \to 0} \left[\frac{V}{1 + \dfrac{R_1 K_c}{(T_1 s + 1)(T_2 s + 1)}} \right] = \frac{V}{R_1 K_c + 1}$$

Example 4–7. For the proportional-control system in Fig. 4–4, calculate the offset.

$$E_o = \lim_{s \to 0} \frac{-\dfrac{R_1 U}{T_1 s + 1}}{1 + \dfrac{R_1 K_c}{(T_1 s + 1)(T_2 s + 1)}} = \frac{-R_1 U}{R_1 K_c + 1}$$

Compare this result to that of equation 4–23.

Example 4–8. Determine the offset for the integral-control system of Fig. 4–6.

$$E_o = \lim_{s \to 0} \left[\frac{-\dfrac{U}{Ts + 1}}{1 + \dfrac{R}{T_i s (Ts + 1)}} \right] = \underline{0}$$

Thus integral control eliminates offset.

Example 4–9. Determine the velocity error for the system in Fig. 4–6.

$$E_v = \lim_{s \to 0} \left[\frac{1}{s} \frac{A}{1 + \dfrac{1}{T_i s} \left(\dfrac{R}{Ts + 1} \right)} \right] = \frac{A T_i}{R}$$

Therefore this type of system may have a steady velocity error.

Example 4–10. Determine the velocity error for the system in Fig. 4–4 with proportional-derivative control:

$$E_v = \lim_{s \to 0} \left[\frac{1}{s} \frac{A}{1 + \dfrac{R_1 K_c (1 + T_d s)}{(T_1 s + 1)(T_2 s + 1)}} \right] \to \underline{\infty}$$

The limit is infinite, meaning that the deviation increases without limit and that the controlled variable will gradually fall further and further behind the set point.

Two-Position Control

Two-position control has the widest industrial and domestic use on processes having not more than two energy-storage elements. In operation, two-position control is very simple, but in theory the action is difficult to analyze because of the discontinuous nature of changes in the manipulated variable. Nevertheless, problems of two-position control can be solved by quantitative consideration. In the discussion that follows, two-position control will be considered as having a differential gap and dead time, because few, if any, industrial controlled systems are without them.

The most elementary case of two-position control is illustrated in Fig. 4–18. The level control LC turns on the inflow when the level is

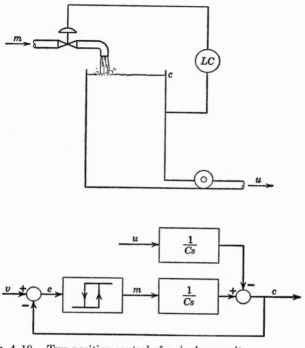

FIG. 4–18.   Two-position control of a single-capacitance process.

too low, and turns it off when the level is too high.   For an increase in level (valve open),

$$C\dot{c} = m - u \qquad \text{when} \quad c < v + G, \dot{c} > 0 \qquad (4\text{--}60)$$

and for a decrease in level (valve closed),

$$C\dot{c} = -u \qquad \text{when} \quad c > v - G, \dot{c} < 0 \qquad (4\text{--}61)$$

where C = vessel capacitance = vessel area
$\quad\;\; c$ = controlled variable = vessel head
$\quad\; m$ = manipulated variable = inflow
$\quad\;\; u$ = load variable = outflow
$\quad\;\; v$ = set point
$\quad\; G$ = differential gap

For constant values of manipulated variable, set point, and load, the above two equations may be integrated. For an increase in level

$$e_1 = \left(\frac{M - U}{C}\right) t + K_a \qquad \text{when} \quad e_1 < + G, \dot{e}_1 > 0 \quad (4\text{--}62)$$

For a decrease in level

$$e_1 = \left(\frac{-U}{C}\right) t + K_b \qquad \text{when} \quad e_1 > - G, \dot{e}_1 < 0 \quad (4\text{--}63)$$

where $e_1 = -e = (c - v) =$ deviation
  $U =$ value of load variable u
  $M =$ maximum value of manipulated variable m
  $K =$ constant of integration

Equations 4–62 and 4–63 describe the action of the system and are plotted in Fig. 4–19. As might be expected, the oscillation consists of a

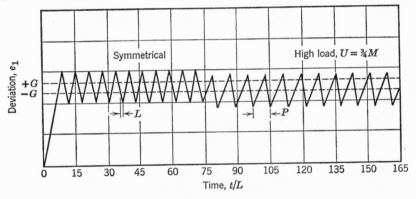

FIG. 4–19.   Two-position control of a single-capacitance process.

series of connected straight lines. The controlled variable "overshoots" the differential gap by a time equal to the dead time, L. Thus

$$A = G + \frac{ML}{2C} \qquad (4\text{--}64)$$

where $A =$ amplitude of oscillation. The double amplitude or total amplitude is $2A$. The amplitude of oscillation is not dependent upon the magnitude of the load variable. From Fig. 4–19 it is noted that a change of load variable may cause an unsymmetrical action, but whatever reduction of amplitude is gained on one side is lost on the other side. The amplitude also depends upon the size of the inlet valve M, the dead time L and the process capacitance C. For small amplitude the process capacitance should be large, the dead time should be small, and the inlet valve size should be just larger than that necessary to handle the largest load.

The period of cycle is calculated from the amplitude divided by the rate of change of the controlled variable:

$$P = \left(L + \frac{2GC}{M}\right) \frac{M^2}{U(M - U)} \tag{4-65}$$

where P = period of oscillation. Large, but not excessive, period is usually considered desirable because this reduces wear on the controlling mechanisms. Large period and small amplitude requires large process capacitance C and small inlet valve size M.

Example 4–11. The process of Fig. 4–18 has a steady outflow of 0.5 cu ft per sec, a vessel area of 1.0 sq ft and a dead time of 0.5 sec. The differential gap is 1 in. Calculate the amplitude and period of oscillation.

First calculate the valve size M. This should be about 50 per cent greater than the maximum outflow:

$$M = 1.5 \times 0.5 = 0.75 \text{ cfs}$$

The amplitude is

$$A = 1 + \frac{0.75 \times 0.5 \times 12}{2} = \underline{3.25 \text{ in.}}$$

The period is

$$P = \left(0.5 + \frac{2 \times 1 \times 1}{12 \times 0.75}\right) \times \left[\frac{(0.75)^2}{0.5(0.75 - 0.5)}\right] = \underline{3.2 \text{ sec}}$$

The second example of two-position control is shown in Fig. 4–20, differing from the previous example only in having a time-constant response. For an increase in level (valve open),

$$T\dot{c} + c = Rm + u \qquad \text{when} \quad c < v + G, \dot{c} > 0 \tag{4-66}$$

and for a decrease in level (valve closed),

$$T\dot{c} + c = u \qquad \text{when} \quad c > v - G, \dot{c} < 0 \tag{4-67}$$

where T = vessel time constant = RC
R = outlet-valve resistance
C = vessel capacitance = vessel area
c = controlled variable = vessel head
m = manipulated variable = inflow
u = load variable = downstream head
v = set point (at center of differential gap)
G = differential gap

For constant values of manipulated variable, set point, and load, the above two equations can be integrated. For an increase in level

$$e_1 = (e_a + V)(1 - e^{-t/T}) \quad \text{when} \quad e_1 < +G, \dot{e}_1 > 0 \quad (4\text{-}68)$$

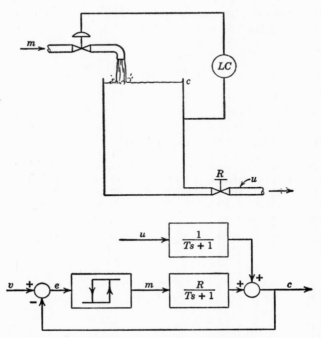

FIG. 4–20. Two-position control of a single-capacitance process.

For a decrease in level

$$e_1 = K_b(e^{-t/T}) + e_b \quad \text{when} \quad e_1 > -G, \dot{e}_1 < 0 \quad (4\text{-}69)$$

where $e_1 = -e = (c - V)$ = deviation
$e_a = RM + U - V$ = maximum potential
$e_b = (U - V)$ = minimum potential
M = maximum value of manipulated variable
U = value of load variable
V = value of set point
K_b = constant of integration

These two equations describe the response of the controlled variable and are plotted in Fig. 4–21. The oscillations are composed of segments of exponential curves. Without the operation of the controller, the controlled variable would have followed the dotted curves to the potential values (e_a, e_b). The "overshoot" beyond the differential gap is due to the dead time L. The period of oscillation depends directly upon the process time constant and upon the amplitude of oscillation. The amplitude is reduced by a small value of dead time L and a large value of process time constant T.

Two-position control of processes having more than one capacitance is similar in general respects to the control of single-capacitance processes. The additional capacitances of the system act to "round-off" the peaks of the controlled variable oscillation.

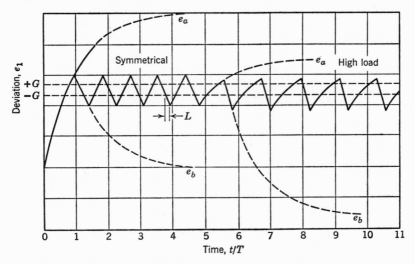

FIG. 4–21.   Two-position control of a single-capacitance process.

The differential gap is often intentionally introduced in two-position control in order to increase the period of oscillation and thereby reduce wear on the controlling mechanisms. As shown by equation 4–65 it is effective for this purpose. A negative differential gap is sometimes employed to reduce the amplitude of cycle, and, according to equation 4–64, this would be effective. If used carefully, and if the system parameters such as resistances and capacitances are constant, the amplitude of oscillation may be reduced somewhat.

In conclusion, two-position control is best suited for the control of single-capacitance processes in which the process capacitance is very large and dead time (or equivalent dead time) very small. There is little effect due to changes of load variables other than to alter the symmetry of the cycle,

Single-Speed Floating Control

Single-speed floating control is often useful for control of processes or systems having little or no capacitance and self-regulation. The controller is assumed to have a neutral zone; otherwise the controlled variable would oscillate continuously, because the manipulated variable would be changing continually in one direction or the other. A single-speed floating controller without a neutral zone acts in a manner similar to two-position control.

The operation of single-speed floating control is illustrated by the diagrams of Fig. 4–22. For a process such as liquid-flow rate which has no capacitance, a change in load variable (u_0 or u_2) causes an immediate but proportional change in controlled variable c. Then, as the controlled

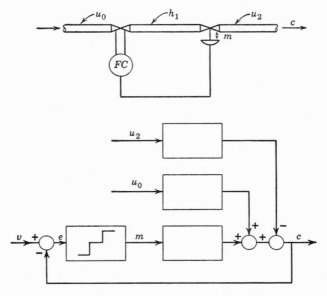

FIG. 4–22.   Single-speed floating control of liquid-flow rate.

variable moves out of the neutral zone, the throttling valve begins to close at a constant rate and the controlled variable returns to the neutral zone as shown in Fig. 4–23. (Compare this result to the integral control in Fig. 4–10 for the same process.) Therefore, single-speed floating control is stable for processes without capacitance or energy-storage elements as long as dead time is small. With dead time, the overshoot into the neutral zone requires increasing of the width of neutral zone

N and decreasing the floating rate so that the overshoot is less than the width of the neutral zone.

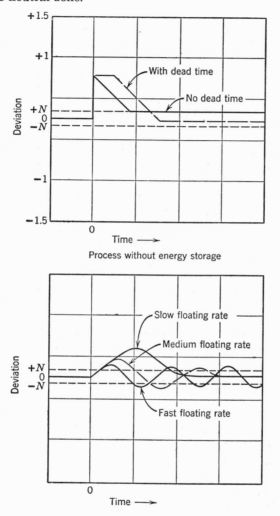

Process without energy storage

Single-capacitance process with self-regulation

Fig. 4–23.   Response of single-speed floating control.

The operation of single-speed floating control of processes without self-regulation is unstable.   When a change in load variable occurs, the controlled variable moves out of the neutral zone, and the inlet valve begins to move at a constant rate.   The controlled variable oscillates continuously across the neutral zone because the controlled variable, on each swing, is returned to the neutral zone at a rate equal to that rate at which it left the neutral zone on a previous swing. If dead time is present the amplitude of oscillation increases on each swing because each succeeding slope through the neutral zone becomes greater.

Single-speed floating control of a process with a single time constant is shown in Fig. 4–23. The response of the controlled variable to a change in load variable is indicated in Fig. 4–23 for various values of floating rate (rate of change of manipulated variable). A fast floating rate causes continuous oscillation of the controlled variable because the process has not had time to reduce the slope in the neutral zone on each successive swing. The proper floating rate combined with a neutral zone of proper width will produce a well-damped response of the controlled variable.

Single-speed floating control for processes having more than one capacitance is not generally successful, because in order to achieve stability the floating rate must be made so small that excessive over-shoot and amplitude of oscillation results.

Summarizing, single-speed floating control is most effective for control of processes having little or no energy storage. Dead time or equivalent dead time should be small. Offset is restricted to the neutral zone.

Ziegler–Nichols Method

The calculation of the response of the controlled system is usually difficult because of the mathematical complexity of solving the high-order differential equations for each new control problem. In addition, one solution of these equations is generally not sufficient because it is desired to explore the effects of several parameters of the system. This situation often forces the use of computing machines (differential analyzers) in finding and making compromises in design of various portions of the controlled system.

The Ziegler–Nichols method affords a systematic way of determining controller settings for best performance of a controlled system and, in addition, provides a simple quantitative picture of control system behavior. This method is based on the approximation of the behavior of a complex dynamic system by the behavior of a system composed only of a single dead-time element and a time-constant element. The apparent dead time and apparent time constant are then used to calculate performance of the system.

The determination of the system apparent dead time and apparent time constant may be made either by calculation or by test. Generally if a system is complex dynamically, it is also difficult to calculate a response.   Consequently the Ziegler–Nichols method is primarily an experimental one.

The open-loop transient test is used to determine the magnitude of the apparent dead time and apparent time constant.   As shown in Fig. 4–24, the closed loop is opened at a point immediately following the controller, and the entire system is maintained in a steady state at the normal operating values of all variables.   Generally the loop is cut just

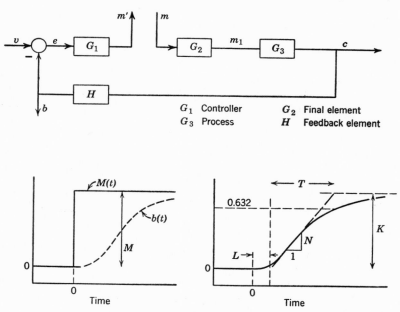

G₁ Controller   G₂ Final element
G₃ Process   H   Feedback element

Fig. 4–24.   Open-loop transient test.

after the controller mechanism by employing the manual control apparatus.   A step change of the variable m is introduced, and the result of this change is recorded at point b just before the controller. Thus, a step-change response is obtained for the open-loop system excluding the controller itself.   The following precautions must be employed during this test:

1. The step change must be as small in magnitude as can be recorded and interpreted.

2. The step change should begin with the controlled variable just below the set point and end just above the set point.

3. The step changes should be made in both directions if it is suspected that the system is not linear.

4. None of the variables should be allowed to attain maximum or minimum values or in any way become limited during the test.

5. There should be no appreciable friction or backlash causing hysteresis or no appreciable dead zone in any elements of the system.

6. All elements having appreciable lag must be included in the open loop test. If the controller has a lag, the controller should be set for proportional control action only and the response recorded at m' in Fig. 4–24 instead.

The recorded open-loop transient response is almost always an S-shape curve as indicated in Fig. 4–24. The zero point of the step change must be carefully marked.

The open-loop response may be approximated by making the measurements shown in Fig. 4–24. First, a line is drawn tangent to the point of inflection of the response curve. Second, a horizontal line is drawn tangent to the final value of the response curve. The measurements made are

K = Magnitude of change in units of recorded variable
N = Reaction rate in units per minute
L = Apparent dead time in minutes
M = magnitude of change in units of variable being changed

A simple check of the approximation may be made as follows: A horizontal line at 63.2 per cent of the total change should give a value of T in minutes approximately equal to the value of K/N. If this value does not check within 15 per cent, either the slope line is drawn incorrectly or there may be a serious nonlinear behavior of the system. If the apparent dead time and the apparent time constant T taken in each direction are within about 10 per cent, a simple average may be used. If they are not within 10 per cent, there is a serious nonlinear behavior in the system.

The lag ratio should next be calculated:

$$R = \frac{NL}{K} = \frac{L}{T} \text{ (dimensionless)} \qquad (4\text{–}70)$$

If the process has no self-regulation, the value of K is extremely large and the lag ratio R is nearly zero. If, on the other hand, the process-reaction rate N is extremely large (rapid), then the lag ratio R is also extremely large.

The following equations may be used for calculating the desired factors regarding performance of the controlled system. The Cohen–

Coon equations[1] are given for proportional, proportional-integral, proportional derivative, and proportional-integral-derivative control. The equations for integral control and two-position control are presented by the author.[2]

Proportional Control. The control action is described by

$$\frac{m}{e} = K_c$$

The setting of proportional sensitivity for one-quarter ratio of succeeding amplitudes of transient response,

$$K_c = \frac{M}{NL}\left(1 + \frac{R}{3}\right)\frac{\text{units of } m}{\text{units of } e} \qquad (4\text{-}71)$$

For this setting, the following transient response characteristics result:

$$P = 4L\left(\frac{12 + 3R}{10 + 7R}\right)\text{min} \qquad (4\text{-}72)$$

where P = period of oscillation. Also,

$$E_o = \frac{NL}{M}\left(\frac{3}{3 + 4R}\right)\frac{\text{units of } c}{\text{units of } m \text{ disturbance}} \qquad (4\text{-}73)$$

where E_o = offset. The step disturbance may be located at any point in the loop but it is expressed in terms of the equivalent value of manipulated variable m, usually a valve-position change, giving the same steady-state offset.

$$D = 1.5E_o \qquad (4\text{-}74)$$

where D = maximum deviation.

Integral Control. The control action is described by

$$\frac{m}{e} = \frac{1}{T_i s} \qquad (4\text{-}75)$$

The setting of integral time for one-quarter ratio of succeeding amplitudes of transient response is

$$T_i = \frac{NL^2}{4M}\left(\frac{1 + 5R}{R^2}\right)\frac{\text{unit of } c}{\text{units of } m \text{ per min}} \qquad (4\text{-}76)$$

[1] "Theoretical Consideration of Retarded Control" by G. H. Cohen and G. A. Coon, *ASME Trans.*, Vol. 75, p. 827, July, 1953.

[2] "Phase Plane Analysis" by D. P. Eckman, *Mech. Engrg.*, Vol. 75, p. 582, July 1953.

For this setting the following transient-response characteristics result:

$$P = 4.8L \left(1 + \frac{1}{R}\right) \tag{4-77}$$

where P = period of oscillation.

Proportional-Derivative Control   The control action is described by

$$\frac{m}{e} = K_c(1 + T_d s) \tag{4-78}$$

The settings for one-quarter ratio of amplitudes and minimum offset are

$$K_c = \frac{M}{NL} \left(\frac{5}{4} + \frac{R}{6}\right) \frac{\text{units of } m}{\text{units of } c} \tag{4-79}$$

$$T_d = L \left(\frac{6 - 2R}{22 + 3R}\right) \text{min} \tag{4-80}$$

For these settings the following transient characteristics result:

$$P = 4L \left(\frac{5 + 6R}{6 + 10R}\right) \text{min} \tag{4-81}$$

$$E_o = \frac{NL}{M} \left(\frac{8}{10 + 9R}\right) \frac{\text{units of } c}{\text{units of } m \text{ disturbance}} \tag{4-82}$$

$$D = 1.5E_o$$

If independent adjustments are employed at the controller $(K_c + K_D s)$, set the derivative adjustment K_D to the value given by the product $K_c T_d$. Notice that settings of derivative time cannot be obtained for processes having an apparent dead time L greater than three times the apparent time constant K/N.

Proportional-Integral Control.   The control action is described by

$$\frac{m}{e} = K_c \left(1 + \frac{1}{T_i s}\right) \tag{4-83}$$

The settings for one-quarter ratio of amplitudes and a compromise between minimum area and period are

$$K_c = \frac{M}{NL} \left(\frac{9}{10} + \frac{R}{12}\right) \frac{\text{units of } m}{\text{units of } c} \tag{4-84}$$

$$T_i = L \left(\frac{30 + 3R}{9 + 20R}\right) \text{min} \tag{4-85}$$

If independent adjustments are employed at the controller ($K_c + K_i/s$), set integral adjustment (K_i) to the value given by the ratio K_c/T_i.

Proportional-Integral-Derivative Control. The control action is described by

$$\frac{m}{e} = K_c \left(\frac{1}{T_i s} + 1 + T_d s \right) \tag{4-86}$$

The settings for one-quarter ratio of amplitudes, asymptotic return, and minimum area are

$$K_c = \frac{M}{NL} \left(\frac{4}{3} + \frac{R}{4} \right) \tag{4-87}$$

$$T_d = L \left(\frac{4}{11 + 2R} \right) \tag{4-88}$$

$$T_i = L \left(\frac{32 + 6R}{13 + 8R} \right) \tag{4-89}$$

Note: $\dfrac{T_i}{T_d} \cong 6.$

If the control action is described by

$$\frac{m}{e} = K_c' \left[\frac{1}{T_i' s} + \left(1 + \frac{T_d'}{T_i'} \right) + T_d' s \right] \tag{4-90}$$

the settings must be calculated by trial and error from

$$K_c' = \frac{K_c}{1 + \dfrac{T_d'}{T_i'}} \tag{4-91}$$

$$T_d' = \frac{K_c T_d}{K_c'}$$

$$T_i' = \frac{K_c' T_i}{K_c} \tag{4-92}$$

If the control action is given by

$$\frac{m}{e} = \frac{K_i}{s} + K_c + K_d s \tag{4-93}$$

the settings must be calculated from

$$K_c = \frac{M}{NL} \left(\frac{4}{3} + \frac{R}{4} \right)$$

$$K_d = \frac{M}{2N} \qquad (4\text{--}94)$$

$$K_i = \frac{(3 + 2R)M}{6NL^2}$$

Two-Position Control. The open-loop test for two-position control is conducted in much the same manner as for any other control except that it is sometimes necessary to employ larger changes in the manipulated variable m. This is because the final element very often has only two positions, a relatively large value and a relatively small value.

The amplitude and period of resulting oscillation for the closed-loop system may be calculated from

$$A = \frac{K(M_{max} - M_{min})}{2M} (1 - e^{-R}) + Ge^{-R} \qquad (4\text{--}95)$$

and

$$P = 4L \left[\frac{1}{R} \tanh^{-1} \left(\frac{AM}{KM_{max} - VM} \right) \right] \qquad (4\text{--}96)$$

where A = amplitude of cycle, units of c
M_{max} = maximum value of manipulated variable, units of m
M_{min} = minimum value of manipulated variable, units of m (This is often zero.)
G = amplitude of differential gap, units of c
P = period of cycle, minutes
V = set points, units of c

Note that the amplitude A and the differential gap G are expressed in half-amplitude—that is, twice these values give the total cycle and total gap. The equation for amplitude is adequate for any two-position control, but the equation for period is valid only when the two-position cycle is relatively symmetrical. When the lag ratio R is less than about 0.2, equation 4–95 may be written

$$A = G + \left[\frac{K(M_{max} - M_{min})}{2M} - G \right] R \qquad (4\text{--}97)$$

Example 4–12. An open-loop transient-response test shows a temperature system to have an apparent dead time L of 0.8 min, a reaction rate N of 0.5

degrees per minute, and a process ultimate temperature change K of 10 degrees for a change in manipulated variable M of 10 per cent of valve setting. Calculate the proportional sensitivity for proportional control.

From equation 4–70

$$R = \frac{NL}{K} = \frac{0.5 \times 0.8}{10} = 0.04$$

From equation 4–71

$$K_c = \frac{10}{0.5 \times 0.8}\left(1 + \frac{0.04}{3}\right) = 25 \text{ per cent/degree}$$

Example 4–13. For a process with $R = 0.5$, what is the decrease in period of oscillation if derivative control is employed with proportional control?

From equations 4–72 and 4–81

$$\frac{P_{p+d}}{P_p} = \frac{(5 + 6R)(10 + 7R)}{(6 + 10R)(12 + 3R)} = \frac{8}{11}$$

or a decrease of about 27 per cent.

Example 4–14. For a process with $R = 0$, what is the decrease in offset allowed when derivative control is employed?

$$\frac{E_{op+d}}{E_{op}} = \frac{8}{3} \times \left(\frac{3}{10}\right) = 0.80$$

or a decrease of about 20 per cent.

Example 4–15. An open-loop transient test shows a pressure system to have an apparent dead time L of 0.04 minutes, a reaction rate N of 2.5 psi per minute, and a process ultimate change K of 10 psi for a change of valve setting M of 5 per cent. If the set point is 100 psi, and the differential gap is 0.5 psi, calculate the amplitude and period of on–off control.

$$R = \frac{NL}{K} = \frac{2.5 \times 0.04}{10} = 0.01$$

For small R, use equation 4–97

$$A = 0.5 + \left[\frac{10(100 - 0)}{2 \times 5} - 0.5\right]0.01 = \underline{1.5 \text{ psi}}$$

For small R equation 4–96 is

$$P = \frac{4L}{R}\tanh^{-1} Z = \frac{4L}{R}\left(\frac{1}{2}\ln\frac{1 + Z}{1 - Z}\right)$$

or

$$P = \frac{4L}{R}Z = \frac{4L}{R}\frac{AM}{(KM_{\max} - VM)}$$

$$P = \frac{0.16}{0.01}\frac{1.5 \times 5}{10 \times 100 - 100 \times 5}$$

$$= 0.24 \text{ min} = \underline{14.4 \text{ sec}}$$

PROBLEMS

4–1. Explain physically why offset occurs, using the mechanical float-level control of Fig. 3–3 in the previous chapter.

4–2. Explain physically why offset is zero, using the mechanical integral control of Fig. 3–4 in the previous chapter.

4–3. If a process-control system contains a capacitance element $1/Cs$, prove that integral control is not necessary to eliminate static error if only time-constant elements are in the remainder of the system.

4–4. Prove that velocity error is not zero if proportional-integral control is used and if the remainder of the system contains only time-constant elements.

4–5. Sketch the resulting oscillations for on–off control when (a) differential gap G is zero; (b) dead time L is zero; (c) capacitance C is made small; (d) control-element size M is only 10 per cent larger than load flow U.

4–6. For processes with small dead time, how much should the proportional sensitivity be increased when derivative action is added?

4–7. For processes with small lag, how much should the proportional sensitivity be decreased when integral action is added?

4–8. In Fig. 4–1, $G_1 = K_c$, $G_2 = \dfrac{1}{Cs}$, $N = \dfrac{1}{Cs}$. Show that the time constant of the system response is C/K_c. Would this system have offset?

4–9. In Fig. 4–1, $G_1 = K_c\left(1 + \dfrac{1}{T_is}\right)$, $G_2 = \dfrac{1}{Cs}$, $N = \dfrac{1}{Cs}$. Calculate the condition for critically damped response.

4–10. In Fig. 4–1, $G_1 = K_c(T_ds + 1)$, $G_2 = \dfrac{1}{Cs}$, $N = \dfrac{1}{Cs}$. Calculate the system time constant.

4–11. In Fig. 4–1, $G_1 = K_c$, $G_2 = \dfrac{R}{Ts + 1}$, $N = \dfrac{1}{Ts + 1}$. Calculate the offset.

4–12. In Fig. 4–1, $G_1 = K_c + \dfrac{K_i}{s}$, $G_2 = \dfrac{R}{Ts + 1}$, $N = \dfrac{1}{Ts + 1}$. Calculate the relation necessary for a damping ratio of 0.707.

4–13. In Fig. 4–1, $G_1 = K_c$, $G_2 = \dfrac{R_1}{T_1s(T_2s + 1)}$, $N = \dfrac{R_1}{T_1s(T_2s + 1)}$. Calculate the proportional sensitivity for critical damping. Calculate the static error.

4–14. In Fig. 4–1, $G_1 = K_c(T_ds + 1)$, $G_2 = \dfrac{R_1}{T_1s(T_2s + 1)}$, $N = \dfrac{R_1}{T_1s(T_2s + 1)}$. Calculate the proportional sensitivity for a damping ratio of one third. Calculate the period of oscillation.

4–15. In Fig. 4–1, $G_1 = K_c$, $G_2 = \dfrac{R_1}{(T_1s + 1)(T_2s + 1)}$, $N = \dfrac{1}{T_1s + 1}$. Calculate the period of oscillation and the offset.

chapter 5

Measuring
(Feedback) Elements

Measurement of the value of the controlled variable is necessary in order to determine the magnitude of deviation. The performance of the measuring means is therefore an important factor in the operation of an automatic controller.

The characteristics of a measuring means, such as a thermometer, pressure gage, or flowmeter, are important in three ways:

1. The principle of operation of the measuring means often determines the method by which the automatic controller mechanism operates.

2. The characteristics of the measuring means affect the indication of the value of the controlled variable.

3. The dynamic characteristics of the measuring means directly influence the operation of the automatic controller.

The principle of operation of measuring means will be reviewed from the standpoint of automatic control; that is, no emphasis is placed upon the display (the indication or recording) provided by the measuring means. For a broad study of the subject of measurement, the reader should consult the related textbook, *Industrial Instrumentation*.[1]

Types of Measuring Means

The basic operation performed by the measuring means is to convert or transduce the controlled variable into another variable that may be employed for operation of the automatic controller. As shown in Fig. 5–1, the measuring means H converts the controlled variable into the

---

[1] D. P. Eckman, John Wiley and Sons, Inc., New York, 1950.

feedback variable b in order that the controller may determine the actuating signal e:

$$e = r - b$$

where r = reference input. The actuating signal may be different than the deviation $(v - c)$ because the feedback variable b may have a different value than the controlled variable c.

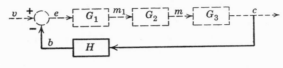

G_1 Controlling element
G_2 Final control element
G_3 Process
H Measuring element

FIG. 5–1.   The measuring element.

The feedback variable b may be a mechanical displacement, a force, a pressure, or an electrical signal:

1. A *displacement* element converts the controlled variable into a mechanical displacement.   (Example: a mercury thermometer converts temperature into a height of mercury column by thermal expansion.)

2. A *force* element converts the controlled variable into a force or torque.   (Example: a displacement float-level gage converts liquid level into a buoyant force on the float.)   Pressure elements may be considered force elements when the pressure is applied to the area of an elastic element such as a bellows or piston.   Almost any force element may produce a displacement by applying the force to a spring.   A mutually exclusive classification of displacement, force, and pressure elements could probably not be made.

3. An *electric* element converts the controlled variable into some form of electrical quantity such as voltage or current.   (Example: a thermocouple converts temperature into a direct current voltage.)

Whether a system is force balance, displacement balance, or electrical balance depends upon its design as a pneumatic or hydraulic mechanism or as an electrical mechanism.

Temperature Elements

Temperature may be measured by mechanical, fluid or electrical means.

Expansion thermometers employ the thermal expansion of an elastic member to produce a motion of an indicating pointer proportional to the temperature. Expansion thermometers are displacement type because they convert temperature into a proportional displacement.

1. *Mercury-in-glass thermometers* are the simplest and most widely used temperature-measuring element in both laboratory and industry. The temperature range of the industrial mercury-in-glass thermometer is about −38 to 950 F. The mercury thermometer is employed for two-position control by utilizing an electrical contact at the surface of the mercury.

2. *Bimetallic thermometers* are also widely used in industry. The bimetal is usually Invar for the low-expansion metal and either brass or a nickel alloy for the high-expansion metal. The temperature range of the industrial bimetallic thermometer is about −40 to 800 F. The bimetallic element is often employed for two-position control, as in domestic and industrial thermostats.

3. *Liquid-expansion thermometers* utilize the thermal expansion of a fluid to provide an indication of the temperature. A cylindrical bulb filled with a liquid is subjected to the temperature to be measured. A small-diameter tube or capillary connects the bulb with the receiving element in the controller. This receiving element consists of a bourdon tube, a helix, a spiral, or a bellows. Expansion of the fluid inside the system causes the free end of the bourdon tube or bellows to move, and this motion is utilized to operate the controlling means. The range of the liquid-expansion thermometer is about −35 to 1000 F.

Pressure thermometers employ the principle that the pressure of a gas or vapor is proportional to temperature. The pressure is then measured by a bourdon tube or a bellows, and the force produced by the system pressure is used to operate the controlling means. Pressure thermometers are therefore force elements. When deflection of the bourdon tube or bellows is allowed, a displacement element results.

1. *Gas-expansion thermometers* operate at essentially constant volume, the gas expanding according to its temperature. The range of the gas thermometer is about −200 to 800 F. Nitrogen is the most commonly used gas.

2. *Vapor-actuated thermometers* operate from the vapor pressure of a liquid that partially fills the system. Since the vapor pressure depends solely upon the temperature at the free surface of the liquid, the vapor-actuated thermometer indicates only the temperature existing at the free surface. Vapor thermometers may be used for temperatures as low as −50 F and as high as 600 F.

A *thermocouple* is composed of two dissimilar wires welded together at one end. When the temperature at the welded junction changes, an electrical potential is generated and appears at the free ends of the wire. This potential is the result of two distinct functions known as the Thomson effect and the Peltier effect.

The Thomson effect is that portion of the total potential caused by the temperature gradient over a single section of homogeneous wire. The Peltier effect is that portion of the total potential produced by the contact of two dissimilar wires. Both potentials vary with temperature. Thus, the thermocouple is an electric element.

The five most commonly used industrial thermocouples are listed in Table 5–1. Data on thermocouple emf versus temperature relationships are given in the related book, *Industrial Instrumentation*.

Table 5–1.   Characteristics of Thermocouples

Thermocouple (Positive Metal First)	Useful Range, °F	Millivolts per °F*
Copper–Constantan	−300 to 600	0.0330
Iron–Constantan	0 to 1300†	0.0350
Chromel–Alumel	600 to 1800‡	0.0215
Pt 10% Rh–platinum	1300 to 2900	0.00651
Pt 13% Rh–platinum	1300 to 2900	0.00754

* At listed maximum temperature.
† Add 200 F in reducing atmosphere.
‡ Add 200 F in oxidizing atmosphere.

The thermocouple measuring junction is usually located some distance from the controller, and thermocouple lead wires are used to extend the reference junction to the controller. There are two methods of selecting lead wires: (1) the thermocouple wires themselves may be extended to the controller if the thermocouple wire is not expensive, and (2) the lead wires may be made of less expensive thermocouple metals having the same thermoelectric properties as the thermocouple.

A thermal well, protects the thermocouple from corrosion and contamination. The iron–Constantan thermocouple may have the iron wire in the form of a closed-end tube with the insulated Constantan wire running through the center and swaged into the end of the tube to form the hot junction. Such a design reduces mass and speeds the response.

The *resistance thermometer* is widely used because of its recognized accuracy and simplicity in industrial operations. The resistance thermometer is an electric element and operates on the principle that the electrical resistance of a wire changes with temperature. The industrial resistance thermometer bulb consists essentially of a coil of fine wire wound on or in a frame of insulating material, often mica or glass. Platinum, nickel, and copper resistance bulbs are used, and some of their characteristics are shown in Table 5–2.

Table 5–2. Characteristics of Resistance Thermometer Bulbs

Wire Material	Bulb Resistance, ohms	Useful Range, °F
Platinum	10–35	−300 to 1200
Nickel	100–300	−300 to 600
Copper	10	−40 to 250

Resistance thermometer bulbs are generally used with a thermal well, except when temperature measurements are made in dry air.

The *thermistor* is another electric element employed as a temperature measuring means and is similar to a resistance thermometer. Thermistors are made from a mixture of metallic oxides and provide a specific resistance versus temperature relation. The resistance may either decrease or increase with increasing temperature.

The *radiation element* operates by measuring the thermal radiation from a heated body. Radiation in a band from approximately 0.1 to 8.0 microns in the visible and infrared portion of the spectrum is directed by a lens or mirror to the thermopile or vacuum thermocouple. A thermopile is a number of thermocouples connected in series, the measuring junctions having been flattened and blackened to provide high absorption of radiation. The reference junction is thermally connected to the housing of the radiation unit. The radiation unit is therefore an electric element.

The radiation unit is directed (sighted) on the surface, the temperature of which is being measured. The temperatures between 800 and 3200 F are best suited to the radiation unit, but temperatures as low as 200 F may be measured.

Pressure Elements

The measurement of pressure or vacuum for purposes of control is generally accomplished by applying the unknown pressure to a movable, elastic member of constant area. The force thus created is balanced by a spring force or other balancing force and the resulting movement operates the controlling means. Mechanical pressure elements may therefore be either displacement- or force-type depending upon the physical arrangement.

1. *Bourdon tube, spiral,* and *helix elements* are the most common actuating elements for the pressure gage. These types of elements do not require a spring since the elastic modulus of the metal is utilized to

graduate the deflection due to changes in pressure. Bourdon tube gages are almost always employed for measuring static pressure, not differential pressure.

2. The *bellows* pressure gage is used for the measurement of differential pressure by applying the two unknown pressures to the two bellows. The force of the bellows is balanced by a spring, and the resulting displacement is proportional to the applied differential pressure. Absolute pressure may be measured by evacuating one bellows to a very low absolute pressure, and applying the unknown absolute pressure to the opposite bellows.

3. The *bell* pressure gage is useful for the measurement of low pressures near atmospheric. The bell is suspended on a beam in a sealing liquid, and the unknown pressure is applied underneath the bell. The force of the pressure on the bell is balanced either by weights or by a spring. Differential pressures are measured by applying the second pressure over the bell.

4. The *manometer* differential pressure gage operates from a metal float in an enlarged leg of a mercury U-tube. The metal float follows the changes in level of the mercury in the chamber as the differential pressure changes. The motion of the float is transmitted through a pressure-tight shaft and is utilized for operating the controlling means.

5. In the *ring-balance* differential pressure gage the ring is balanced on a rotating shaft or knife-edge bearings. The differential pressure displaces the sealing liquid in the ring and the rotation of the ring results from the net torque due to the different pressures acting against the closed ends of the ring.

6. The *electrical pressure* gage employs an unbonded or bonded strain gage for indicating the pressure acting against the bellows area.

Liquid-Level Measurement

Measurement of liquid level is accomplished by two different methods. Head measurement by a float following the liquid-level surface provides accurate measurement of liquid volume independent of liquid density. Pressure measurement by a pressure gage connected to the bottom of a tank provides accurate measure of liquid weight independent of liquid density.

1. The *float and tape method* is employed for open vessels. Other mechanisms employ a free float on a pivoted arm to operate an indicating means.

2. The *diaphragm–box system* is used for pressure measurement in open vessels. The metal box contains a flexible diaphragm which acts

to compress the gas in the pressure receiver line when the liquid level increases. The pressure receiver is then calibrated in terms of liquid head. The bubbler system and the air-trap system are similar means of liquid-level measurement.

3. The *displacement-float meter* may be used in either open or closed pressure vessels. The buoyant force caused by the displaced liquid is used to operate the indicating means.

Many electrical types of liquid-level control devices do not indicate or record the level. An electrode is sometimes introduced to make electric contact through the liquid and operate a relay for controlling the level. Another type utilizes a column of the liquid to break a light beam and actuate a photocell relay. In some devices a column of liquid serves as a portion of a variable electric capacitor to operate an electronic control circuit.

Fluid Flow Rate Measuring Elements

The control of fluid flow rate in closed pipes is accomplished generally by one of two means; the head flowmeter, or the area flowmeter.

The *head flowmeter* operates by measuring the pressure differential across a suitable restriction to flow. The most common restrictions are the orifice, flow-nozzle, Venturi, Pitot tube, and Venturi-Pitot Ring. The pressure-differential is measured by any of the pressure-differential meters described in a previous section of this chapter. For further details on the theory and use of head flowmeters the reader is referred to the textbook *Industrial Instrumentation*.

1. An *orifice* may be installed with flange taps or with pipe taps in which the upstream tap is 2.5 pipe diameters and the downstream tap is 8.0 pipe diameters from the orifice, or with vena-contracta taps which locate the upstream tap 1.0 pipe diameter from the orifice and the downstream tap at the vena contracta. Flange taps are the simplest and most economical, pipe taps provide the smallest pressure differential, and vena-contracta taps provide the largest pressure differential.

2. The *flow-nozzle* is arranged with a well-rounded entrance section so that the permanent pressure loss is small. It is therefore useful in measuring large quantity flow rates of steam in power plants.

3. The *Venturi tube* has both a smooth entrance and exit so that the permanent pressure loss is very small. It may be used to measure the flow of fluids containing solid particles but is employed principally for measuring large flow rates of liquids.

4. The *Pitot tube* operates by converting velocity head into static head. The differential head is thus proportional to velocity at the streamline

centering on the forward opening. The pitot tube requires calibration in a particular application. It is most useful in measuring flow rate in very large pipes and ducts.

5. The *Venturi-Pitot ring* operates on the principle of the pitot tube, but two factors of design serve to increase the differential head for a given flow rate. First, the venturi section increases velocity so that velocity head is increased, and second, the pitot has both forward and rearward openings to increase differential head.

The pressure differential across the restriction is given by a form of Bernoulli's law for incompressible fluids so that the flow rate varies as the square-root of pressure differential. Thus a pressure-differential meter used with an orifice is calibrated for flow rate with a parabolic scale having wider graduations at high flow than at low flow. The flow coefficients must be taken from tabulated data.

The *area flowmeter* operates on the principle that the variation of area of flow-stream required to produce a constant pressure-differential is proportional to flow rate. The rotameter is one form of the area meter. The fluid passes up the tube through the annular space around the float. The float is supported in the fluid stream by the pressure differential, buoyancy, and drag acting upward against the weight acting downward. A scale etched on the glass metering tube is calibrated in flow rate and is read by noting the position of the float against the scale.

The *electromagnetic flowmeter element* is an electric element operating on the principle that the liquid flowing through a nonmagnetic tube in a magnetic field induces a voltage that is proportional to flow rate and field intensity. The field is supplied by an electromagnet. Electrodes sealed in the tube detect a direct-current or alternating-current voltage. The flowing fluid should have some electric conductivity. The flow rate is measured independently of viscosity, velocity disturbance, etc.

The *Coriolis flowmeter* element operates by passing the fluid out one radial tube and back another radial tube. The force difference between the two paths is caused by the Coriolis acceleration. The force is measured by an elastic member, strain gages, and slip rings. The flow rate is measured independently of viscosity, velocity disturbance, etc.

Pneumatic Transmission

It is often required to measure the value of a controlled variable where the location of the point of measurement is at a considerable distance from the location of the controller. Most measuring devices such as a mercury thermometer, pressure gage, or flow-rate meter would then require fluid-line connections of great length. This cannot be done because excessive measuring lag would result. Therefore some transmission or telemetering means must be employed. Pneumatic transmission is one method of transmitting the value of the controlled variable.

The pneumatic transmission system shown in Fig. 5–2 may be used

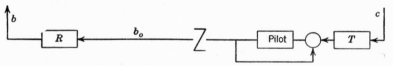

FIG. 5–2.   Pneumatic transmission.

for distances up to many hundreds of feet. The controlled variable is converted to an air pressure at the transmitter T. The air pressure is then conducted through a single tube to the receiver R where it is transduced to a position or force for operation of the controller.

The details of a pneumatic transmission system are illustrated in Fig. 5–3 for a particular system transmitting a measured pressure c of range 0 to 100 psi gage. The transmitter consists of a double-bellows

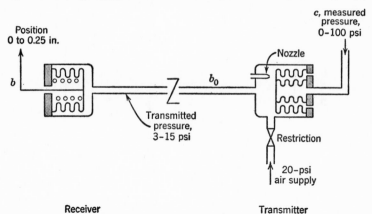

FIG. 5–3.   A pneumatic transmission system.

system with the measured pressure in the smaller bellows balanced by a transmitted pressure acting against the larger bellows. The transmitter acts as follows: For a measured pressure c of 50 psi, the transmitted pressure b_0 is 9 psi. When the measured pressure c increases suddenly to 51 psi, the bellows assembly moves to the left and covers the exhaust nozzle. This increases the transmitted pressure b_0 because air flows into the system through the supply restriction. The transmitted pressure b_0 increases to 9.12 psi and balances the new measured pressure c. It is apparent that the transmitted pressure is proportional to the measured pressure. Usually an amplifying pilot is employed at the transmitter in order to increase the air-flow capacity of the transmitter. Other controlled variables such as temperature or flow rate may be transmitted by suitably designed transmitters.

The connecting tube carries the transmitted pressure to the receiver. This tube is almost always one-quarter in. O.D. standard copper, aluminum, or plastic tubing.

The receiver is simply a pressure-gage element calibrated for 3–15 psi input pressure range.

Practically the only limitation of distance of pneumatic transmission is the lag of transmitting the signal through a long connecting tube. The capacitance of the tube is caused by the volume of the tube and it

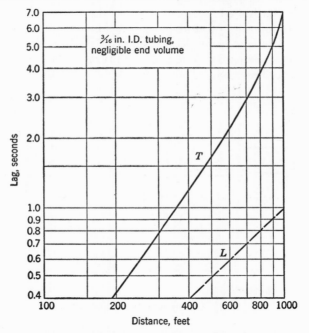

FIG. 5–4.   Approximation of transmission lag.

is distributed along the length of the tube. The resistance of the tube is due to fluid friction and is likewise distributed along the tube. Because of these distributed parameters, the calculation of the lag is extremely difficult and it is necessary to rely upon experimental tests to determine the lag.[1] The results of such a test, shown in Fig. 5–4, are given in

[1] J. C. Moise, *A Theoretical and Analytical Investigation of Long Pneumatic Transmission Lines*, Doctoral thesis, Case Institute of Technology, Cleveland, Ohio, 1952.

terms of the approximate first-order time constant T that most nearly represents the test data. The dead time L due to the time for transmission of the pressure wave down the tube is also indicated in Fig. 5–4. Thus pneumatic transmission may be employed up to 350 ft distance if a time constant of about 1 second and a dead time of one-third second are not important in automatic control, and up to about 1000 ft distance if a time constant of about 7 seconds and a dead time of one second are not important.

Two methods are used to improve the speed of pneumatic transmission. First, as mentioned previously, an amplifying pilot shown in Fig. 5–5 may be used.

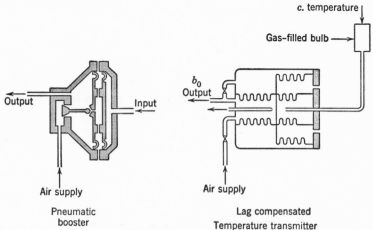

FIG. 5–5.   Pneumatic transmission pilots.

The amplifying pilot provides a gain of one so that the output (transmitted) pressure is the same as the input pressure. The pilot is simply inserted in the transmission line. Its advantage derives from the large ports of the pilot valve so that a large flow of air is allowed when a change of pressure takes place. The operation is as follows: An increase in input pressure acts against the diaphragm and pushes the pilot stem to the left. This opens the supply port and allows air to flow into the output volume. The increased output pressure acts to the right against the second diaphragm and exactly balances the input pressure. On a decrease in input pressure, air is exhausted from between the diaphragms.

The lag-compensated transmitter provides a boosting action that tends to overcome transmission lag. The operation is as follows: An increase in temperature at the thermometer bulb increases the pressure in the right inner bellows. This moves the bellows assembly to the left, covers the exhaust nozzle, and increases the output pressure to a large magnitude. Then, as air flows through the restriction to the outer bellows chamber, the bellows moves gradually to the right and reduces the output pressure to its new but larger value. The action is similar to a derivative effect and is described more precisely by

$$\frac{b_0}{c} = \frac{T_D s + 1}{T_L s + 1} \tag{5-1}$$

where T_L = time constant lag of transmitter
$\quad b_0$ = transmitted pressure
$\quad T_D$ = compensating time constant
$\quad c$ = controlled variable

If the upper restriction were not present in Fig. 5–5, the compensation T_D would be zero. Thus, the right-hand (derivative) term of equation 5–1 indicates a pure derivative effect in the presence of a time-constant lag T_L. The net effect is that of reducing the time-constant lag of the system. The dead-time lag is also partially compensated.

Electric Transmission

Electric transmission or telemetering systems operate by transducing the controlled variable into an electric signal, usually voltage or a current. Electric systems have a great advantage of nearly unlimited

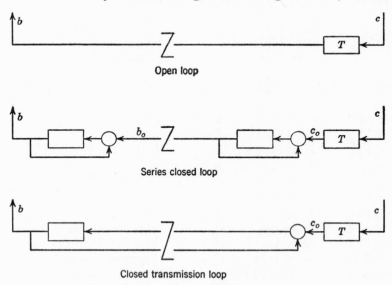

FIG. 5–6.   Transmission methods.

distances of transmission either by wire-carried signal or by radio linkage. Electric transmission systems employed in automatic control are of several types as shown in Fig. 5–6. The transducer is indicated at T. The open-loop system employs a transducer such as a thermo-couple in which the feedback signal b is a voltage. The series closed-loop system is employed in three forms; closed-loop amplifiers at both transmitting and receiving end, or at either end only. The closed-transmission-loop system is sometimes advantageous for particular transducers.

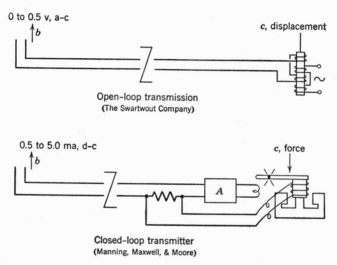

Fig. 5–7. Electrical transmitters.

The open-loop transmitter employing a differential transformer is shown in Fig. 5–7. The differential transformer consists of two to four coils with a movable core centered in the coils. The primary coils are connected to a source of alternating voltage. The voltage induced in the secondary coils will depend upon the position of the core. The transmission signal is a 60-cycle voltage of 0 to 0.50 volts. The advantage of this system is that the arrangement is simple and the speed of response is limited only by the transducer itself. The disadvantage, as with any open-loop system, is that careful ambient temperature and pressure compensation may be required and supply voltages must be constant.

The closed-loop transmitter in Fig. 5–7 employs a null-balance stage in the transmitter. The transducer provides a force C acting on the balance arm. The position of the balance arm is detected by the oscillator coil and amplifier A is energized. The direct-current output of the amplifier is fed back to the voice coil-magnet drive on the balance arm. Thus the output direct current of 0.5 to 5.0 milliamperes is proportional to input force. The advantages of this system are that the direct-current transmission signal is not easily interfered with and the signal may be manipulated easily, giving great flexibility.

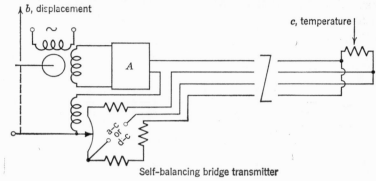

Self-balancing bridge transmitter

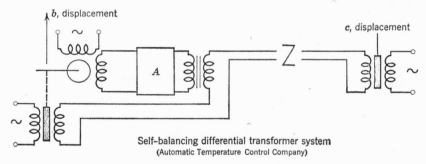

Self-balancing differential transformer system
(Automatic Temperature Control Company)

FIG. 5–8.   Electrical transmitters.

Closed-transmission-loop systems are shown in Fig. 5–8. The self-balancing bridge transmitter employs the Wheatstone bridge. A change in temperature c at the resistance element (or thermistor) causes an unbalance of the bridge which is detected and amplified to drive the reversible motor. The motor rebalances the bridge. The output variable b is the displacement of the output arm, which may be used to operate a control means.

The self-balancing differential transformer system of Fig. 5–8 employs an input transformer and a feedback transformer interconnected so that the differential voltage of the secondaries is proportional to relative unbalance. The two differential transformers must be operated from the same line source so that the primaries are in phase. The closed-transmission-loop systems have the advantage of flexibility.

The impulse-duration transmission system is shown in Fig. 5–9. The transmitter consists of a synchronous motor driving an electric contact through a cam in such a way that the duration of make of the contact is proportional to the variable being measured. The receiver is a clutch

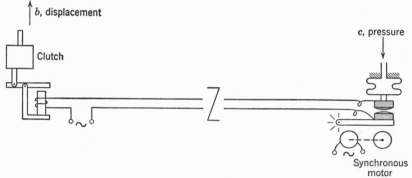

FIG. 5–9.   Impulse-duration transmission.

controlled synchronous motor driving in such a way that, from a given starting point of drive, the impulse signal actuates a magnet clutch to drive an output arm in one direction. When the signal ends the opposing clutch is actuated to drive the output arm in the opposite direction. Thus the output-arm position b is determined once each cycle. The advantage of this two-wire system is that no synchronization is required, and the signal requires only two wires. The speed is generally slow, with a cycle of from 5 to 60 seconds.

There are many other forms of electric transmission such as synchro systems, and potentiometer systems. These are too numerous to review here.

First-Order Response

Speed of response of the primary measuring element and the measuring means of a controller is the most important single factor affecting the operation of an automatic controller. Since automatic control is a continuous, dynamic function, the rate of detection and the time element in response of the measuring means form an essential part of automatic control analysis.

If we were suddenly to immerse the bare bulb of an expansion thermometer in an agitated salt bath maintained at a constant temperature, the thermometer pen would rise as indicated by the curve of Fig. 5–10.

The curve appears to be exponential, and it approaches the bath temperature gradually. This curve shows that if it requires 12 seconds for the thermometer to indicate 90 per cent of the change, it takes another

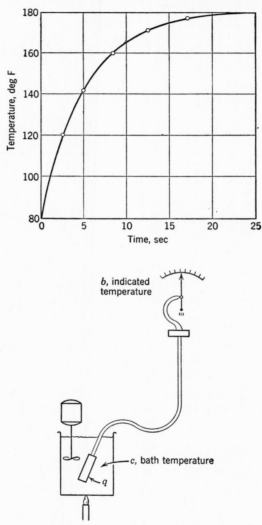

FIG. 5–10.   Response of thermometer element.

12 seconds to reach 99 per cent, and another 12 seconds to reach 99.9 per cent of the final value. The difficulty of expressing lag in terms of time for indicating a complete change is that theoretically the final temperature will never be reached.

The response curve for a simple thermal element is derived from the laws of conservation of energy and heat transfer. As indicated in Fig. 5–10, the increase in energy is equal to the inflow of energy, or

$$(WP)\dot{b} = q \tag{5-2}$$

where W = weight of element, lb
   P = specific heat of element = Btu lb^{-1} deg^{-1}
   b = temperature of element, deg
   q = heat flow to element, Btu/sec

For convection transfer of heat

$$q = HA(c - b) \tag{5-3}$$

where H = convection coefficient of heat transfer, Btu/ft^2 deg^{-1} sec^{-1}
   A = surface area of element, ft^2
   c = temperature of surrounding fluid, deg

Combining equations 5–2 and 5–3 to eliminate heat flow q, a first order differential equation results:

$$T\dot{b} + b = c \tag{5-4}$$

where T = time constant = WP/HA. The operational form of the equation is found by setting $s = d/dt$. Solving for the relation between output variable b and input variable c, the system function is obtained

$$\frac{b}{c} = \frac{1}{Ts + 1} \tag{5-5}$$

The operational diagram for the thermometer is shown in Fig. 5–11.

The response to a sudden (step) change of temperature is found by solving equation 5–4 for particular conditions:

$$\left(\frac{b - b_0}{c - b_0}\right) = 1 - e^{-t/T} \tag{5-6}$$

where b_0 = initial temperature of element. This response is plotted in Fig. 5–11. The element time constant T may be evaluated experimentally from the response curve. When

$$\frac{t}{T} = 1.0$$

the value of the temperature ratio is

$$\frac{b - b_0}{c - b_0} = \left(1 - \frac{1}{e}\right) = (1 - 0.368) = 0.632$$

Therefore, the time constant of a simple thermal element is the time required to reach 63.2 per cent of the final value.   Note also that the initial slope intersects the final value at a time T.

The general approach to the response of a measuring means is indicated by the block diagram in Fig. 5–11.   The controlled or measured variable c is the input to some measuring device, and the output is the

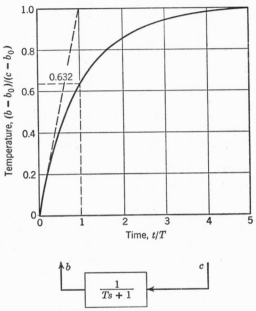

FIG. 5–11.   First-order response.

indicated variable b.   The indicated variable b may or may not actually be indicated on a calibrated scale.

The time response of many simple physical systems in engineering may be characterized by the general system function

$$\frac{K}{Ts + 1} \qquad (5\text{--}7)$$

where T = time constant
K = system steady-state gain

Systems exhibiting this system function are termed time constant elements.

Example 5–1.   A test of a system shows a response similar to that in Fig. 5–11 which indicates a first-order response, and 7.0 sec is required to indicate one third of the total change.   What is the element time constant?

Tables for e^{-x} show

$$1 - e^{-x} = 0.333 \qquad \text{for } x = 0.406$$

Then

$$\frac{t}{T} = 0.406 \quad \text{or} \quad T = \frac{7.0}{0.406} = \underline{17.1 \text{ sec}}$$

Thermal-Element Lag

Temperature-measuring elements such as the expansion thermometer, thermocouple, and resistance thermometer possess appreciable measuring lag because of the heat capacity of the materials of construction and the heat transfer characteristics of the surrounding media. Heat is transferred to the thermal element by conduction, convection, and radiation but the conduction heat transfer is usually small compared to the convection and radiation transfer of heat.

The bare thermocouple and bare thermometer bulb installed in rapidly moving fluid have almost first-order response as may be seen by the actual test curves of Fig. 5–12. The element time constant can be calculated if all the material and fluid characteristics were known. From equation 5–4, the time constant is

$$T = \frac{WP}{HA} \tag{5–8}$$

Therefore a small time constant requires small weight but large surface area, low specific heat, and high heat transfer coefficient.

The heat transfer coefficient can be calculated for *forced convection* transfer of heat from a fluid flowing at right angles to a cylindrical thermal element from

$$N_u = n(N_p)^{0.3}(N_r)^m \tag{5–9}$$

where N_u = Nusselt number = HD/K

H = convection coefficient, Btu/ft^2 F^{-1} sec^{-1}

D = diameter of tube or rod, ft

K = thermal conductivity of fluid, Btu/ft F^{-1} sec^{-1}

m = a constant given below

n = a constant given below

N_p = Prandtl number = $gC\mu/K$

C = specific heat of fluid, Btu/lb deg^{-1}

μ = absolute viscosity, lb sec/ft^2 = $\nu\gamma/g$

ν = kinematic viscosity, ft^2/sec

γ = fluid density lb/ft^3

N_r = Reynolds number = VD/ν

V = velocity of fluid, ft/sec

The constants of the equation depend upon Reynolds number as follows:[1]

N_r	n	m
40–4000	0.68	0.47
4000–40,000	0.19	0.62
40,000–400,000	0.26	0.80

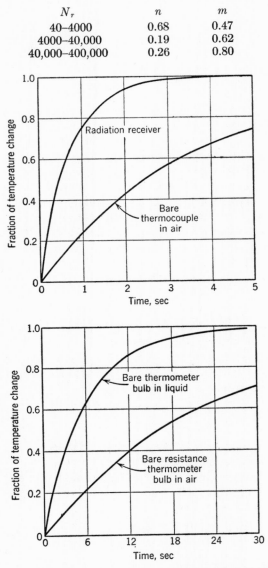

FIG. 5–12.   Response of thermal elements.   (Not necessarily typical of each type.)

[1] E. R. G. Eckert, *Introduction to The Transfer of Heat and Mass*, McGraw-Hill Book Company, New York, 1950.

The velocity of fluid flow V is a most important factor in response. Equation 5–9 shows that the thermal-element time constant should vary

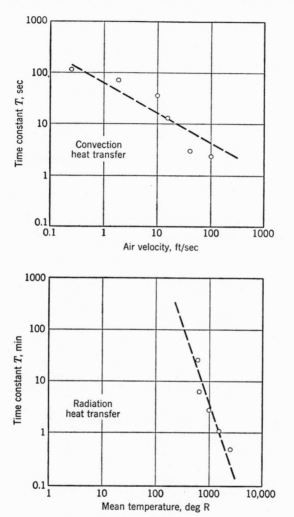

Fig. 5–13. Effect of fluid velocity and mean temperature on thermal-element time constant.

inversely as the 0.6 power of velocity. The data of Fig. 5–13 show reasonable agreement.

The characteristics of the fluid surrounding the element are also important.   Equation 5–9 indicates

$$H \sim \frac{K^{0.7} C^{0.3} \gamma^{0.6}}{\mu^{0.3}}$$

so that high thermal conductivity, high specific heat, high density, and low viscosity are necessary for fast response.

Example 5–2.   A mercury thermometer bulb is $\frac{1}{2}$-in. long by $\frac{1}{8}$-in. diameter. The glass envelope is very thin.   Estimate the time constant in water flowing at 10 ft per sec at a temperature of 140 F.

$$N_p(\text{water}) = \frac{C\nu\gamma}{K} = 3.02$$

$$N_r = \frac{VD}{\nu} = \frac{10 \times 0.125}{0.5 \times 10^{-5} \times 12} = 21,000$$

$$N_u = 0.19(3)^{0.3}(20,000)^{0.62} = 122$$

$$H = \frac{K}{D} N_u = \frac{0.38 \times 122 \times 12}{3600 \times 0.125} = 1.2$$

$$\frac{WP}{A} = \frac{\pi D^2 L \gamma_m P_m}{4\pi DL} = \frac{D\gamma_m P_m}{4} = 0.073$$

$$T = \frac{WP}{HA} = \frac{0.073}{1.2} = \underline{0.06 \text{ sec}}$$

For *radiation transfer* of heat to a thermal element from a black-body source, the heat flow q in Btu per sec is given by:

$$q = KEA \left[\left(\frac{c}{100} \right)^4 - \left(\frac{b}{100} \right)^4 \right] \tag{5–10}$$

where K = radiation constant = 47.4×10^{-6} Btu ft^2/sec deg^{-4}
$\quad\ E$ = emissivity of thermal-element material
$\quad\ A$ = surface area of thermal element, ft^2
$\quad\ c$ = temperature of source, deg R
$\quad\ b$ = temperature of receiving element, deg R

This is a nonlinear equation and may be replaced by

$$q = H_r A (c - b) \tag{5–11}$$

if the coefficient of radiation transfer H_r is defined by

$$H_r = \frac{1}{A} \frac{\partial q}{\partial c} = \frac{4KE\theta^3}{100} \tag{5–12}$$

where θ is the average of the source and element temperatures in deg R/100.   This approximation is in error by only 10 per cent for a source temperature twice the element temperature.

The time constant for a thermal element responding to radiation transfer of heat depends greatly upon the average operating temperature θ. As equation 5–12 indicates, the time constant should vary inversely as the cube of temperature. The data in Fig. 5–13 illustrates this effect. The emissivity of the thermal-element material should be as large as possible and thermal response is often improved by roughening and blackening the surface of the thermal element. In some cases it is necessary to sacrifice response by using a thermal element of low emissivity in order to reduce the radiation error.

Example 5–3. A thermal well made of standard $\frac{1}{2}$-inch iron pipe is used in a furnace (reducing atmosphere) at 1400 F. (O.D. = 0.84 in., 0.85 lb per ft). The well is 2 ft long. Estimate its time constant.

The element probably receives most heat by radiation. Assume emissivity is 0.8.

$$H_r = 4 \times 48 \times 10^{-6} \times \frac{0.8}{100} \times \left(\frac{1860}{100}\right)^3 = 0.01$$

$$T = \frac{1.70 \times 0.11 \times 12}{0.01 \times \pi \times 0.84 \times 2} \simeq \underline{42 \text{ sec}}$$

Pressure-Element Lag

Fluid capacitance and resistance are the sources of measuring lag in pressure elements when long fluid-filled lines are necessary to connect

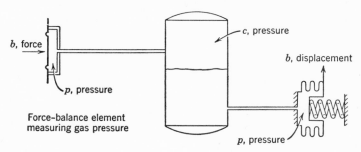

b, force

p, pressure

Force–balance element measuring gas pressure

c, pressure

b, displacement

p, pressure

Displacement element measuring liquid pressure

Fig. 5–14. Pressure elements.

a pressure gage to the point of measurement. Inertia of moving fluids and moving pressure-element parts also cause measuring lag, but this will be neglected. The volume of connecting lines is assumed small compared to pressure-element volume.

The bellows pressure gage of Fig. 5–14 is a deflectional system in which the displacement of the bellows and spring is proportional to the

pressure in the bellows. For a change of pressure c, liquid must flow
from the vessel to the element. Employing the continuity relation, then

$$(A\gamma)\dot{b} = w \qquad (5\text{--}13)$$

where A = bellows effective area, ft^2
γ = fluid density, lb/ft^3
b = bellows displacement, ft
w = fluid flow rate, lb/sec

The displacement of the spring is proportional to pressure:

$$pA = Kb \qquad (5\text{--}14)$$

where p = bellows pressure, lb/ft^2
K = spring gradient, lb/ft

The flow of liquid w into the bellows through the long connecting line
depends upon the pressure difference and resistance of the line and is
given by

$$w = \frac{1}{R}(c - p) \qquad (5\text{--}15)$$

where R = resistance of line, sec/ft^2
c = pressure to be measured, lb/ft^2

Combining these equations to eliminate pressure p, the differential
equation relating output deflection to input pressure is

$$T\dot{b} + b = \frac{A}{K}c \qquad (5\text{--}16)$$

where T = element time constant.

For incompressible fluids operating into an elastic element the time
constant is

$$T = R\left(\frac{\gamma A^2}{K}\right) \qquad (5\text{--}17)$$

The capacitance of the system is given by the parameters enclosed by
the parenthesis. Naturally small capacitance results in small element
time constant and requires a small bellows area and large spring gradient.
Therefore, small displacement leads to small element time constant.
The resistance R of the connecting line should also be small. Line
resistance is discussed later in this section.

The diaphragm pressure gage of Fig. 5–14 is considered to be a null
system in which a balancing force b, supplied by some external mechanism, maintains the diaphragm in a fixed position. Then for a fixed-

volume pressure chamber the rate of change of pressure is given by

$$C\dot{p} = w \tag{5-18}$$

where C = capacitance = $V/(nRT_1)$, ft^2
  V = volume, ft^3
  n = polytropic constant
  R = gas constant, ft/deg
  T_1 = temperature, deg R
  w = flow rate, lb/sec

The balancing force b is assumed to balance the chamber pressure:

$$b = pA \tag{5-19}$$

where b = balancing force, lb
  p = chamber pressure, lb/ft^2
  A = diaphragm effective area, ft^2

The flow of gas through the connecting line is given by equation 5–15. Combining these equations, the differential equation is

$$RC\dot{b} + b = Ac \tag{5-20}$$

For compressible fluids operating into elements of more or less fixed volume, the time constant is therefore

$$T = RC = R\left(\frac{V}{nRT_1}\right) \tag{5-21}$$

Therefore small volume and small line resistance are conducive to fast response.

The resistance of a long connecting line having bends, fittings, and valves depends upon whether laminar or turbulent flow exists. Actually under transient conditions the flow increases from zero to some high velocity, usually turbulent, then decreases to zero if there are no leaks in the line. Thus the calculation of line resistance is made very difficult and for approximation purposes it is usually assumed that laminar flow exists. According to the Poiseuille–Hagen law, the laminar resistance is

$$R = \frac{dp}{dw} = \frac{128\nu L}{\pi g D^4} = \frac{128\mu L}{\pi D^4 \gamma} \tag{5-22}$$

where R = resistance, sec/ft^2
  ν = kinematic viscosity-ft^2/sec
  L = line length, ft
  D = line inside diameter, ft
  μ = absolute viscosity-lb sec/ft^2
  γ = fluid density, lb/ft^3

The laminar resistance is usually less than the actual resistance by as much as 10 to 100 per cent. The best method of determining resistance is by actual test of the element time constant. The capacitance may be calculated with reasonable accuracy.

Summarizing, the pressure-element time constant may be calculated from

$$T = \frac{128\mu L}{\pi D^4}\left(\frac{A^2}{K}\right) \quad \text{(liquid)} \tag{5-23}$$

and

$$T = \frac{128\mu L}{\pi D^4}\left(\frac{V_0}{nP_a}\right) \quad \text{(gas)} \tag{5-24}$$

where V_0 = volume of element at operating pressure, ft^3

n = polytropic constant ($n = 1$ = isothermal)

P_a = average absolute pressure, lb/ft^2

A = element area, ft^2

K = element spring rate, lb/ft

μ = absolute viscosity of gas, lb sec/ft^2

L = length of line, ft

D = inside diameter of line, ft

Example 5–4. One pressure element (null type) has no elasticity but 1.0-cu in. volume. Another pressure element (deflectional type) has an area of 2.5 sq in. and a spring gradient of 100 lb per in. but negligible end volume. Which one is likely to have the smallest lag when measuring an air pressure of 10 lb per sq in. at normal temperature? Compare the capacitance of these elements.

For null type,

$$C = \frac{V\gamma}{nP_a} = \frac{1 \times 0.123}{1728 \times 1 \times 24.7 \times 144} = \underline{2.0 \times 10^{-8} \text{ ft}^2}$$

For deflectional type,

$$C = \frac{A^2\gamma}{K} = \frac{(2.5)^2 \times 0.123}{(144)^2 \times 100 \times 12} = \underline{3.0 \times 10^{-8} \text{ ft}^2}$$

Example 5–5. Calculate the laminar resistance of 100 ft of $\frac{3}{16}$-in. I.D. tubing for air and water at 68 F.

For water,

$$R = \frac{128\nu L}{g\pi D^4} = \frac{128 \times 1.1 \times 10^{-5} \times 100 \times 12^4}{32.2 \times 3.14 \times (0.187)^4}$$

$$R = \underline{23,000 \text{ sec/ft}^2}$$

For air,

$$R = \frac{128\nu L}{g\pi D^4} = \frac{128 \times 16.8 \times 10^{-5} \times 100 \times 12^4}{32.2 \times 3.14 \times (0.187)^4}$$

$$R = \underline{370,000 \text{ sec/ft}^2}$$

Second-Order Response

The response of many temperature and pressure elements cannot be adequately described by a first-order differential equation. Pressure elements, for example, may have inertia effects in addition to fluid effects. Temperature elements often possess more than one energy storage or capacitance. Therefore, a second-order differential equation must be used to describe adequately many pressure- and temperature-measuring elements.

The response of fluid manometers or U-tubes is second order because inertia of the manometer fluid is involved. Applying Newton's second law to the manometer of Fig. 5–15,

$$\left(\frac{AL\gamma}{g}\right)\ddot{b} = -(RA^2\gamma)\dot{b} - (A\gamma)b + cA \tag{5–25}$$

or

$$\left(\frac{L}{g}\right)\ddot{b} + (RA)\dot{b} + b = \frac{1}{\gamma}c \tag{5–26}$$

where L = length through manometer liquid, ft
$\quad b$ = displacement difference, ft
$\quad R$ = fluid resistance of manometer tube, sec/ft^2
$\quad A$ = area of manometer tube, ft^2
$\quad c$ = measured pressure, lb/ft^2
$\quad \gamma$ = manometer fluid density, lb/ft^3

This second-order differential equation describes the response of the manometer. Solutions to this equation are expressed in simpler form by combining coefficients of the equation in a certain manner to obtain combinations having particular significance. Equation 5–26 may be written

$$\frac{b}{c} = \frac{1}{\gamma}\frac{1}{T^2s^2 + 2\zeta Ts + 1} \tag{5–27}$$

where $T = \sqrt{L/g}$ = characteristic time (the inverse is the natural undamped frequency)

$$\zeta = \frac{RA}{2}\sqrt{\frac{g}{L}} = \text{damping ratio} = \frac{16\nu}{D^2}\sqrt{\frac{L}{g}}$$

These quantities are characteristics of the system. When the damping ratio is less than one, ($\zeta < 1$), the system is underdamped as shown by the response to a step change in measured pressure in Fig. 5–15. When the damping ratio is one ($\zeta = 1$), the system is critically damped, and when the damping ratio is greater than one $(\zeta > 1)$, the system is overdamped.

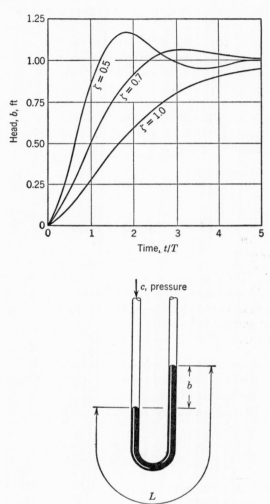

FIG. 5–15.   Step response of a typical second-order system.

For best response a manometer should have a short length so that the characteristic time T is small. However, the length of a manometer is specified by the pressure to be measured and the density of the manometer fluid. Consequently, fast response is obtained by selecting a dense manometer fluid. The damping ratio should be approximately

0.6 to 0.8 (see Fig. 5–15) so that fast response is obtained without excessive oscillation.

Many dynamic systems in engineering are described by a second-order linear differential equation with constant coefficients. Such equations can always be expressed in the following form where the coefficient of the zero order term is one:

$$A\ddot{b} + B\dot{b} + b = Kc \qquad (5\text{–}28)$$

When the system is underdamped, equation 5–28 may be written

$$\frac{b}{c} = \frac{K}{T^2s^2 + 2\zeta Ts + 1} \qquad (5\text{–}29)$$

where $T = \sqrt{A}$ = characteristic time

$\zeta = \sqrt{B^2/4A}$ = damping ratio

When the system is overdamped, equation 5–28 may be written

$$\frac{b}{c} = \frac{K}{(T_1s + 1)(T_2s + 1)} \qquad (5\text{–}30)$$

where $T_1, T_2 = \dfrac{B}{2}[1 \pm \sqrt{1 - 4A/B^2}]$ are the two time constants of the system. For a critically damped system the two time constants are equal. These system functions are indicated in Fig. 5–16.

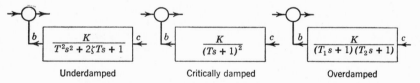

| Underdamped | Critically damped | Overdamped |

FIG. 5–16. System functions for second-order systems.

Example 5–6. For the bellows gage of Fig. 5–14 with a mass M of the spring and bellows, derive an expression for the characteristic time and damping ratio.

When measuring liquid pressure, Newton's second law yields

$$M\ddot{b} = pA - Kb$$

Also, the motion of the bellows depends upon the flow rate in the line:

$$(A\gamma)\dot{b} = w = \frac{1}{R}(c - p)$$

Combining,

$$\frac{M}{K}\ddot{b} + \left(\frac{RA^2\gamma}{K}\right)\dot{b} + b = \frac{A}{K}c$$

Therefore $T = \sqrt{\dfrac{M}{K}}$

$$\zeta = \frac{RA^2\gamma}{2\sqrt{MK}}$$

The natural frequency is

$$f_n = \frac{\omega_n}{2\pi} = \frac{1}{2\pi T} = \frac{1}{2\pi}\sqrt{\frac{K}{M}}$$

Example 5–7. A pressure of 15 psi maximum is to be measured with a mercury U-tube. What is the smallest characteristic time?

$$T = \sqrt{\frac{L}{g}} = \sqrt{\frac{P_m}{\gamma g}} = \sqrt{\frac{15 \times 144}{848 \times g}} = \underline{0.89 \text{ sec}}$$

The response of many thermal elements are second order when a thermal well surrounds the element. In a number of applications it is not possible to expose the bare thermocouple, resistance thermometer bulb, or expansion thermometer bulb to the fluid whose temperature is being measured. The thermal well provides physical protection as well as protection from corrosion and contamination.

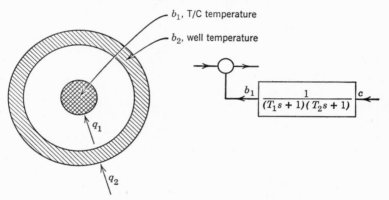

FIG. 5–17.   Second-order response of thermocouple and well.

The cross section of a thermocouple and well in Fig. 5–17 indicates the temperatures and flow of heat. The equations for the system are (neglecting thermal conductivities of materials)

$$C_2\dot{b}_2 = q_2 - q_1 \tag{5–31}$$

$$q_2 = \frac{1}{R_2}(c - b_2) \tag{5–32}$$

$$C_1\dot{b}_1 = q_1 = \frac{1}{R_1}(b_2 - b_1) \tag{5–33}$$

where C_2 = well capacitance = $W_2 C_{p2}$, Btu/deg

C_1 = thermocouple capacitance = $W_1 C_{p1}$, Btu/deg

W = weight, lb

C_p = specific heat, Btu/deg lb^{-1}

R_1 = heat-transfer resistance, well to $T/c = 1/H_1 A_1$

R_2 = heat-transfer resistance, fluid to well = $1/H_2 A_2$

H = heat-transfer coefficient, Btu/ft^2 sec^{-1} deg^{-1}

A = area, ft^2

b_1 = temperature at thermocouple, deg

b_2 = temperature of well, deg

c = measured temperature, deg

In this analysis the heat transfer resistance due to conduction is neglected because it is usually small compared to fluid film (convection) resistance. Eliminating heat flows and temperature b_2 from the above equations

$$\frac{b_1}{c} = \frac{1}{(R_2 C_2 R_1 C_1)s^2 + (R_1 C_1 + R_2 C_1 + R_2 C_2)s + 1} \tag{5-34}$$

This system function can be factored into two time constants:

$$\frac{b_1}{c} = \frac{1}{(T_1 s + 1)(T_2 s + 1)} \tag{5-35}$$

where

$$\frac{1}{T_1}, \frac{1}{T_2} = \frac{R_1 C_1 + R_2 C_1 + R_2 C_2}{2 R_1 C_1 R_2 C_2}\left[1 \pm \sqrt{1 - \frac{4 R_2 C_2 R_1 C_1}{(R_1 C_1 + R_2 C_1 + R_2 C_2)^2}}\right]$$

A close inspection of the damping ratio will show that it cannot be less than one. Therefore, the response of the system can be expressed by two time constants, T_1 and T_2.

Example 5–8. A thermal well has a time constant of 60 sec when installed without a thermocouple in it. The thermocouple shows a time constant of 3 sec when suddenly inserted into the well. The weight of the thermocouple junction is 1 oz and the weight of the thermal well is 0.5 lb. Assume the specific heats to be the same. Calculate the time constants.

$$\frac{R_1 C_1 + R_2 C_1 + R_2 C_2}{2} = \frac{R_1 C_1}{2} + \frac{C_1}{2 C_2} R_2 C_2 + \frac{R_2 C_2}{2}$$

$$\frac{R_1 C_1 + R_2 C_1 + R_2 C_2}{2} = \frac{3}{2} + \frac{\frac{1}{16}}{2 \times 0.5} 60 + \frac{60}{2}$$

$$\frac{R_1 C_1 + R_2 C_1 + R_2 C_2}{2} = 35.2$$

$$\frac{4 R_2 C_2 R_1 C_1}{(R_1 C_1 + R_2 C_1 + R_2 C_2)^2} = \frac{60 \times 3}{(35.2)^2} = 0.15$$

$$T_1, T_2 = 35.2[1 \pm \sqrt{1 - (0.15)}]$$

$$T_1, T_2 = \underline{68 \text{ sec}}, \underline{2.6 \text{ sec}}$$

PROBLEMS

5–1. A thermometer having a time constant of 5 sec is placed in a bath the temperature of which is changing linearly at a rate of 1 deg per sec. How much does the thermometer read in error?

5–2. The time constant of a thermometer in flowing liquid is 10 sec. If the fluid velocity is doubled, estimate the new time constant.

5–3. The time constant of a thermocouple in a furnace at 1000 F is 2 sec. What would the time constant be at 1800 F?

5–4. A bellows pressure gage (area 2 sq in., spring 200 lb per in.) is connected by a $\frac{3}{16}$-inch I.D. tubing 50 ft long. Measuring water pressure, what is its time constant?

5–5. A mercury U-tube has 2 ft total length of mercury in a $\frac{1}{8}$-in. I.D. diameter tube. What is the period of oscillation and the damping ratio?

5–6. A thermal well and thermocouple each have a simple time constant. For these elements in series show that there is little difference in response by neglecting the smaller time constant if it is one tenth or less of the larger number. Assume a linearly changing input and solve differential equations.

chapter 6

Controlling Elements

The automatic controller may operate through purely mechanical means, but more often an auxiliary source of fluid or electric power is employed to actuate the control mechanism and to drive a final control element. The controlling means is usually classified according to the kind of power employed directly in operation: self-operated, pneumatic, hydraulic, and electric. The combination of electrically operated control elements and fluid-power-operated final control element is particularly used.

The automatic controller consists of the measuring element H of Fig. 6–1, the actuating signal element (the circle), the control element

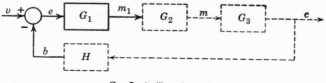

G_1 Controlling element
G_2 Final control element
G_3 Process
H Measuring element

FIG. 6–1. The controlling means.

G_1, and the final control element G_2. In self-operated controllers, these elements are contained usually in one contiguous assembly. Power-operated controllers, on the other hand, and particularly those involving transmission of signals employ separate devices for the measuring element H and the final element G_2.

Self-Operated Controllers

Many automatic controllers operate by employing power developed by the measuring means. These controllers are usually simple and inexpensive, and are widely used in both industrial and domestic service.

The *pressure regulator* or pressure-reducing valve of Fig. 6–2 may be either a "flow" type or a "dead-end" type. The only difference between these two types is that the "dead-end" type incorporates a relief valve,

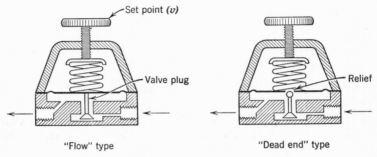

FIG. 6–2.   Pressure regulators.

indicated by the opening through the diaphragm in Fig. 6–2. The set point is determined by the adjustment of the spring compression. The diaphragm "measures" the outlet pressure, and the actuating signal is the net force acting on the valve plug. The manipulated variable is the flow rate past the valve plug. The operation is as follows: When the outlet pressure is too low, the diaphragm moves downward because downward spring force is greater than the upward force, due to pressure acting against the area of the diaphragm. This increases the flow into the outlet and raises the outlet pressure so that the upward pressure force equals the downward spring force. Conversely, if the outlet pressure is too high, the valve plug reduces the flow at the outlet.

The "dead-end" type regulator releases fluid from the outlet through the relief valve when the outlet pressure is too high. Therefore it may be used only on fluids such as air that may be released to the atmosphere.

The "flow" type regulator can only reduce the flow to zero; it cannot allow flow out of the system. Thus, it is useful for water and fuel-gas pressure control.

A pressure regulator has a proportional-control action because the flow rate is proportional to the actuating signal. The proportional sensitivity is the change in flow rate per unit change of valve-plug displacement and is governed by the spring gradient and the valve-flow characteristic. The proportional sensitivity is usually not adjustable.

The *float-level controller* of Fig. 6–3 is widely used for control of liquid level in open or closed vessels. For such applications the valve stem is connected to an arm on the shaft, and the shaft runs through sealed bearings to the interior of the tank. The float is fastened to the arm on the inside end of the shaft, and the valve must be operated by direct mechanical power from the float. Consequently, the valve plug is almost always designed for minimum fluid forces. The control action is, of course, proportional, and the proportional sensitivity may sometimes be made adjustable through adjustable linkage.

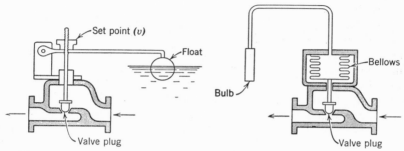

FIG. 6–3.   Direct-connected level   FIG. 6–4.   Thermostatic valve.
controller.

A "radiator thermostat valve" is constructed along similar lines (Fig. 6–4). Temperature is measured by the thermometer bulb and the liquid expansion operates the bellows and valve plug. Sometimes a powerful bimetallic element is used in place of the liquid-expansion element. A set-point mechanism, omitted from the figure, usually consists of a threaded portion on the bellows container so arranged as to raise or lower the bellows position. The operation is as follows: When the temperature increases, the liquid expands, and the bellows forces the valve plug downward. This reduces the flow of steam or hot water into the controlled space. The control action is proportional and the proportional sensitivity is governed by the size of the thermal element and the flow characteristic of the valve.

These are but a few examples of the hundreds of self-operated controllers employed in industry for pressure, temperature, and liquid-level control. Nearly all self-operated controllers employ proportional-control action in which the value of manipulated variable is proportional to actuating signal. Generally, the proportional sensitivity is not adjustable.

Pneumatic Proportional Controllers (Displacement Type)

Pneumatically operated controllers for industrial process control are simple and easily maintained and provide high-power amplification using compressed air as a source of auxiliary power.

The pneumatic controller consists of two parts: a controller mechanism incorporating the control action and providing an air-pressure output and a final control element which positions a control valve in accordance with the air-pressure output of the controller. Consequently, the output air pressure of the controller will be considered proportional to the manipulated variable. Final control elements are considered in Chapter 7.

The displacement-type pneumatic controller operates by converting the controlled variable and set point into corresponding displacements and manipulating these displacements in order to produce a pressure output. The *actuating signal means* in Fig. 6–5 consists of a differential link, one end of which is positioned mechanically by the measuring means according to the magnitude of the controlled variable c, and the other end is positioned to correspond to the set point v. The difference is the actuating signal and is the displacement of the center of the link.

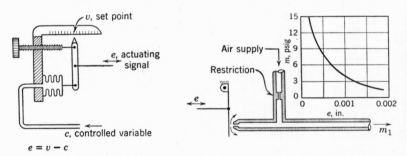

FIG. 6–5. A mechanical actuating signal means.

FIG. 6–6. Flapper–nozzle amplifier.

A *proportional controller* of very simple type is the nozzle–flapper arrangement of Fig. 6–6. Air at about 20 psig is supplied through a small orifice or restriction (about 0.010 in. I.D.) to the open nozzle. The nozzle orifice is about 0.015 in. I.D. A flapper is positioned against the nozzle opening in accordance with the actuating signal e so that the nozzle back pressure m_1 is inversely proportional to the distance between nozzle opening and flapper. A motion of the flapper of about 0.0015 in. is sufficient for nearly full output range. This device may produce proportional control if the flapper is accurately positioned by a measuring means.   Over a reasonably linear range

$$m_1 = K_c e + M_1 \qquad (6\text{-}1)$$

where m_1 = output pressure (nozzle back pressure)

K_c = proportional sensitivity

e = actuating signal

M_1 = normal output pressure

The proportional sensitivity is the change in output pressure per unit of actuating signal e and may be adjusted by moving the flapper pivot point.

The *proportional controller* of Fig. 6–7 employs a power-amplifying pilot for providing a larger quantity of air flow than can be provided

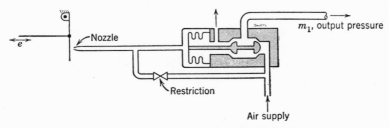

FIG. 6–7.   Proportional controller with pilot.

through the small restriction of Fig. 6–6.   The nozzle back-pressure, instead of operating a final control element directly, is carried to the bellows chamber and acts against the area of the bellows.   Because the bellows has some stiffness (spring gradient) the pilot valve plug is positioned between the inlet and outlet ports in accordance with the nozzle back-pressure.   A low nozzle back-pressure positions the valve plug to the left, throttles the exhaust port, and causes a high output pressure m_1.   A high nozzle back-pressure positions the valve plug to the right, throttles the supply port, and causes a low output pressure m_1.   The advantages of adding the pilot are: (1) the actuating signal e versus output pressure m_1 relation may be made linear; and (2) the capacity for air flow can be considerably increased.

A *proportional controller* incorporating a negative feedback circuit is shown in Fig. 6–8.   The system is similar to the mechanism of Fig. 6–7 except that the output m_1 is connected to a feedback bellows which operates to reposition the flapper.   The nozzle restriction is usually incorporated into the body of the pilot and is omitted from the figure.   This type of controller incorporates a closed loop, whereas the controllers discussed above are the open-loop type.   The operation is as follows: When the actuating signal increases, the flapper covers the nozzle, the nozzle back-pressure is increased, and the output m_1 increases. (A direct-acting pilot is assumed.) The increased output pressure acts against the bellows and repositions the flapper to the left away from the nozzle. If the operation is made stable by proper design, there results a

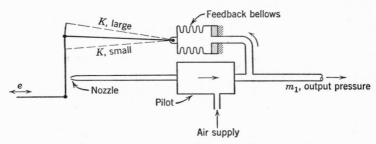

FIG. 6–8. Proportional controller with pilot and feedback.

slight increase in output m_1 corresponding to the increase in actuating signal e. When the feedback link is in the upper position, the feedback is small, the resultant output pressure change is large, and the proportional sensitivity is large (proportional band small). When the feedback link is in the lower position, the proportional sensitivity is small (proportional band large). The advantages of adding the negative feedback are the same as for its use on process control: (1) The effect of variations of supply pressure, temperature, and output leakage is reduced to a minimum (usually made negligible); (2) The proportional sensitivity or proportional band may be varied over a wide range, usually as much as 1200 to 1. With this system displacement amplification up to 10,000 to 1 is easily obtained.

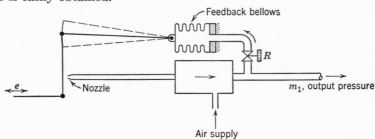

FIG. 6–9. Proportional-derivative controller.

Proportional-derivative control is obtained by adding a feedback restriction as shown in Fig. 6–9. This results in delayed negative feedback. The operation cannot be described adequately by employing a sudden (step) change in actuating signal, so we will assume that the actuating signal changes linearly with time. The flapper then moves slowly to the right, covers the nozzle, and causes a slow increase in output pressure m_1. There is a flow of air through the feedback restriction resulting from the fact that the pressure in the feedback bellows is considerably less than it would have been without the restriction in the line. This delays and reduces the feedback, and, since the feedback is negative, the output pressure is higher and leads instead of lags the actuating signal e. Thus the delayed negative feedback produces derivative response. The operational equation describing the proportional-derivative action is ideally

$$\frac{m_1}{e} = K_c(1 + T_d s) \qquad (6\text{--}2)$$

where K_c = proportional sensitivity (inverse of proportional band)
T_d = derivative time

The derivative time is the product of the resistance of the feedback restriction and the capacitance of the feedback bellows. Therefore, adjustment of the restriction R adjusts the derivative time T_d.

A *proportional-integral controller* is illustrated in Fig. 6–10. It differs from the proportional controller of Fig. 6–8 only in the addition of the

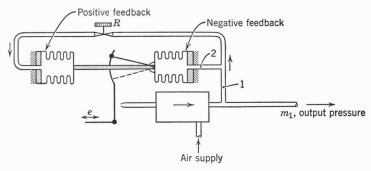

FIG. 6–10.   Proportional-integral controller.

so-called positive feedback bellows and restriction. The free ends of two bellows are rigidly connected, and the flapper is attached to the bellows rod by the adjustable link indicated in the figure. The operation is as follows: When the actuating signal e suddenly increases (a step change), the flapper covers the nozzle and increases the output pressure m_1. The output pressure is transmitted to the negative feedback bellows, repositions the flapper, and stabilizes the output pressure at the new value. But there is now a pressure drop across the restriction because the pressure in the positive feedback bellows remains at its former value.

Thus there is a small flow of air into the positive feedback bellows, the flapper is moved slowly toward the nozzle and the output pressure steadily increases. The rise in output pressure continues until the supply pressure limit is reached. The output pressure m_1 therefore has an added portion representing the integral of the step change in actuating signal. Ideally the operational equation for the system would be

$$\frac{m_1}{e} = K_c\left[\frac{1}{T_i s} + 1\right] \tag{6-3}$$

where T_i = integral time (inverse of reset rate)

K_c = proportional sensitivity (inverse of proportional band)

The proportional sensitivity K_c is adjusted by selecting a position of the flapper connecting link. The integral time is adjusted by setting the restriction R.

Proportional-integral-derivative control is achieved by adding a restriction in the negative feedback line in Fig. 6–10 as was done in Fig. 6–9. This combination provides an addition of the reset and derivative responses and the explanation of its operation proceeds as outlined above for each response. If the restriction is added in the feedback line at point 2 in Fig. 6–10, the response may be represented by

$$\frac{m_1}{e} = \frac{K_c}{\left(1 - \dfrac{T_2}{T_3}\right)}\left[\frac{1}{T_3 s} + \left(1 + \frac{T_2}{T_3}\right) + T_2 s\right] \tag{6-4}$$

where T_2 = time constant of negative feedback bellows and resistance R_2 (derivative time)

T_3 = time constant of positive feedback bellows and resistance R (integral time)

This arrangement thus provides the proper control action as long as the two resistances are not set at the same value. Such controllers are arranged so that the derivative time T_2 cannot be set to a value equal to or greater than the integral time T_3.

If the restriction is added in the feedback line at point 1, Fig. 6–10, the response may be represented by

$$\frac{m_1}{e} = K_c\left[\frac{1}{T_3 s} + \left(1 + \frac{T_1}{T_3}\right) + T_1 s\right] \tag{6-5}$$

where T_1 = time constant of negative feedback bellows and resistance R_1 (derivative time)

T_3 = time constant of positive feedback bellows and resistance R (integral time)

This arrangement provides the desired control action and avoids any limitations of setting derivative time.

Pneumatic Proportional Controllers (Force Type)

The force-type pneumatic controller operates by converting the controlled variable and set point into corresponding forces and manipulating these forces in order to produce a pressure output. The advantages of this type of pneumatic controller is that greater flexibility is provided for achieving various kinds of control action. Industrial controllers of this type are often termed "stack controllers."

The actuating signal mechanism is shown in Fig. 6–11. The set-point means is a "dead-end" type pressure regulator which provides a pressure

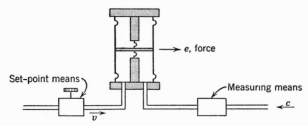

FIG. 6–11.   Actuating-signal means for a force-type pneumatic controller.

corresponding to the set point v. The measuring means consists of a suitable pneumatic transmitter arranged to provide a pressure corresponding to the controlled variable. These two pressures are introduced to the set of three diaphragms which subtracts the controlled variable c from the set point v and produces a force corresponding to the actuating signal.

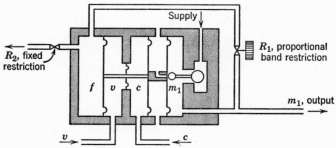

FIG. 6–12.   Force-type proportional controller.

The *proportional controller* of Fig. 6–12 employs the actuating-signal means of Fig. 6–11 as the left-hand set of three diaphragms. The right-

hand diaphragm operates a pilot to convert the actuating-signal force
into a pressure output m_1. The restrictions R_1 and R_2 allow adjustment
of the proportional sensitivity K_c of the controller.

The operation is as follows: When the controlled variable exceeds the
set point, the actuating signal force acts to the right and pushes the pilot
stem to open the supply port. The output pressure m_1 increases and
this pressure causes a force to the left in chamber m_1 (negative feedback),
thus balancing the actuating signal. Now, if restriction R_1 is closed
there is a fixed proportional sensitivity of one (proportional band 100
per cent). On the other hand, if restriction R_1 were wide open, restriction R_2 to atmosphere being fixed, the pressure in chamber f would
always be the same as that in chamber m_1. In the latter case there is
no negative feedback and the proportional sensitivity is very high. For
settings of restriction R_1 between full open and closed, the pressure in
chamber f is governed by the flow through the two orifices in series (R_1
and R_2) so that positive feedback cancels a varying portion of the
negative feedback. Therefore, the restriction R_1 adjusts the proportional
sensitivity of the controller.

Integral response can be added to a proportional controller by the
addition of delayed positive feedback as shown in Fig. 6–13. The pro-

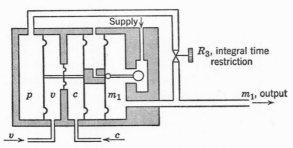

FIG. 6–13. Proportional-integral controller (fixed band).

portional-band adjusting restrictions and chamber have been omitted for
simplicity so that this controller has a fixed proportional sensitivity of
one and an adjustable integral time. The operation is as follows:
Suppose that the controlled variable increases suddenly to a new steady
value. This causes a force to the right which is balanced by a higher
output pressure m_1. There is now a pressure drop across the resistance
in the line leading to chamber p. Air flows into the chamber causing a
force to the right which further increases the output pressure m_1. This
action continues with the output pressure gradually increasing and
integral action results. The mechanisms of Fig. 6–12 and 6–13 can be

combined to provide adjustable proportional sensitivity (restriction R_1) and adjustable integral time (restriction R_3).

A *derivative action* can be added to the proportional controller by providing delayed negative feedback as shown in Fig. 6–14. The proportional-sensitivity adjusting restrictions and chamber and the integral restrictions and chamber have been omitted for simplicity, so that this controller has a fixed proportional sensitivity of one and an adjustable derivative time. The operation is as follows: When the controlled variable increases gradually, a steadily increasing actuating signal causes an increasing force to the right and an increasing output pressure

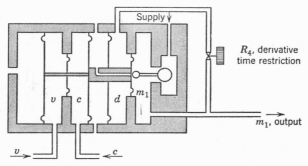

FIG. 6–14. Proportional-derivative controller (fixed band).

m_1. The negative feedback is negligible in chamber m_1, because the area of the diaphragm is small. The feedback is therefore delayed through restriction R_4 into chamber d. The delayed negative feedback causes a higher output pressure, and therefore the output pressure leads the input pressure by a time equivalent to the time constant of the resistance R_4 and the capacitance of chamber d.

The mechanisms of Fig. 6–12, 6–13, and 6–14 are combined by adding proper combinations of diaphragms and restrictions to produce proportional, proportional-derivative, proportional-integral and proportional-integral-derivative controllers. However, this combination may be made in two ways. First, if the controller has both delayed negative feedback and delayed positive feedback it is of a noncascade type, and the ideal response may be represented by

$$\frac{m_1}{e} = K_c \left[\frac{1}{T_i s} + 1 + T_d s \right] \tag{6-6}$$

where K_c = proportional sensitivity
T_i = integral time
T_d = derivative time

Second, if a proportional-derivative control unit output is connected as the input to a proportional-integral control unit, it is a cascade type and the ideal response may be represented by

$$\frac{m_1}{e} = K_c \left[\frac{1}{T_i s} + \left(1 + \frac{T_d}{T_i} \right) + T_d s \right] \tag{6-7}$$

Where the symbols are the same as above. This equation is easily derived by combining equations 6–2 and 6–3 to eliminate the intermediate variable. This type of controller has certain advantages with respect to start-up of batch processes.

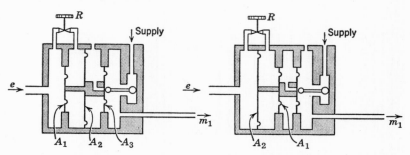

Modified proportional–integral control   Modified proportional–derivative control

FIG. 6–15. Passive-type pneumatic control (direct and inverse derivative of the Moore Products Co.).

The force-type control mechanism of Fig. 6–15 employs a somewhat different principle of operation to provide a very useful combination control action. With the device in the left-hand figure, a modified or limited proportional-reset action is obtained as follows: an increase in actuating-signal pressure e acts against the small diaphragm and causes the pilot to increase slightly the output pressure m_1. There is now a pressure drop across the restriction R and as air flows slowly into the second chamber, the pressure there slowly increases. The output pressure therefore slowly increases until it equals the actuating-signal pressure. The equation for this response can be shown to be

$$m_1 = K \left[\frac{\alpha T s + 1}{T s + 1} \right] e \tag{6-8}$$

where m_1 = output pressure
K = proportional sensitivity = A_2/A_3
α = gain ratio = A_1/A_2
T = time constant of restriction and chamber
e = actuating-signal pressure

When the gain ratio α is small (it is usually set at about one tenth), the effect of the control action is somewhat like a proportional-integral action in which the time constant T adjusts the integral-like time constant.

With the device on the right in Fig. 6–15, the first and second diaphragms are reversed, with the result that the gain ratio α is also inverted and a modified proportional-derivative action is obtained. The action is described by equation (6–8), but with the gain ratio α equal to approximately ten. The time constant T then becomes a derivative-like adjustment.

Air Supply for Pneumatic Systems[1]

The greatest problem connected with pneumatic controllers is the maintenance of a clean, dry air supply at constant pressure. Moisture, oil, corrosive liquids, or foreign particles carried into the pneumatic system from the air supply will eventually cause trouble.

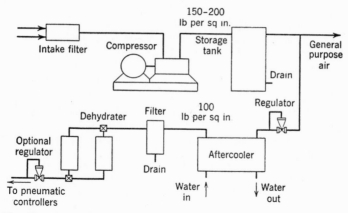

FIG. 6–16. Complete air-supply system for large installation of pneumatic control equipment.

An air supply arrangement, as in Fig. 6–16, may be used for a large amount of control equipment. An intake filter is located outside the compressor room through which the air passes to the compressor. A steam- or electric-driven compressor of desired capacity at a delivery pressure between 150 and 200 lb per sq in. gage is common. The air passes into a storage tank, through a pressure regulator holding the pressure to 100 lb per sq in., and then to an aftercooler. The aftercooler

[1] Reproduced by permission from *Principles of Industrial Process Control*, John Wiley and Sons, Inc., New York, 1949.

or condenser requires a water supply. A porous stone filter removes oil, and a dehydrator completes the removal of moisture. A second pressure regulator is sometimes added to provide constant reduced pressure in the supply lines leading directly to the control rooms for a group of pneumatic control equipment.

In the majority of small installations an arrangement as shown in Fig. 6–17 is satisfactory, especially where excessively low or high temperatures are not encountered and where the intake air is relatively dry. An intake filter removes dust and solids from the intake air. A com-

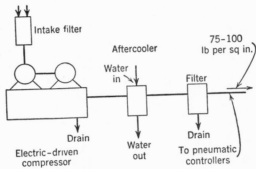

Fig. 6–17.   Air-supply system for small installation of pneumatic control equipment.

pressor with attached storage tank contains a pressure-actuated switch to maintain relatively constant pressure in the tank. An aftercooler and large-capacity filter removes excess oil, moisture, and solids.

Solids are removed most easily by a suitable intake filter at the compressor. The intake filter should be located at a point where it may gather the cleanest air possible; this point is generally outside the building housing the compressor. Edge-type, gauze, or waste filters may be placed at various points in the system to separate solid particles or foreign matter. Clean connecting lines of brass or copper are desirable to eliminate rust.

Moisture is usually adequately removed with a storage tank of proper size and a compressor aftercooler. Where moisture conditions are severe, chemical or electric driers in addition to aftercooling may be required to remove moisture more completely. Chemical driers containing silica gel, activated alumina, calcium chloride, alcohol, glycol, or other drying agents are common equipment. When the drying agent requires replacement or regeneration, a two-section dehydrator should be installed, only one section being used at a time while the other section is being regenerated. If the drying agent is a liquid, an additional unit may be needed for removing the drying agent carried over in the dry air. Lines should be trapped and installed on a slope to drain properly. Check valves should be inserted if there is a possibility that liquids or other gases might back into the lines from other sources.

Oil should be prevented from entering into the system. The air compressor should never be overloaded, since it will pump more oil when running at high loads. A water-sealed rotary compressor where no oil comes in contact with the air is sometimes preferred. The air compressor should receive careful maintenance in order to obtain high efficiency at all times. An aftercooler aids in removing oil vapor as well as moisture. Filters of the porous stone, fuller's earth, centrifugal, or waste type effectively remove larger suspensions of oil. Solvent-type filters may be used to remove oil, although it may then be necessary to remove the solvent dissolved in the air.

An individual filter should be placed at each controller to remove any remaining moisture, oil, or solids just before the air enters the controller. The waste-type filter is most common and is quite satisfactory under ordinary conditions. An individual small-capacity pressure regulator should accompany each controller or group of controllers in order to provide proper pressure regulation.

Moisture-free compressed air does not freeze even at subzero temperatures. Therefore, methods of effectively removing moisture also aid in avoiding trouble due to freezing of air lines. Antifreeze injection systems are not adequate, since the total amount of entrained fluid in the air may be increased.

Locating the air lines so as to avoid low-temperature areas as much as possible is of considerable aid in eliminating either condensation or freezing. It may be possible to maintain the temperature of a group of air lines above freezing by means of a steam tracer. Burying the lines in the ground below the frost line, with suitable traps to remove condensate may be effective.

It is sometimes possible to substitute other compressed gases than air for the operation of pneumatic controllers where an adequate air supply cannot be provided. Such gases must not bring about any corrosive action or deterioration of the parts of the control system. For strictly emergency short-time operation of a single control system bottled nitrogen may be feasible.

Hydraulic Controllers

Hydraulically-operated controllers for industrial process control provide great power and positiveness of action since they employ a source of high-pressure oil as auxiliary power. In certain instances high-pressure water is used as a power source.

The hydraulic controller usually consists of two operating units, a pilot valve to control oil pressure and flow output and a power cylinder and piston to provide the required displacement of a valve or other final control element. The output displacement will be considered proportional to the manipulated variable.

The operation of hydraulic controllers may be illustrated by Fig. 6–18. The measuring means is the diaphragm which produces a force proportional to the magnitude of the controlled variable c. The set-point means is the spring and knob by which a force proportioned to the value of the set point v is imposed. The actuating signal means is the dif-

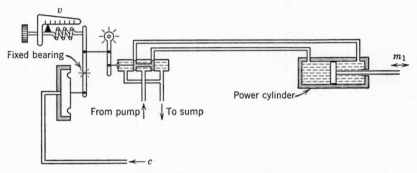

Fig. 6–18.   Hydraulic integral control.

ferential link connecting the diaphragm and spring. Oil at high pressure is supplied to the pilot valve. The operation is as follows: When the actuating signal increases, the pilot valve stem is moved to the left. This supplies oil to the right side of the power cylinder and exhausts oil from the left side. Consequently the power piston moves to the left. Its rate of motion is proportional to the actuating signal. The resulting integral action is described by

$$m_1 = \frac{1}{T_i s} e \qquad (6\text{–}9)$$

where m_1 = position of power piston
$\quad\;\; T_i$ = integral time
$\quad\;\; e$ = actuating signal

The integral time is sometimes made adjustable at the linkage between input arm and pilot stem.

Power is supplied to hydraulic systems by means of an electric motor-pump assembly as shown in Fig. 6–19. The pump, usually a gear type, draws oil from the sump through the filter. The sump collects the return oil from the system and serves to dissipate heat. This latter function is very important in hydraulic systems, and it may infrequently be necessary to employ an oil cooler. The pump and motor run continuously.

An accumulator is sometimes connected to the pump outlet to serve as a reservoir of high pressure oil. The accumulator contains a diaphragm with the gas side filled to several hundred pounds per square

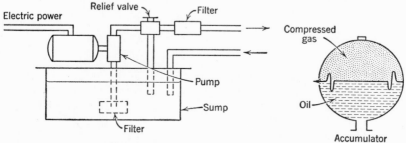

FIG. 6–19. Hydraulic power supply.

inch of gas, usually nitrogen. With suitable check valves, the accumulator may run the control system for several minutes in the event of electrical failure. The main sources of difficulty in hydraulic systems are dirt and heat. Extreme care must be taken to insure that the system is initially clean. After that, particles of metal and oil deposits are bound to occur, and the system must be periodically cleaned. Heat causes great variations in viscosity of the oil, and cooling must be arranged. Usually a large sump may dissipate sufficient heat by radiation.

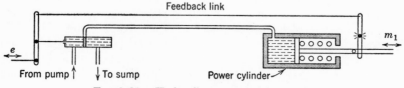

FIG. 6–20. Hydraulic proportional control.

The hydraulic proportional controller in Fig. 6–20 illustrates the one-tube hydraulic system. It is similar in many respects to a pneumatic controller. The operation is as follows: When the actuating signal increases, the pilot valve stem is moved to the left. This action partially opens the connecting tube to the sump, the oil pressure at the power cylinder is reduced, and the spring pushes the power piston to the left. The feedback link then moves to the right, tends to close the pilot valve, and balances the power piston at its new position. Thus, the position of the power piston m_1 is proportional to the actuating signal e,

$$m_1 = K_c e \qquad (6\text{-}10)$$

where K_c = proportional sensitivity

The proportional sensitivity may be adjusted by moving the connection of the feedback link. The one-tube hydraulic controller is often employed for speed control of engines.

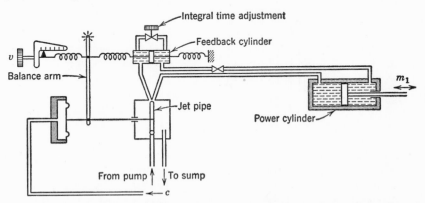

FIG. 6–21. Hydraulic proportional-integral control (Askania Regulator Company).

A hydraulic proportional-integral controller of a somewhat different type is shown in Fig. 6–21. The diaphragm causes a force proportional to the value of the controlled variable to act against the balance arm. The set-point spring also causes a force on the balance arm, as does the feedback spring. The motion of the balance arm displaces a free-swinging nozzle which directs a jet of oil at high pressure into a distributor block connected to both sides of the power cylinder. The operation is as follows: With an increase in controlled variable, the jet pipe swings to the right and increases the pressure in the right side of the distributor block. This increases the pressure on the left side of the power cylinder and decreases the pressure on the left side of the feedback cylinder. The power-cylinder piston moves to the right and causes oil to flow into the right side of the feedback cylinder. The feedback piston moves to the left, increases the force on the balance arm, and returns the jet pipe to a balanced position. This is proportional action. However, the pressure drop across the feedback piston causes a flow of oil through the integral needle valve and allows the feedback piston to move to the right. This action moves the jet pipe to the right and causes continuing motion of the power piston. This is the integral action. The combination is proportional-integral action:

$$\frac{m_1}{e} = K_c\left[1 + \frac{1}{T_i s}\right] \tag{6-11}$$

where K_c = proportional sensitivity
      T_i = integral time

The proportional sensitivity is adjusted by suitable levers between the feedback spring and balance arm. The integral time is adjusted at the needle valve on the feedback piston.

Many other types of hydraulic systems are in use, but the three described here are the most common for process control. Integral action, and any combination of proportional, integral, and derivative actions may be obtained.

Electrical Proportional Controllers (Feedback Type)

Electrically operated controllers for industrial process control are very flexible in operation and are particularly useful when long distances are necessary between various portions of the closed loop. Electrical proportional controllers fall naturally into two classes:

1. Those employing direct feedback transmission from the power actuator.

2. Those providing a direct current or voltage output to which a power actuator responds.

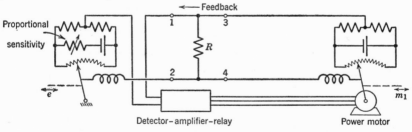

Fig. 6–22. Electrical proportional control (Leeds & Northrup Co.).

The *d-c bridge proportional controller* is illustrated in Fig. 6–22. The slider or contact arm displacement on the left slidewire of Fig. 6–22 is proportional to the actuating signal. Usually this contact arm and potentiometer are mounted in a self-balancing potentiometer or resistance thermometer so that sufficient power is available to provide accurate positioning. The slidewire is located in a fixed bridge so that the d-c voltage to the amplifier is proportional to the actuating signal. The amplifier is a combined detector, rectifier, power amplifier, and relay which closes a forward drive circuit or reverse drive circuit to the electric power motor when the actuating signal bridge voltage is not balanced by the feedback voltage. The power motor also operates a contact arm on an identical fixed bridge to provide a d-c feedback voltage across resistor R. When the feedback voltage equals the input voltage the two contact arms are in correspondence so that the motor output arm displacement m_1 is directly proportional to the actuating signal e. The power motor may be used to position a throttling fluid valve or other final control element. The control action is given by

$$m_1 = K_c e \qquad (6\text{--}12)$$

where m_1 = position of power-motor output arm
K_c = proportional sensitivity
e = actuating signal

Proportional sensitivity adjustment is provided by the variable resistor in the actuating signal (left) bridge.

The *proportional-derivative* circuit is shown in Fig. 6–23. This circuit provides a delayed negative feedback and produces a response proportional to the rate of change of the actuating signal. (Compare

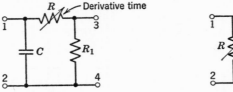
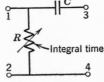

Proportional–derivative circuit   Proportional–integral circuit

FIG. 6–23.   Feedback circuits for the electric controller of Fig. 6–22.

the electrical system to the pneumatic system of Figs. 6–9 and 6–14.) The derivative time is proportional to the electrical time constant RC and is selected by adjusting resistor R.

The *proportional-integral* circuit is also shown in Fig. 6–23 and is inserted at the points indicated in Fig. 6–22. This circuit provides an "advanced feedback" and results in an integral action added to the proportional action. The operation is as follows: Upon a motion of the contactor arm to the left in Fig. 6–22, away from the set point, a d-c voltage is passed to the amplifier and drives the power motor in one direction. The feedback voltage provided by the power-motor slidewire causes a current to flow into the capacitor C, charging the capacitor and resulting in a voltage drop across the resistor R. This is proportional action. Now, however, in order to maintain a steady current through resistor R, the capacitor must be continually charged. This can only be done by a slow and continuous motion of the power-motor arm to the left. This is integral action. The integral time is proportional to the electrical time constant RC and is selected by adjusting resistor R. Proportional-integral derivative action is provided by inserting a suitable combination of the feedback circuits of Fig. 6–23 in the circuit of Fig. 6–22.

The *a-c bridge proportional controller* is shown in Fig. 6–24. As in the previous electric controller the actuating-signal slidewire (at the left) has a sliding contactor positioned according to the actuating signal, usually by means of a self-balancing potentiometer or resistance thermometer. The power-motor slidewire on the right has its contactor

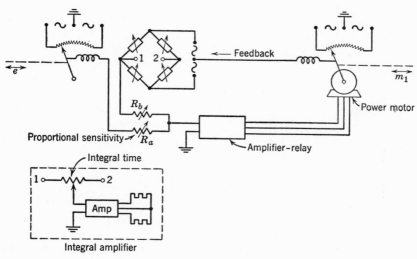

FIG. 6–24.   Electric proportional-integral control (Minneapolis-Honeywell Regulator Co.).

positioned by the output arm of the power motor. The feedback bridge provides integral action as will be explained later. The operation is as follows: When an increase in actuating signal moves the slidewire contactor to the left, a-c voltage and resulting current is carried by resistor R_a. This causes a voltage at the input of the amplifier-relay. The a-c amplifier operates an electric relay to close a forward drive circuit or a reverse drive circuit when the current through resistor R_a is not balanced by a feedback current through resistor R_b. The feedback voltage from the power-motor slidewire is applied to the integral bridge. Neglecting the operation of this bridge, the net effect of the feedback voltage is to cause a current through resistor R_b which must balance the current through resistor R_a. This is proportional action and the power-motor arm must "follow" the actuating signal contactor. Integral action is as follows: Whenever there is a current through resistor R_a, caused by the actuating-signal voltage, the controlled variable is not at the set point. The integral bridge, consisting of the four thermistors, is not balanced because of the necessary current through resistor R_b. Therefore, a voltage results at points 1 and 2 of the bridge and the integral amplifier is energized. The integral amplifier operates heaters which heat the thermistors of the reset bridge. The action of the integral amplifier is to change the current through resistor R_b, again energizing the amplifier-relay and driving the power-motor arm further to the left. This in turn causes further unbalance at the integral bridge which results in a continuous motion of the power-motor arm. The proportional sensitivity is adjusted by setting the ratio of resistors R_a and R_b. The integral time is adjusted by setting the integral amplifier input resistance.

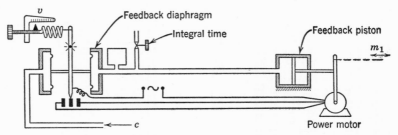

FIG. 6–25.   Electric proportional-reset controller (The Hays Corp.).

The *pneumatic-feedback electric controller* is shown in Fig. 6–25. The controlled variable c is a pressure and acts against the diaphragm causing a force to the right against the balance arm. The set point is a spring force acting on the balance arm. If the controlled variable increases, the balance arm moves to the right and causes the contact to close a circuit to the power-motor. The output arm of the power-motor moves counter clockwise and moves the piston of the feedback cylinder to the left. This action compresses the air in the feedback system and the feedback diaphragm provides a feedback force balancing the actuating signal force. This is proportional action. The pressure in the feedback system is now greater than atmospheric pressure and air flows out the integral restriction to atmosphere. This decreases the force on the balance arm, again operates the power motor to continue the counter-clockwise motion. This is the integral action. For an opposite change of the controlled variable, a vacuum is caused in the feedback system. The proportional sensitivity may be adjusted through suitable levers at the feedback diaphragm or by a change in volume of the feedback system. The integral time is adjusted by setting the restriction to atmosphere.

The principal characteristic of the electrical controllers described in this section is the use of the reversible electric motor as a final control element with the position of the output-arm fed back in a proper manner to provide the desired control action. The advantages of this system are that the actuation is electrical and therefore distance between elements is theoretically unlimited. Another advantage is that the actuator is enclosed within the controller loop.

Electronic Proportional Controllers

The electronic proportional controller is distinguished by the use of an electronic d-c amplifier with appropriate feedback for providing the desired control action. Generally too, the output is simply a direct current which is transmitted to any type of final control element arranged for operation from a direct current.

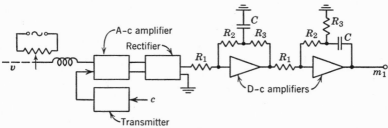

Fig. 6–26.   Electronic proportional-integral derivative controller (general scheme similar to that provided by the Swartwout Company).

The *a-c voltage-input proportional controller* is illustrated in Fig. 6–26 and differs from the preceding electric controllers in that the actuating signal is an a-c voltage rather than a mechanical displacement. The measuring means consists of a resistance thermometer element or an electrical pressure gage providing a 60-cycle voltage proportional to the controlled variable. The set point means is a potentiometer providing a 60-cycle voltage proportional to the set point. The difference in these voltages is the actuating signal which is passed to the a-c amplifier. A rectifier follows to convert the a-c signal to a proportional d-c voltage.

The first d-c amplifier has a "delayed" negative feedback and provides proportional-derivative action as has been described previously for other electric controllers as well as for pneumatic controllers. Proportional-integral action is provided by the second d-c amplifier with "advanced" negative feedback as has been described for the electric controller of Fig. 6–23. Adjustable proportional sensitivity is provided by an adjustable gain of the a-c amplifier. Adjustable derivative time is provided by the setting of the feedback resistor of the first d-c amplifier. Adjustable integral time is provided by the setting of the feedback resistor of the second d-c amplifier. The output of the controller is a d-c current which is carried through wires to a final control element. The combination of proportional-derivative action and proportional-integral action in cascade has an advantage with respect to start-up of control systems. For the proportional action of the a-c amplifier and rectifier,

$$\frac{m_3}{e} = K_3 \tag{6–13}$$

For the proportional-derivative amplifier circuit,

$$\frac{m_2}{m_3} = K_2(1 + T_d s) \tag{6–14}$$

For the proportional-integral amplifier circuit

$$\frac{m_1}{m_2} = K_1\left(1 + \frac{1}{T_i s}\right) \tag{6–15}$$

where e = actuating signal = $v - c$
  K_3 = gain of a-c amplifier and rectifier
  K_2 = gain of first d-c amplifier = $(R_2 + R_3)/R_1$
  K_1 = gain of second d-c amplifier = R_2/R_1
  m_1 = output current (or voltage) of second d-c amplifier
  m_2 = output voltage of first d-c amplifier
  m_3 = output voltage of a-c amplifier
  T_d = derivative time = $R_2 R_3 C/(R_2 + R_3)$
  T_i = integral time = $R_2 R_3 C/(R_2 + R_3)$

Combining to eliminate the intermediate voltages m_2 and m_3,

$$\frac{m_1}{e} = K_1 K_2 K_3 \left[\frac{1}{T_i s} + \left(1 + \frac{T_d}{T_i}\right) + T_d s\right] \tag{6–16}$$

The combination provides proportional-integral-derivative action as shown by equation 6–16 wherein the derivative time and integral time also affect the overall proportional sensitivity. The latter is also affected by the gain of each amplifier. However the gains of the d-c amplifiers are generally fixed and the gain of the a-c amplifier made adjustable.

The *"voice-coil" motor* shown in Fig. 6–27 is the primary transducing device employed with electronic controllers in order to convert direct current into a mechanical force. The operation is based upon the force caused in a conductor carrying a current through a steady magnetic field. The force is linearly proportional to the product of current and field strength.

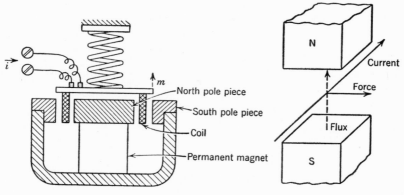

FIG. 6–27.   The "voice-coil" motor.

The motor is constructed by winding a coil of fine wire in a cylindrical form. The coil is maintained in an air gap between pole pieces connected to a permanent magnet. The construction is therefore the same as a permanent magnet loud-speaker. A current through the coil causes a force to push the coil up or down through the gap. The spring converts the motor to a deflectional system so that displacement is proportional to current.

The *d-c current input proportional controller* is shown in Fig. 6–28. The difference between this controller and the controller of Fig. 6–26 lies in the arrangement of the actuating-signal means. The transmitter produces a direct current of a few milliamperes proportional to the controlled variable c. This current passes through the "voice-coil" on the balance detector and causes a force to act on the balance beam opposing the action of the set-point spring. The resulting deflection of the balance beam "couples" the oscillator coil. The signal from the oscillator coil is amplified to a d-c voltage by the preamplifier, and the voltage is negatively fed back to a second "voice-coil" on the balance beam thus restoring force balance at the beam. The output signal of the preamplifier is a d-c voltage proportional to the difference between set point v and controlled variable c and is the actuating signal voltage. This voltage is acted upon by the proportional-derivative amplifier and network (first d-c amplifier). This amplifier has a delayed negative feedback and the derivative time is adjusted by the resistor. The output voltage of the first d-c amplifier is passed to the second d-c amplifier for proportional-integral action. Integral time is adjusted by the resistor R_i and the proportional sensitivity is adjusted by resistor K_c. The output of the second amplifier is a direct current of a few milliamperes.

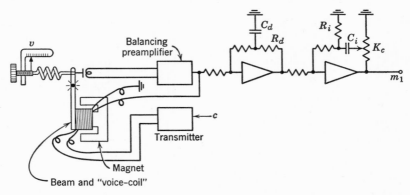

FIG. 6–28. Electronic proportional-integral derivative controller (general scheme
similar to Manning, Maxwell & Moore, Inc.).

The principal advantage of the electric controller of the electronic d-c output current type is that it may be connected by simple two-wire cables, and it provides great flexibility in obtaining combinations of controller action.

Theory of Automatic Controller Circuits

All automatic controllers employ the basic principles of amplifiers and lag elements in order to produce proportional, integral, and derivative action or whatever action is desired. Every automatic controller mechanism employing feedback is a miniature controlled system within itself and is subject to all the analysis techniques employed for automatic control. Consequently, operational diagrams may be drawn to illustrate analogous forms of pneumatic, hydraulic, and electric controllers.

Several amplifiers employed in automatic controllers are shown schematically in Fig. 6–29. The mechanical and fluid amplifiers are used for either displacement or force amplification by suitable modification. The electronic amplifier is employed for either voltage or current amplification. Magnetic and transistor amplifiers are also employed as well as many ingenious combinations and modifications of all these amplifiers.

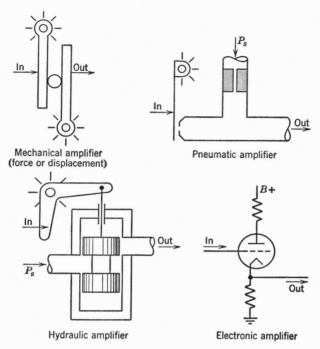

Fig. 6–29. Amplifiers for control elements.

Proportional controllers usually employ feedback as shown in Fig. 6–30. The pilot gain is usually large and the equation for the operation is easily shown to be

$$\frac{m_1}{e} = -K_c \left(\frac{1}{\dfrac{K_c}{K_p} + 1} \right) \qquad (6\text{–}17)$$

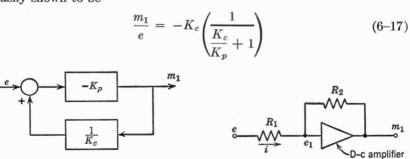

Fig. 6–30. Analog circuits for proportional control.

where K_p = pilot amplifier gain
$\quad\;\; K_c$ = feedback gain

Since the pilot gain K_p is usually large (10^2 to 10^6) then

$$\frac{m_1}{e} = -K_c \tag{6-18}$$

The feedback gain becomes the proportional sensitivity of the controller. The following figures show the use of these principles: Fig. 6–8, pneumatic; Fig. 6–12, pneumatic; Fig. 6–20, hydraulic; and Fig. 6–28, electrical. The electrical d-c voltage analog of Fig. 6–30 may be analyzed by assuming a current flow i into the input resistor R_1:

$$e - e_1 = iR_1 \tag{6-19}$$

The current flow into the amplifier is negligible (grid current only) so all current i passes through the feedback resistor R_2:

$$e_1 - m_1 = iR_2 \tag{6-20}$$

The amplifier has a fixed gain K and in addition changes the sign of the voltage:

$$m_1 = -Ke_1 \tag{6-21}$$

Combining the above three equations to eliminate current i and voltage e_1,

$$\frac{m_1}{e} = -\frac{R_2}{R_1}\frac{1}{1 + \dfrac{R_1 + R_2}{KR_1}} \tag{6-22}$$

The amplifier gain K is usually large (10^2 to 10^6) so that the above equation reduces to

$$\frac{m_1}{e} = -\frac{R_2}{R_1} \tag{6-23}$$

The negative sign shows that the output voltage (reference to ground) is negative for a positive input voltage. As a proportional controller the proportional sensitivity is adjusted by selecting the ratio of resistances (R_2/R_1).

Proportional-derivative controllers employ either one of two basic principles: (1) delayed negative feedback, or (2) advanced input, as shown in Fig. 6–31. The delayed negative feedback employs a feedback capacitance to ground. Thus the output voltage m_1 must continually change in order to charge the capacitor, yielding a derivative effect. The operational equation may be derived by the same procedure as before. Since the amplifier gain is very large (10^2 to 10^6), the operational equation for the left circuit of Fig. 6–31 is

$$\frac{m_1}{e} = -K_c(T_d s + 1) \qquad (6\text{–}24)$$

where $K_c = 2R/R_1$
$\quad\ T_d = RC/2$

The derivative time T_d is adjusted by setting either or both resistors; the proportional sensitivity is adjusted by setting the ratio of resistors.

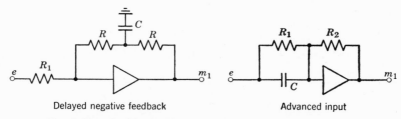

Delayed negative feedback   Advanced input

FIG. 6–31.   Analog circuits for proportional-derivative control.

The delayed negative feedback principle has been illustrated previously in Figs. 6–9 and 6–14 (pneumatic) and Figs. 6–23, 6–26, and 6–28 (electrical).

The advanced input method is not employed as often but is very easy to accomplish with fluid amplifiers. The operational equation may be shown to be

$$\frac{m_1}{e} = -K_c(T_d s + 1) \qquad (6\text{–}25)$$

where $K_c = R_2/R_1$
$\quad\ T_d = R_1 C$

This method is illustrated by the pneumatic circuit of Fig. 6–15 although there the gain is not large.

Proportional-integral controllers may be one of three types: (1) delayed positive feedback (Fig. 6–32); (2) advanced negative feedback (Fig. 6–33); (3) delayed input (Fig. 6–33).

The delayed positive feedback method employs a negative feedback through lower resistor R_4, thereby producing a proportional action. Two feedback amplifiers are involved. The delayed feedback through upper resistors R, R_1, and R_4 is positive because of the additional feedback amplifier. The positive feedback produces a regeneration of amount controlled by capacitor C and resistors R. The operational equation may be shown to be, if the resistor $R_1 = 2R$,

$$\frac{m_1}{e} = -K_c\left(1 + \frac{1}{T_i s}\right) \tag{6-26}$$

where $K_c = R_4/R_2$
$\quad\quad T_i = RC/2$

The integral time is set by adjusting either one or both resistors R. The proportional sensitivity is set by ratios of feedback resistors. This

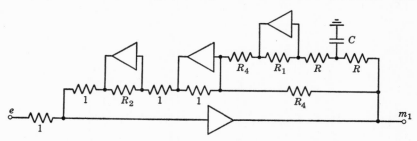

FIG. 6-32. Analog circuit for proportional-integral control—delayed positive feedback.

method employing mechanical feedback amplifiers and a pneumatic amplifier is exemplified by the pneumatic controllers of Figs. 6–10 and 6–13.

The advanced negative feedback method of Fig. 6–33 is commonly employed in electric controllers. By inspection of Fig. 6–33 it is seen

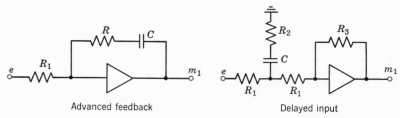

Advanced feedback   Delayed input

FIG. 6-33. Analog circuits for proportional-integral control.

that unless the input voltage is zero there must exist a rate of change of output voltage in order to maintain a current into the condenser and thus its charge. The operational equation is

$$\frac{m_1}{e} = -K_c\left(1 + \frac{1}{T_i s}\right) \tag{6-27}$$

where $K_c = R/R_1$
$\quad\quad T_i = RC$

The integral time is adjustable by resistor R and the proportional sensitivity by the ratio of resistors. The electrical systems of Figs. 6–26 and 6–28 use this method.

The delayed input method of Fig. 6–33 is sometimes employed as a lag network in order to achieve proportional-integral action. The operational equation is

$$-\frac{m_1}{e} = K_c \left(\frac{\alpha Ts + 1}{Ts + 1}\right) \tag{6–28}$$

where $K_c = R_3/2R_1$
$\alpha = 2R_2/(2R_2 + R_1)$
$T = (2R_2 + R_1)C/2$

If it is arranged that resistor R_2 is much smaller than resistor R_1 and if capacitor C is large, then the coefficient α of equation 6–28 is negligible and the response approaches proportional-integral action. This method is that employed in the pneumatic controller of Fig. 6–15.

Other control actions such as proportional-integral-derivative action may be obtained via a suitable combination of the five circuits of Figs. 6–30, 31, 32, and 33. These combinations and many others that are in infrequent use are too numerous to review here. Many of these combinations perform according to the equation

$$\frac{m_1}{e} = \frac{K_i}{s} + K_c + K_d s \tag{6–29}$$

where K_i is some integral-like adjustment, K_c is some gain adjustment, and K_d is some derivative-like adjustment. The three adjustable coefficients are not always individually adjustable by physical knobs at the controller. It is usually the case that the knobs actually adjust a combination of coefficients (K_i, K_c, K_d). The manufacturer of the controller should be consulted as to the arrangement of the adjustable parameters of the controller.

Electrical Proportional Controllers for Electric Heating

The throttling or modulating of electrical heat by amplitude modulation of electric power proves to be expensive because of the large amount of electrical equipment involved. A simpler expedient is to turn on and off the electric power by means of contactors or relays. The power can be modulated as an average over a period of time by turning on the electric power for varying time fractions of a fixed time cycle. Thus if a relay were turned off every P minutes but turned on for f minutes in each P period, the average electric power could be manipulated. The manipulated variable is then

$$m = \frac{f}{P} \qquad (6\text{--}30)$$

where m = fraction of time on = average power
$\quad\; f$ = time on
$\quad\; P$ = period of cycle (usually fixed)

The period of cycle P is about 10 to 120 sec for most furnaces.

A *proportional controller* for electric heating is shown in Fig. 6–34. The actuating signal e is a position given by a self-balancing potentiometer, for example, and determines the position of the upper contact

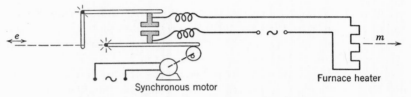

Fig. 6–34. Proportional controller for electric heating.

of a single-pole switch. The lower contact is carried on a movable arm, the end of which is oscillated up and down by a cam and synchronous motor. The time of "make" of the contact is proportional to the height of the upper contact; the higher the contact, the less time on. Therefore, the manipulated variable m is proportional to the actuating signal e, and proportional control results. The proportional sensitivity is set by adjusting the levers. The period is adjustable by setting the cam speed.

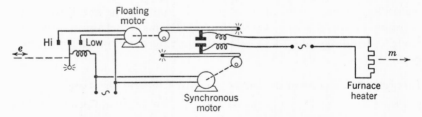

Fig. 6–35. Single-speed floating controller for electric heating.

The *single-speed floating controller* of Fig. 6–35 is commonly used for electric furnaces. A millivoltmeter pyrometer, potentiometer pyrometer, or expansion thermometer contains HI-LOW contacts operated in such a manner that when the controlled variable is below the set point, the low contact is made; above the set point, the HI contact is made.

In a narrow region near the set point, neither contact is made. This latter region is termed the neutral zone.

The HI-LOW contacts supply power to drive a slow-speed motor in one direction or another, and to increase "time on" when the LOW contact is made and to decrease time on when the HI contact is made. The floating motor usually requires several minutes to change from zero "time on" to full "time on." Single-speed floating control action results. In equation form,

$$\left(\begin{array}{lll} \dot{m} = K & \text{when} & c > v + N/2 \\ \dot{m} = O & \text{when} & v + N/2 < c > v - N/2 \\ \dot{m} = -K & \text{when} & c < v - N/2 \end{array}\right) \quad (6\text{--}31)$$

where m = fraction of "time on"
$\quad K$ = floating rate
$\quad c$ = controlled variable
$\quad v$ = set point
$\quad N$ = neutral zone

The floating rate K is adjusted by selecting a gear ratio for the floating motor. The neutral zone N is adjusted by setting the position of the HI-LOW contacts. The period of cycle P is adjusted by selecting a gear ratio for the synchronous motor.

A *proportional-integral controller* for electric heating is shown in Fig. 6–36. This arrangement provides a control action in which the

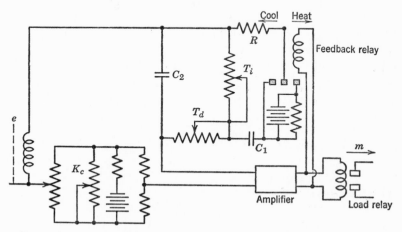

Fig. 6–36.   Proportional-integral control for electric heating (Leeds and Northrup Co.).

fraction of "time-on" of the load relay m is proportional to the actuating signal e. In addition, integral and derivative actions are also provided. The actuating signal is generally a mechanical displacement provided by a self-balancing potentiometer or resistance thermometer. The operation of the circuit is described briefly as follows: Suppose that the actuating signal is positive so that the contactor at e is above the center position. This causes a voltage to appear at the amplifier which closes the load relay and feedback relay. This connects the battery to the resistor R, and capacitors C_1 and C_2 begin slowly to charge. Soon the voltage across capacitor C_2 exceeds the previous input voltage and the amplifier drops out both relays. In actual practice the relays must be interlocked. The feedback relay is then connected so as to discharge the capacitors. If the capacitor charge and discharge rates are the same, then the load relay is on for one-half time and off for one-half time. If the capacitors discharge faster than they charge, the load relay is on for greater than one-half time and if the capacitors discharge more slowly than they charge, the load relay is on for less than one-half time. The fraction of time on m_1 is therefore proportional to the actuating signal because the rates of charge and discharge are determined by the net voltages from the input and feedback.

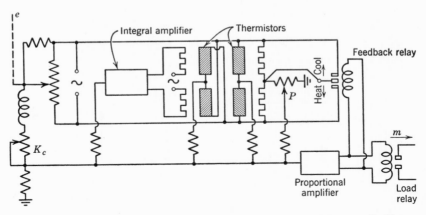

FIG. 6–37. Proportional-integral control for electric heating (Minneapolis-Honeywell Regulator Co.).

The total period of cycling is governed by the gain of the amplifier and the interlocking of the relays. The proportional sensitivity K_c is adjusted by the potentiometer at the input circuit. Integral time T_i and derivative time T_d are adjusted by the resistors in the feedback circuit.

The proportional-integral controller shown in Fig. 6–37 operates in a very similar manner except that the cycling action is governed by the thermal bridge. When the feedback relay closes the upper contact, the lower heater and thermistor rise in temperature and unbalance the center-tap feedback voltage. When the feedback voltage exceeds the input voltage, then the amplifier reverses the feedback relay. The total period of cycling is adjusted at potentiometer P by selecting the overswing voltage of the thermistor bridge. Integral action is provided by the integral amplifier, heaters, and thermistors, the latter being thermally lagged. Whenever the actuating signal is not zero, the integral amplifier turns on the appropriate integral heater thus providing a feedback voltage to actuate the proportional amplifier. Integral time is adjusted by setting the gain of the integral amplifier.

Two-Position and Floating Controllers

Two-position controllers are generally electrical in operation although pneumatic proportional controllers with the proportional sensitivity set very high are sometimes used. The thermostats in Fig. 6–38 illustrate the various differential gaps in two-position control. The thermostat on the left operates load contacts directly from the bimetallic element. The set point is adjusted by setting one contact or by repositioning the whole bimetal element. The gap of this arrangement is theoretically zero although in actual practice there is a very small gap due to contact "stickiness."

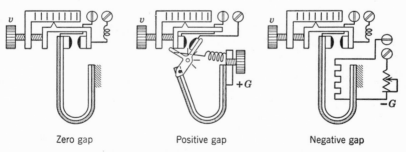

Zero gap   Positive gap   Negative gap

Fig. 6–38. Two-position (thermostat) controllers.

A positive differential gap is often necessary in two-position control in order to save wear on the control apparatus. The mechanism of Fig. 6–38 employs a toggle action to produce a positive gap. The gap is adjustable by the tension of the spring because this determines the suppressive (hysteresis) force acting on the element.

A negative differential gap is often used on domestic thermostats in order to reduce an abnormally long period of oscillation. An auxiliary heater operated by the load contacts or by an auxiliary relay turns on the heater when the contact is made. Thus the bimetal element opens the load contact before the actual temperature attains the same point. The load contact make point is normal. This is sometimes termed "anticipation."

There are many forms of two-position controllers of the "thermostat" or "pressurestat" type for both domestic and industrial application. These offer many arrangements of load contacts, set point, and differential gap. Generally, a solenoid valve of one type or another or an electrical heating element, motor, or other power device is operated by the controller.

For industrial service the controller of Fig. 6–39 is often used because it only requires moving a light aluminum vane in or out of two coils. The vane may be carried directly by the galvanometer pointer of a

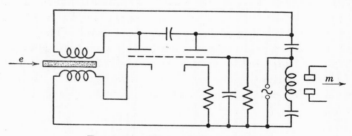

FIG. 6–39.   Two-position controller.

millivoltmeter. The coils may be positioned by a set-point mechanism or may be fixed. The left-hand tube circuit is an oscillator with the vane out of the coils. When the vane is between the coils, the oscillation is greatly reduced. The right-hand tube circuit picks up the oscillation and blocks the relay current. Thus the relay coil is energized when the vane is between the coils and is de-energized when the vane is out of the coils.

For floating controller action a neutral zone is usually necessary. This is obtained by a second contact position in the controller and is often obtained with two independently set on-off control mechanisms.

Single-speed floating control may be achieved by means of the same equipment as for two-position control with an electric-motor-operated valve. The difference lies only in the speed of operation of the motor. In two-position control the motor valve timing is 120 sec or less. In single-speed floating control the timing for valve stroke is usually

120 sec or more. An electrical interrupter is sometimes employed in conjunction with the motor to decrease the speed of opening and closing the valve.

PROBLEMS

6–1. Find $e = f(v, c)$ for a motion of the differential lever.

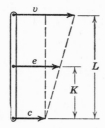

6–2. Show that the pneumatic amplifier has proportional actions described by pressure $m = Ke$.

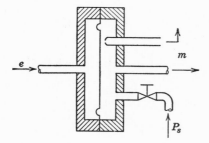

6–3. Show that the pneumatic amplifier has proportional actions described by $m = Ke$.

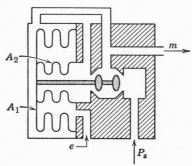

6–4. The flow through the open nozzle when the velocity at the restriction is acoustic velocity is given by $q = K\pi Dep/\sqrt{T}$, where K is the orifice coefficient, and T is upstream temperature. Linearize the equation.

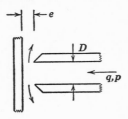

6–5. Assuming a linear relation for the nozzle, derive the output–input relations for the hydraulic controller (A = piston area, K = spring constant, $K_2 = \partial q/\partial p$ nozzle, $K_3 = \partial q/\partial p$ supply, $K_1 = \partial q/\partial e$ nozzle).

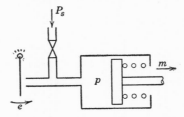

6–6. For the gas-pressure regulator calculate the offset when acoustic velocity exists at the throat.

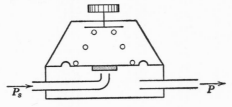

6–7. Calculate the input–output relationship, and state the kind of control action.

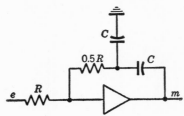

6–8. Calculate the input–output relationship, and state the kind of control action.

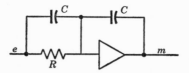

6–9. Calculate the input–output relationship, and state the kind of control action.

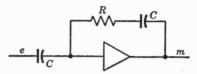

6–10. The device shown in the figure has proportional-integral action. The position of the input shaft e is transmitted directly to the output m through the differential gears. The input e is also integrated by the disk and is added into the output by rotation of the outside gear of the differential. Assuming nominal gear ratios write a description of the operation.

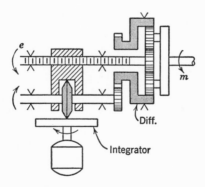

6–11. For the proportional controller (duration type) calculate the output as a fraction "on" per cycle as a function of input e and period of cycling P.

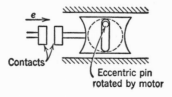

6–12. A new controller action can be synthesized by deriving system functions G and H. If G represents a high-gain amplifier, derive H to give proportional-integral action; $c = \left(1 + \dfrac{1}{Ts}\right)v.$

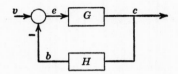

chapter 7

Final Control Elements

The final control element is the mechanism which alters the value of the manipulated variable in response to the output signal from the automatic control device. The position of the final control element in the automatic control loop is shown in Fig. 7–1. The final control

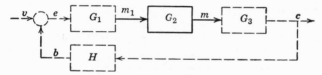

G_1 Controlling element
G_2 Final control element
G_3 Process
H Measuring element

FIG. 7–1. The final control element.

element often consists of two parts: first, an actuator which is used to translate the output signal of the automatic controller into a position of a member exerting large power; and second, a device to adjust the value of the manipulated variable (usually a flow rate of a fluid).

The actuator must provide an accurate output position proportional to the input signal in spite of various forces acting on the output member. The most important forces are

1. Inertia forces caused by the mass of moving parts

2. Static friction forces during impending motion of two adjacent surfaces

3. Thrust forces caused by weight and unbalanced fluid pressure.

195

Thus, the actuator is often required to employ a power-amplifying mechanism. As with automatic controllers, the actuator may operate by pneumatic, hydraulic, electrical, or a combination of these means.

Pneumatic Actuators

Pneumatic actuators may operate directly from the pneumatic output signal from a pneumatic controller, or they may employ a separate source of compressed air. There are five common methods of operation of pneumatic actuators. These are called

1. Spring actuator
2. Spring actuator with positioner
3. Springless actuator
4. Piston actuator
5. Motor actuator.

A *spring actuator* shown in Fig. 7–2 operates directly from the air-pressure output of a pneumatic controller in order to provide an output position proportional to the input air pressure. The diaphragm is

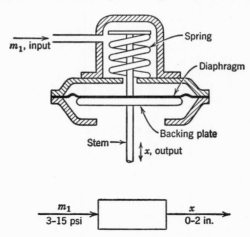

Fig. 7–2. Spring and diaphragm actuator.

usually made of fabric-base rubber, molded to form, and supported by a backing plate. The input air pressure m_1 acts against the diaphragm and causes a downward force which compresses the spring. At static balance, the force of the air pressure against the diaphragm equals the spring compression force:

$$(m_1 - m_0)A = Kx \qquad (7-1)$$

where m_1 = input air pressure, lb/in.^{2}

m_0 = input air pressure at zero stroke, lb/in.^{2}

A = effective area of diaphragm, in.^{2}

K = spring gradient, lb/in.

x = output (stem) displacement, in.

The standard input operating range of spring actuators is 3 to 15 psi gage. The output displacement or stroke is generally between $\frac{1}{4}$ and 3 in. and is limited by the allowable stroke of the diaphragm. For longer strokes a piston–spring combination is employed.

The performance of a spring actuator is generally satisfactory providing it is not used under conditions of excessive force on the stem. Inertia forces due to the mass of moving parts must be limited by the natural frequency of the system,

$$f_n = \frac{1}{2\pi} \sqrt{K/M} \qquad (7\text{–}2)$$

where f_n = natural frequency, cycles/sec

K = spring gradient, lb/in.

M = total mass of moving parts, lb sec^2/in.

The natural frequency should be at least 25 cycles per second, otherwise the actuator stem may oscillate continuously when damping is negligible.

Static friction forces must be limited to a low enough value that excessive hysteresis does not result. For hysteresis less than one per cent of full travel,

$$F_f < \frac{M_r A}{100} \qquad (7\text{–}3)$$

where F_f = static friction force, lb

M_r = input operating range, lb/in.^{2}

This may be a serious limitation. For example, a spring actuator with an effective area of 100 sq in. and an operating range of 3 to 15 psi cannot support more than 12 lb friction if the hysteresis is to remain less than one per cent of full range. Thrust forces are also limited by the ability of the actuator to provide full operating stroke,

$$F_t < m_0 A \qquad (7\text{–}4)$$

where F_t is the total thrust force acting in one direction. This may also be a serious limitation. For example, a spring actuator with an effective area of 100 sq in. and an initial air pressure setting of 3 psi cannot support more than 300 lb unbalanced force. In addition, thrust forces must be relatively constant otherwise the stem position will not be directly related to the input air pressure. The performance of a spring actuator is also influenced by the characteristics of the spring and diaphragm. A well-designed actuator has a linear static relation between input air pressure and output stroke if the effective area of the diaphragm and the spring gradient are constant throughout the stroke. Hysteresis due to the stresses in the spring and diaphragm are usually less than one or two per cent of full stroke.

The spring actuator often requires a positioner as shown in Fig. 7–3 when static friction forces are large or when the response of the motor is too slow. The positioner consists of an input bellows, a nozzle and amplifying pilot, and the feedback levers and spring. An air supply of

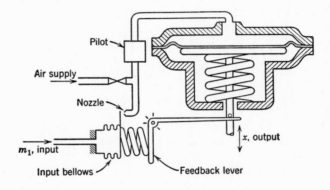

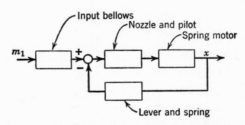

FIG. 7–3.   Spring and diaphragm motor with positioner.

from 20 to 100 psig must be provided. The operation is as follows: When the input air pressure m_1 increases, the input bellows moves to the right and causes the baffle to cover the nozzle. The nozzle back-pressure change is amplified by the pilot and is transmitted to the diaphragm. The diaphragm moves down and the feedback lever compresses the spring to return the baffle to a balanced position. Thus the actuator stem assumes a position dictated by the input air pressure. The spring actuator becomes a power means and the characteristics of the spring and diaphragm are relatively less important. The use of the positioner results in several improvements in performance.

1. Hysteresis is reduced and linearity is usually improved because the static operation is governed by the feedback spring and input bellows.

2. The actuator can handle much higher static friction forces because of the amplifying pilot.

3. Variable thrust forces on the motor stem do not disturb the stem position to any great extent.

4. Speed of response is generally improved because the pneumatic controller must supply sufficient air to fill the small input bellows rather than the large actuator chamber.

The use of a positioner with a spring actuator does not improve the ability of the actuator to handle larger inertia or thrust forces unless special adjustments of motor operating range are made. The only disadvantage in the use of a positioner is that it may require maintenance.

The *springless actuator* shown in Fig. 7–4 is useful for large thrust forces. The only difference between the springless actuator and the

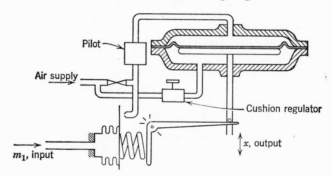

FIG. 7–4.   Springless diaphragm actuator.

spring actuator with positioner of Fig. 7–3, is that the spring of the actuator is replaced by a pressure regulator which maintains a constant pressure on the under side of the diaphragm. An air supply at a pressure of 20 to 100 psig is required. The operation of the springless actuator is as follows: Assume that the cushion regulator is set to provide 9 psig pressure on the under side of the diaphragm. At static balance and with no thrust force on the actuator stem, the upper side pressure must be 9 psig. Then if the input pressure increases, the nozzle back pressure increases, and the upper side pressure is raised to a high value. The actuator stem then moves downward and, as the actuator stem attains the new position, the upper side pressure is returned to 9 psig. If there is an upward thrust force on the actuator stem, the under side pressure remains at 9 psig but the positioner raises the upper side pressure until static balance is achieved. For a downward thrust force the upper side pressure is reduced below 9 psig. Thus, the springless actuator can counteract a thrust force equal to approximately the underside pressure times the area of the diaphragm. This is generally from three to ten times the thrust force handled by a spring actuator with or without a positioner.

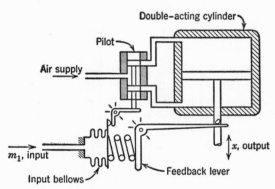

FIG. 7–5.   Double-acting piston-actuator.

The *double-acting piston actuator* of Fig. 7–5 is employed for larger thrust forces than can be handled by the single-acting actuator, and the piston is used in order to obtain long stroke. The pilot is generally a spool-type diverting valve and requires an air supply of 30 to 100 psig pressure. The operation is as follows: When the input pressure m_1 increases, the bellows moves to the right and pushes the pilot spool upward. This action opens the upper side of the cylinder to the air supply and opens the lower side to atmosphere; thus the action is to return the piston to the neutral position. Thus the position of the piston is proportional to the input pressure. A double-acting piston actuator can handle a thrust force equal to about 80 per cent of the supply pressure times the area of the piston.

The *rotary actuator* in Fig. 7–6 is used for very large thrust force or torque. The air motor is a reversible vane-type or positive-displacement-type motor operating from 80 to 100 psig air pressure. The operation is as follows: When the input pressure m_1 increases, the pilot piston moves upward and supplies high pressure to one side of the air motor. The other side of the air motor is exhausted. The motor drives the rack downward, compresses the feedback spring, and returns the pilot piston to the neutral position. Actuators of this kind are employed in sizes from 1 to 15 hp and will handle thrusts as high as 100,000 lb.

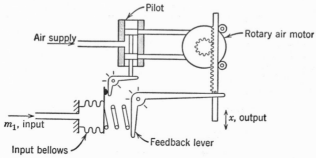

FIG. 7–6. Motor actuator.

Table 7–1 summarizes the application of pneumatic actuators.

Table 7–1. Range of Application of Pneumatic Motor Operators

	Approx. hp	Stroke, in.	Thrust Force, lb	Friction Force for 1% Hysteresis, lb
Spring actuator (3–15 psi range)	0.05	to 3	to 800	to 30
Spring actuator and positioner	0.15	to 3	to 800	to 300
Cushion actuator	0.15	to 3	to 2000	to 300
Double-acting piston actuator	0.1–1	to 36	to 5000	to 600
Rotary motor actuator	1–15	to 60	to 100,000	—

All pneumatic actuators require a source of clean, dry air. The arrangement of proper air supply has been discussed in Chapter 6 (see Figs. 6–16 and 6–17). For pneumatic actuators it is necessary also that the requisite quantity of air be available, because pneumatic actuators require large power input to produce large power output. It is particularly important that supply lines be made large enough so that line losses are small.

Example 7–1. A spring actuator is to be used for positioning a dead weight of 300 lb on its stem. The pressure input is 3 to 15 psig and the stroke is 2 in. What is the minimum diaphragm area and resulting natural frequency?

From equation 7–4,

$$A > \frac{F_t}{m_0} = \frac{300 \text{ lb}}{3 \text{ psi}} = 100 \text{ sq in.}$$

From equations 7–2 and 7–1,

$$f_n = \frac{1}{2\pi} \sqrt{\frac{K}{M}} = \frac{1}{2\pi} \sqrt{\frac{M_r A}{Mx}}$$

$$= \frac{1}{2\pi} \sqrt{\frac{12 \times 100 \times 32.2 \times 12}{300 \times 2}} = 4.4 \text{ cps}$$

Example 7–2. A springless actuator has a diaphragm of 100 sq in. area. Its positioner operates from 3 to 15 psig. The cushion (under-side) pressure is set to 5 psig. What range of thrust load can be accommodated?

Maximum upward thrust $= (15 - 5) \times 100 = 1000$ lb

Maximum downward thrust $= (5 - 3) \times 100 = 200$ lb

Electro-Pneumatic Actuators

When electric control systems are employed, it is often advantageous to use a pneumatic actuator. If a suitable air supply is available, a pneumatic actuator can provide very large power output and may be operated directly from an electric control system. This requires transducing the electrical output of the controller into an input variable for the actuator.

The *electro-pneumatic pilot* of Fig. 7–7 is arranged to convert an electrical signal input to a proportional air pressure output. An electric control system employing this pilot may operate with any of the

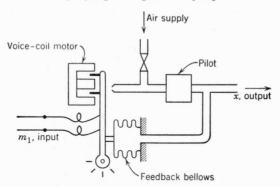

Fig. 7–7.   Electro-pneumatic pilot.

pneumatic actuators previously discussed. The input electric signal (usually a direct current) enters the "voice-coil" motor. The "voice-coil" motor was described by Fig. 6–27 in Chapter 6. The input coil is supported in the field of a permanent magnet so that the coil affords a force proportional to the magnitude of the input d-c current. The force causes a deflection of the balance beam, covers the nozzle, and results in an increase of output pressure. The output pressure acts on the feedback bellows to cause a torque on the balance beam equal but opposite to that of the voice coil. The output pressure therefore is proportional to the input d-c current.

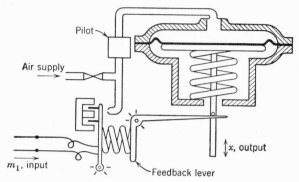

Air supply

Pilot

m_1, input

x, output

Feedback lever

FIG. 7–8.   Electro-pneumatic actuator.

The *electro-pneumatic actuator* of Fig. 7–8 combines the voice coil and the pilot in the positioner of a pneumatic actuator. The motion of the output of the actuator is related to the balance beam through the feedback lever. The output position of the actuator is therefore proportional to input d-c current.

Hydraulic Actuators

Hydraulic actuators, as used for industrial process control, accept a signal from a pneumatic controller or an electric controller and employ hydraulic pressure to drive an output member. The hydraulic actuator is used where high speed and large forces (or large power) are required.

The *hydraulic piston actuator* in Fig. 7–9 has as its input m_1 the position of the vertical lever. For a pneumatic-hydraulic actuator the input would be the position of a bellows. The balance lever pivots at the bottom so that an increase of input (to the left) pushes the pilot piston to the left. This action opens the left end of the piston to supply pressure and opens the right end of the piston to drain. The large power piston, therefore, moves to the right until, as the balance lever rotates about the topmost end, the pilot piston is returned to center, the motion of the output x_1 is therefore proportional to the input motion m_1. The hydraulic actuator requires a continuously running electric motor and pump to provide a source of high-pressure oil, and a drain or sump to collect the return. Hydraulic supply was discussed in detail in Chapter 6.

The *motor actuator* uses a variable-delivery pump shown in Fig. 7–10 in order to produce a proportional output position or speed. The pump consists of a disk driven by a constant-speed electric motor. A number

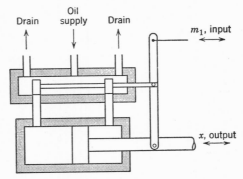

FIG. 7–9.   Hydraulic piston actuator.

of pistons are attached to the disk and reciprocate in a cylinder body. The cylinder body rotates with the disk. When the disk and cylinder body are axial, the pistons remain stationary and there is no oil delivery.

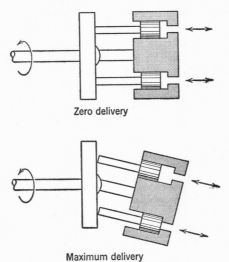

Zero delivery

Maximum delivery

FIG. 7–10.   Hydraulic variable-delivery pump.

When the cylinder body is tilted, the pistons reciprocate and the oil delivery is proportional to the amount of tilt. The actuator is shown in Fig. 7–11. The input signal m_1 is the position of the tilt control lever.

The pump is directly connected to a positive-displacement motor. The motor is physically the same as the pump but has a fixed "tilt" and thus a fixed displacement. The same arrangement may be employed for

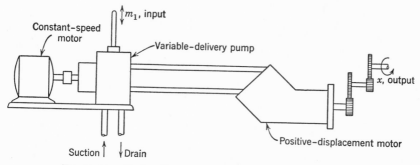

FIG. 7–11. Hydraulic motor operator with rotative output.

position control (output position proportional to input signal) or for speed control (output speed proportional to input signal). Hydraulic motor actuators are used in sizes from three to three hundred horsepower.

The *electro-hydraulic piston actuator* is shown in Fig. 7–12. The input device is the voice-coil motor which positions a three-land pilot spool. The pilot controls the flow of oil to the cylinder, and the piston motor

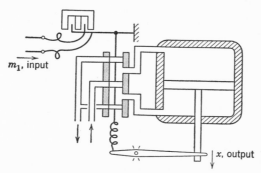

FIG. 7–12. Electro-hydraulic piston actuator.

actuates a spring feedback to the pilot spool. The operation is as follows: An increase in current to the voice coil causes the arm to swing downward thereby pushing down the pilot spool. This action connects the lower side of the cylinder to drain and connects the upper side to supply pressure. The piston then moves downward, and the feedback spring pushes back to rebalance the system at equilibrium. The position of the piston rod is therefore proportional to input direct current.

Hydraulic actuators require a hydraulic power supply. This subject has been discussed in Chapter 6, see Fig. 6–19. Generally, individual power supplies are required at each actuator unless several actuators are grouped close enough together to use a single large unit. Hydraulic power lines should not be run for appreciable distances. The pressure employed in most hydraulic systems usually is from 400 to 1000 psi gage.

Example 7–3. A hydraulic piston actuator with a 4-in. bore and 3-in. stroke is used with a pump having a maximum delivery of 5 gpm. Neglecting acceleration and output load, calculate the time to travel the complete stroke.

$$\text{Traverse time} = \frac{\pi 4^2 \times 3 \times 60}{4 \times 5 \times 231} = 1.96 \text{ sec}$$

Electric Motor Actuators

Electric motor actuators are employed to provide a position output corresponding to an input electric signal. These are of three basic types:

1. The bridge type systems discussed in Chapter 6, see Figs. 6–22, 6–24
2. The relay-type reversible motor drive (see also Fig. 6–25)
3. The amplifier-type reversible motor drive

The *relay-type electric actuator* is shown in Fig. 7–13. A low-inertia reversible a-c motor drives the output through gears. A mechanical feedback is employed such that a rotation at the output rotates a lever

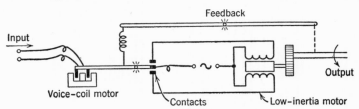

Fig. 7–13.   Relay-type electric actuator.

acting in a feedback spring. The operation is as follows: An increase in direct current at the input coil causes a force to act in the balance beam and pulls the beam down thus "making" the upper contact. This drives the motor in one direction so that the output and feedback rotate, thereby pulling on the spring and rebalancing the voice-coil armature. Output position is therefore proportional to input current. Many variations of this general scheme are employed. The power amplifier may be inserted between the balance beam and motor so that the contacts do not have to carry large current. The amplifier may be actuated by a differential transformer or an oscillator coil on the balance beam. Relays may be eliminated if saturable-core reactors are used.

An *amplifier*-type electric actuator is shown in Fig. 7–14. The input signal is applied directly to the input stage of the d-c amplifier. The difference signal is modulated to an a-c signal of varying phase, amplified, and passed to a two-phase motor. The motor, usually termed a servo-motor, has a low-inertia rotor connected to a low-inertia output gear train. One motor winding is energized from a-c line. When the controlled phase leads the line phase, the motor is driven in one direction, and when the phase lags the line phase, the motor is driven in the opposite direction. The output drives the load and a feedback potentiometer. When the input and output positions match, the difference

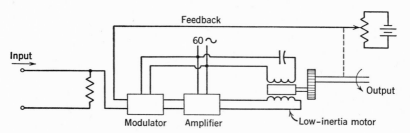

Fɪɢ. 7–14. Amplifier-drive electric motor actuator (The Conoflow Corporation).

signal is zero, both motor windings are energized with the same phase, and the motor is stalled. There are many variations of this general arrangement. For example, a pair of selsyns (synchros) may be used in an a-c system. The amplifier may employ a grid-controlled thyratron, or magnetic amplifiers may be used.

The power of the electric motor actuator is often $\frac{1}{4}$ hp (about 200 watts) or less. One-tenth horsepower (75 watts) or less is more common. Thus the electric motor actuator is generally employed for low power, whereas pneumatic or hydraulic actuators are used for large power.

Example 7–4. An electric motor actuator incorporates a 25-watt motor. Full travel of 2 in. is desired in 10 sec. Assume a gear train efficiency of 50 per cent and calculate the maximum output force.

$$\text{Force} = 0.5 \times \frac{550}{746} \times \frac{25 \times 12 \times 10}{2} = \underline{550\ \text{lb}}$$

Two-Position Motor Actuators

For two-position control an actuator need only assume two positions so as to open and close a fluid valve or other element. The *pneumatic diaphragm actuator* of Fig. 7–15 provides two positions of the stem corresponding to large input pressure and zero (gage) input pressure.

The input pressure is placed over the diaphragm for upward-acting
thrust force or under the diaphragm for downward-acting thrust force.
If the thrust forces cannot be depended upon, a light spring is added
to the actuator stem. For larger strokes and forces a piston–cylinder
combination may be employed.

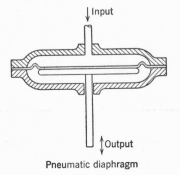

Pneumatic diaphragm

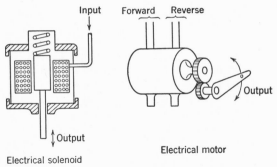

Electrical solenoid

Electrical motor

FIG. 7–15.   Two-position operators.

The *electric solenoid* of Fig. 7–15 is widely employed for two-position
control with either direct or alternating current. Spring-closing or
spring-opening types may be selected depending upon which is desired
for safe operation.

The *electric motor* of Fig. 7–13 may be used in several ways. A reversible electric motor geared to an output arm may be run either forward
or reverse and the output motion limited by the position of limit switch
on the output arm. A nonreversible motor with spring return may also
be used so long as the gear ratio is low enough that the spring will
drive the armature backward through the gear train.

Final Element Power Failure

In the event of power failure the final control element, whether it is pneumatic, hydraulic, or electric, may have one of three possible behaviors:

1. The element may fail open, forward, or upward (closed if a valve, forward if a rotary motor, and upward if a sliding stem). This will be referred to hereafter as "open."
2. The element may fail and hold the position which it was in last. This will be termed "last position."
3. The element may fail reverse or down. This will be termed "closed."

It is possible that any one of these may be desirable in a given instance. For example, it is usually necessary for a boiler draft damper to fail "open" so that gases may pass out of the system. In a continuous blending stream, it is generally desirable for a valve to fail in its "last position" because a minimum amount of product is spoiled while the situation is being remedied. On the other hand, the fuel-oil valve to a furnace should fail "closed" for greatest safety.

Pneumatic or hydraulic piston or diaphragm actuators are easily arranged to fail in the open or closed position by means of a spring force or by the force due to pressure locked on one side. Spring actuators almost always fail either open or closed because of the spring action. Failure in last position is usually more difficult to accomplish but may be done with suitable check valves to lock system pressures. The seals may be expected to last for a number of hours. Various mechanical toggle and pin latches are infrequently used.

Rotary pneumatic, hydraulic, and electric actuators almost always employ some form of gear reduction. The efficiency of these gear trains is usually less than 50 per cent and they are therefore self-locking. That is, the input cannot be driven backward by a torque applied at the output. Such actuators therefore fail in the last position by inherent action. Failure at the open or closed position can only be accomplished by declutching mechanisms and like.

The thrust force on single-seat valves and butterfly valves may either assist or prevent closing or opening on power failure. Generally it is better to arrange that the forces due to pressure differential assist the action desired. It is well to remember, however, that thrust forces are not always in the direction of pressure differential.

Methods of Fluid Control

A source of fluid head is required to provide the transport of fluids through processing equipment. In a tubular heat exchanger, for example, a pump is generally used to move the fluid through the fluid

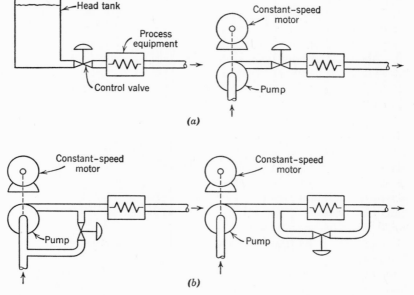

(a)

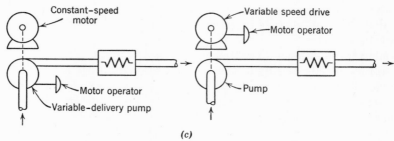

(b)

(c)

Fig. 7–16. Methods of fluid control. (a) Series throttling. (b) Bypass. (c) Variable delivery.

resistance caused by the tubes of the heat exchanger. Several arrangements of the fluid source may be used depending upon the type of fluid and processing equipment. A pump, compressor, blower, or fan is ordinarily used to provide the source of fluid head or pressure. Six arrangements of fluid sources are shown in Fig. 7–16. A control valve or motor operator is used in each arrangement in order to provide a proportioning of the flow of fluid through the process equipment.

Series throttling is probably the most common arrangement of a fluid source. Referring to Fig. 7–16, a head tank provides a source of liquid head or gas pressure. The head in the tank requires separate automatic control in order to maintain a constant head. A control valve in series with the head tank throttles the flow to the process equipment. Alternately a constant-speed motor, turbine, or engine drives a pump. (A turbine or engine requires a speed governor in order to maintain its speed within desired limits). Series throttling from a pump source may be used with any type of axial or radial pump, compressor, blower, or fan, but the head-flow characteristic should be as flat as possible in order to provide constant head. Axial gas compressors do not have a smooth head-flow characteristic and cannot operate at low flow rates. Series throttling cannot be used with a positive-displacement pump or blower because the outlet head becomes excessive at low flow rates.

The *bypass* is a simple arrangement used for positive-displacement pumps, compressors, and blowers. The driving motor, turbine, or engine operates at constant speed. Flow through the process equipment is proportioned by passing a portion of the flow either to the pump inlet or to the downstream side of the process equipment. The economy of the bypass arrangement is not always high, because a considerable portion of the energy stored in the fluid is wasted in the bypass. A better arrangement for a positive-displacement pump is to throttle the delivery.

Variable delivery is a very useful source arrangement for either very low flow rates or for very large flow rates. Referring again to Fig. 7–16, a variable-delivery pump is driven by a constant-speed motor. A motor-operator is connected to the stroke-varying arm of the pump in such a way that the volume delivery of the pump is changed. A relief valve is sometimes necessary at the pump outlet in order to prevent excessive pressure. A variable-speed drive connected to a pump, compressor, or blower is also a variable-delivery source. Two methods are in common use; first, the speed of an electric motor, steam turbine, or steam engine may be changed by throttling the energy supplied to the motor, and second, a variable-speed drive may be interposed between the constant-speed motor and the pump. The variable-speed method has an advantage for very large pumps and compressors because it is less expensive to throttle the steam-flow to a turbine or engine than it is to throttle or bypass the pump outlet.

The choice of any one arrangement of a fluid source depends upon a great number of factors such as the type of fluid, the size of the installation, and the efficiency. The arrangement of the fluid source is very important in automatic control, and it is probably safe to say that most difficulties in automatic control arise because of poorly installed or maintained fluid sources.

Fluid Flow Through Control Valves

A control valve in a pipeline acts as a variable restriction. Referring to Fig. 7–17, the vertical movement of the plug and stem of the control valve changes the area of opening of the port. The flow rate of the

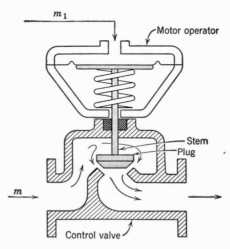

Fig. 7–17. A single-seat control valve and pneumatic actuator.

fluid passing through the port is therefore proportioned or throttled by positioning the valve stem. The stem is in turn positioned by the actuator.

The equation governing the flow of fluid through a restriction such as a valve may be derived from the laws of fluid mechanics. For a control valve, the flow rate of liquid is assumed to be given by

$$m = K_1 a \sqrt{2g(h_1 - h_2)} \qquad (7\text{–}5)$$

where m = flow rate, ft^3/sec
  K_1 = a flow coefficient
  a = area of control valve port, ft^2
  g = acceleration due to gravity, ft/sec^2
  h_1 = upstream static head of flowing fluid, ft
  h_2 = downstream static head of flowing fluid, ft

The area of port opening of the control valve will be assumed proportional to stem position so that

$$K_1 a = Kx \tag{7-6}$$

where K = an overall coefficient, ft^2/ft
x = stem position or lift, ft

Combining equations 7-5 and 7-6 to eliminate a,

$$m = [K\sqrt{2g(h_1 - h_2)}]x \tag{7-7}$$

This equation illustrates that the flow rate m through the control valve is directly proportional to lift x if (1) the differential head $(h_1 - h_2)$ is constant and (2) the overall coefficient K is constant. Unfortunately, these two conditions rarely prevail and it is necessary to study these effects in detail.

A control valve is installed in a pipeline in conjunction with the other equipment necessary to employ the fluid flow for process control. Heat exchangers, pumps, fans, pipe fittings, and hand valves are such equipment.

A *series resistance* may result from the pipeline, orifices, hand valves, heat exchangers, or other equipment installed in series with the valve. Consider, as an example, the series resistance caused by pipe-friction, Fig. 7-18. The head loss in a pipeline can be calculated from the friction formula

$$\Delta h_L = F \frac{L}{D} \frac{v^2}{2g} \tag{7-8}$$

where Δh_L = head loss in feet of flowing fluid
F = friction coefficient (from Moody diagram)
L = equivalent length of pipe including fittings, ft
D = inside diameter of pipeline, ft
v = velocity of flow, ft/sec

The head loss therefore depends upon flow rate. Equation 7-8 may be written in terms of flow rate:

$$\frac{\Delta h_L}{L} = \frac{8}{\pi^2} \frac{Fm^2}{gD^5} \tag{7-9}$$

where m = flow rate, ft^3/sec. Including head loss (Δh_L) in equation 7-7,

$$m = [K\sqrt{2g(H_0 - H_2 - \Delta h_L)}]x \tag{7-10}$$

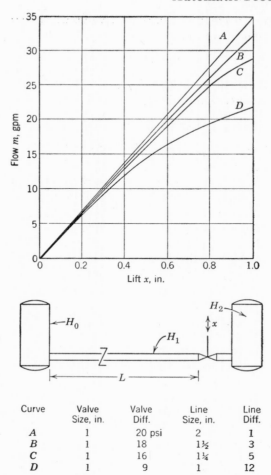

FIG. 7–18.   Effect of line size for a given control valve.

Curve	Valve Size, in.	Valve Diff.	Line Size, in.	Line Diff.
A	1	20 psi	2	1
B	1	18	1½	3
C	1	16	1¼	5
D	1	9	1	12

Substituting equation 7–9 into equation 7–10 to eliminate (Δh_L), there results

$$m = \left[K \sqrt{\frac{2g(H_0 - H_2)}{1 + \alpha_1 x^2}} \right] x \qquad (7\text{–}11)$$

where $\alpha_1 = \dfrac{16FLK^2}{\pi^2 D^5} = \dfrac{\text{line } (\Delta h_L) \text{ at maximum flow}}{\text{valve } (\Delta h) \text{ at maximum flow}}$

Thus the flow is not directly proportional to the valve stem position and the extent of nonlinearity depends upon line pressure differential.

This equation is plotted in Fig. 7–18 for a 1-in. size control valve installed in different size pipelines. The pressure source H_0 and pressure termination H_2 are considered constant, and the equivalent line length L is about 100 ft. The friction factor F and overall valve coefficient K are considered constant. The effect of the larger head loss caused by smaller pipeline size is very noticeable at high flow rates. The smaller lines do not allow the control valve to pass the desired maximum flow of 35 gpm. In order to obtain the desired maximum flow rate, four steps may be taken:

1. Decrease head loss so that differential head at the control valve is greater.
2. Increase pressure source H_0.
3. Decrease pressure termination H_2.
4. Increase control-valve size.

In many cases the pipeline installation may be made so as to reduce head losses by selecting larger sizes of lines or equipment. The pressure source may sometimes be increased by selecting larger pumping equipment. Usually it is not possible to change the pressure termination. Lacking any of these alternatives, the control valve size must be increased.

The effect of increasing valve size in order to obtain any desired maximum flow may be calculated as follows: Rewriting equation 7–10 by dividing through by the maximum flow rate,

$$\frac{m}{M} = \sqrt{\frac{H_0 - H_2 - \Delta h_L}{H_1 - H_2}} \frac{x}{X} \tag{7-12}$$

where m = flow rate at any lift
$\quad M$ = maximum flow rate (at full open)
$\quad H_0$ = constant upstream pressure source
$\quad H_2$ = constant downstream pressure termination
$\quad \Delta h_L$ = total head loss for all series flow equipment
$\quad x$ = lift
$\quad X$ = maximum lift (at full open)
$\quad H_1$ = valve upstream pressure (at full open)

Total head loss may be expressed in a similar manner. Rewriting equation 7–9 by dividing through by the maximum flow rate,

$$\left(\frac{m}{M}\right)^2 = \frac{\Delta h_L}{H_0 - H_1} \tag{7-13}$$

Combining equations 7–12 and 7–13 to eliminate the head loss term and solving for the flow rate,

$$\frac{m}{M} = \frac{1}{\sqrt{\alpha - (1 - \alpha)\left(\dfrac{x}{X}\right)^2}} \frac{x}{X} \qquad (7\text{–}14)$$

where $\alpha = \dfrac{H_1 - H_2}{H_0 - H_2} = \dfrac{\text{valve head differential at maximum flow}}{\text{valve head differential at zero flow}}$

This equation is plotted in Fig. 7–19. A control valve of sufficient size is used so that the desired maximum flow is obtained in each case. Any flow equipment in series with a control valve results in a change of the

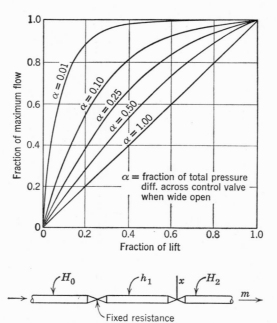

FIG. 7–19. Control-valve operation with series resistance.

flow-lift characteristic of the control valve. It is quite apparent from a study of Fig. 7–19 that a differential head at the control valve of less than 25 per cent of total differential head causes an inability of the control valve to throttle the fluid flow; that is, the valve effectively acts as if it were only open or closed. The consequences of the "loss of control" are discussed later in this section.

A *centrifugal pump or fan source* is often employed in fluid-flow systems and has a characteristic that the outlet head decreases with increas-

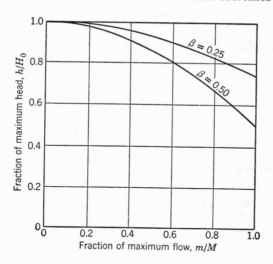

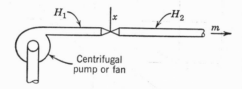

FIG. 7–20. Control valve with a pump or fan source.

ing flow rate. This is termed the pump or fan head characteristic and is illustrated in Fig. 7–20. The head is approximately related to flow at constant speed by

$$\frac{h_1}{H_0} = 1 - \beta \left(\frac{m}{M}\right)^2 \tag{7–15}$$

where h_1 = outlet head

H_0 = outlet head with outlet closed (zero flow)

β = a capacity constant

m = outlet flow rate

M = desired maximum flow rate

In general, the capacity coefficient β is about 0.2 to 0.4 for many centrifugal pumps and fans.

The flow through the control valve is

$$\frac{m}{M} = \sqrt{\frac{h_1 - H_2}{H_1 - H_2}} \frac{x}{X} \tag{7–16}$$

where H_1 = upstream head at maximum flow. Combining equations 7–15 and 7–16 to eliminate head h_1 and if downstream head H_2 is constant,

$$\frac{m}{M} = \frac{1}{\sqrt{\alpha + (1 - \alpha)\left(\dfrac{x}{X}\right)^2}} \frac{x}{X} \tag{7–17}$$

where $\alpha = \dfrac{H_1 - H_2}{H_0 - H_2} = \dfrac{\text{valve head differential at maximum flow}}{\text{valve head differential at zero flow}}$. Equa-

tion 7–17 is exactly the same as equation 7–14 for the case of series resistance. Therefore the graph of Fig. 7–19 is also valid for a centrifugal pump or fan source. If wide throttling of the valve is desired, the

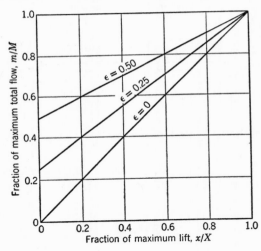

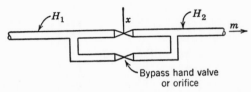

FIG. 7–21. Control-valve operation with parallel resistance.

number α above must be as close to one as possible. This requires that the pump or fan characteristic should be as flat as possible or else that the pump capacity should be as large as possible. Generally the proper pump size is selected by means of an economic study. *Many times, however, an economic study indicates a pump too small to provide an adequate differential head for the control valve.*

The *bypass or parallel resistance* is shown in Fig. 7–21. Assuming the differential head constant, the flow through the bypass is given by

$$M_2 = K_2\sqrt{2g(H_1 - H_2)} \qquad (7\text{--}18)$$

where M_2 = flow rate through bypass (assumed constant) ft^3/sec
K_2 = bypass flow coefficient
H_1 = upstream head, ft
H_2 = downstream head, ft

The flow through the control valve is given by

$$m_1 = [K\sqrt{2g(H_1 - H_2)}]x \qquad (7\text{--}19)$$

where m_1 = flow through control valve, ft^3/sec
x = lift of control valve, fraction

Adding equations 7–18 and 7–19 for total flow

$$\frac{m}{M} = \epsilon + (1 - \epsilon)\frac{x}{X} \qquad (7\text{--}20)$$

where $\epsilon = \dfrac{M_2}{M} = \dfrac{\text{flow through bypass with control valve closed}}{\text{total flow with valve open}}$

The effect of the bypass is simply to reduce the amount of control of flow rate, and to alter the minimum flow as shown in Fig. 7–21.

The overall effect of either a series or parallel resistance, or a centrifugal pump or fan source, is to alter the flow-lift characteristic of a control valve. It is recalled that the proportional sensitivity of a proportional controller is given by

$$K_c = \frac{\Delta m}{\Delta e} = \left(\frac{\Delta m}{\Delta x}\right)\left(\frac{\Delta x}{\Delta e}\right) \qquad (7\text{--}21)$$

where K_c = proportional sensitivity
m = manipulated variable (fluid-flow rate)
e = deviation
x = control-valve position or lift

Therefore, changes in proportional sensitivity result directly from changes in slope of the control valve flow-lift characteristic. Thus, it is possible to alter the overall proportional sensitivity of the controller by as much as 50 to 1 by different arrangements of the control valve installation. This change of proportional sensitivity may or may not be desirable in automatic control.

Summarizing control valve operation it is possible to state two operating principles for automatic control valves:

1. *A fluid throttling control valve cannot operate with minimum differential head.*

2. *The differential head at a fluid-throttling control valve is never arbitrary.* It is a result of specifying flow rate, series and parallel resistances, and pressure source and termination.

As a consequence of these principles it is imperative that the control valve arrangement be selected with a great deal of care. The pressure source should provide sufficiently high head so that adequate throttling of the fluid flow is obtained in spite of head losses caused by series resistances. A bypass resistance should be carefully and not indiscriminately employed.

Example 7–5. A control valve is installed in the exit line of a heat exchanger. The pressure at the inlet of the exchanger H_0 is constant. The pressure drop across the heat exchanger at maximum flow is 40 psi. The control-valve downstream pressure is 20 psig and is constant. What control valve pressure drop must be used and what upstream pressure at the heat exchanger is required?

If the throughput at the heat exchanger changes over wide limits, good throttling at the control valve is necessary. Consequently the control-valve pressure drop should not be less than 50 per cent of total. Thus, 40 psi differential pressure at the valve is desired and the upstream pressure at the heat exchanger must be 100 psig at maximum flow.

Example 7–6. A centrifugal pump is available as a fluid source for a heat exchanger. At maximum flow the head is 100 psig, and at shut-off the head is 140 psig. At maximum flow, line losses are 15 psi and the heat exchanger pressure drop is 75 psi. The control-valve back pressure is atmospheric. Can this pump be used?

Referring to equation 7–14,

$$\alpha = \frac{100 - 15 - 75}{140} = \frac{10}{140} = 0.071$$

Thus the control-valve pressure differential is only 7 per cent at maximum flow. This pump should not be used, because with such a small pressure differential the valve will not throttle the flow adequately.

Sliding-Stem Control Valves

Control valves in which the plug is operated by means of reciprocating motion are termed sliding-stem valves and are of the following types:

1. Single-seat plug valves.
2. Double-seat plug valves.
3. Lifting-gate valves.

The single-seat and double-seat control valves are shown in Fig. 7–22. The single-seat valve has only one port opening between seat and plug and the entire flow passes through this port. It has the following

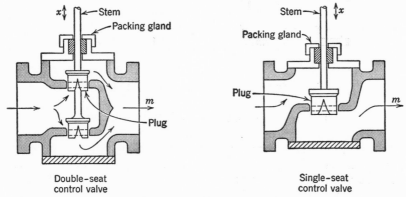

Double-seat
control valve

Single-seat
control valve

FIG. 7–22.   Sliding-plug control valve.

features: (a) It is simple in construction.   (b) It can be shut off to provide zero flow.   (c) There is a large force acting on the valve stem because of the differential head acting across the port and seat area.

The double-seat valve has two port openings and two seats and two plugs. The port openings are not usually identical in size. This type has the following features: (a) Net force acting on the valve stem is generally small (therefore "pressure balanced").   (b) It cannot be shut off tightly because of differential temperature expansion of valve plug and valve body.

A few types of plugs for single-seat and double-seat valves are shown in Figs. 7–23 and 7–24.   The piston type plug has one or more grooves

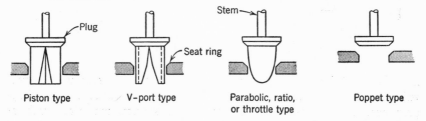

Piston type   V–port type   Parabolic, ratio,   Poppet type
                                            or throttle type

FIG. 7–23.   A few types of single-seat valve plugs.

along its length and the flow passes vertically in the grooves between the plug and seat ring. The V-port type plug is open on the inside and the flow passes horizontally through the triangular shaped area over the

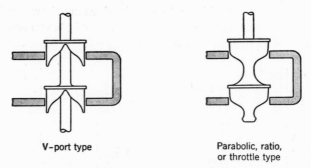

V-port type

Parabolic, ratio,
or throttle type

FIG. 7–24.   Two types of double-seat valve plugs.

seat ring. The parabolic plug presents an annular area to flow between the plug and seat ring. The poppet-type plug offers a cylindrical-shaped flow area and is used with small total lift.

The gate valve in Fig. 7–25 is often used for fluids containing solid matter, because it presents an open area directly to the flow of fluid

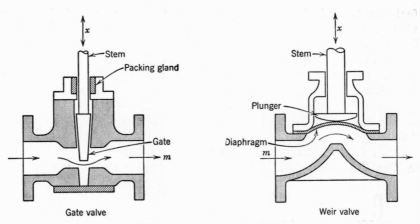

Gate valve

Weir valve

FIG. 7–25.   Single-seat valves with a lifting-gate action.

and does not involve a change of direction of flow stream. A gate valve can usually be shut-off tightly by wedging into the seat. The chopping action at shut-off is very useful for stringy materials such as paper pulp.

The weir valve in Fig. 7–25 is particularly suited to certain chemical fluids, because it has a smooth contour inside the body with no "pockets" for solid matter, and because it has no packing gland around the stem. The flexible diaphragm of rubber or other nonmetallic material is positioned by the plunger and stem. Fluid pressure inside the valve body holds the diaphragm smoothly against the plunger.

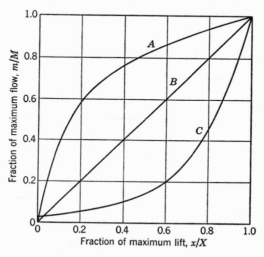

A Decreasing sensitivity type
B Linear type
C Equal-percentage type

Fig. 7–26.   Control-valve "characteristics."

The flow-lift characteristics of sliding-stem valves generally fall into three approximate categories as shown in Fig. 7–26. These are:

A. Decreasing sensitivity type. The valve sensitivity $(\Delta m/\Delta x)$ at any flow decreases with increasing flow. The maximum port area is sufficiently large that pressure losses elsewhere than at the valve port may restrict the maximum flow.

B. Linear type. The valve sensitivity $(\Delta m/\Delta x)$ is more or less constant at any flow.

C. Increasing sensitivity type. This is termed the equal-percentage, logarithmic, parabolic, or "characterized" type of valve because the flow-lift curve plotted on semilogarithmic coordinates is approximately a straight line. The valve sensitivity $(\Delta m/\Delta x)$ increases with increasing flow rate. The valve sensitivity at any given flow rate is a constant percentage of the given flow rate, thus the term equal-percentage.

Actual flow characteristics of a number of control valves, all of $2\frac{1}{2}$-in. size, are shown in Fig. 7–27. These are given for a constant

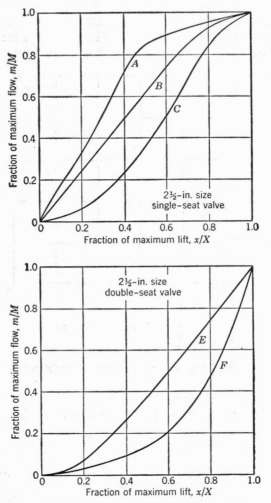

FIG. 7–27. Actual flow-lift characteristics of sliding-stem control valves.

A. Weir (Fig. 7–25)   E. V-port or throttle plug (Figs. 7–23, 7–24)
B. Poppet (Fig. 7–23)   F. Ratio plug (Fig. 7–23)
C. V-port (Figs. 7–23, 7–24)

differential head across the control valve. The flow characteristic is further altered in any actual installation by any series resistance, pump source, or bypass resistance, as discussed previously.

The rangeability of a control valve is the ratio of maximum controllable flow to minimum controllable flow:

$$R = \frac{m \ (\text{maximum controllable})}{m \ (\text{minimum controllable})} \qquad (7\text{--}22)$$

where R = rangeability number. Turndown is a similar concept based on the ratio of normal maximum flow to minimum controllable flow.

$$T = \frac{m \ (\text{normal maximum})}{m \ (\text{minimum controllable})} \qquad (7\text{--}23)$$

Normal maximum flow is generally taken as 70 per cent of maximum flow so that

$$T \cong 0.7R \qquad (7\text{--}24)$$

The minimum controllable flow of a control valve depends upon its construction. Clearances must be allowed in order to prevent binding and sticking, and the flow through these clearances constitutes the minimum controllable flow. The minimum controllable flow for a single-seat valve is not zero unless the throttling seat and shut-off seat are identical and have perfect alignment. The rangeability of a sliding-stem control valve is usually between 20 and 70.

The importance of rangeability and turndown lies in the application of the control valve. For example, if the design of an oil burner and furnace requires a 30 to 1 range of oil flow to accommodate various loads on the furnace, the turndown must be at least 30 and the rangeability must be at least 43.

Example 7–7. Flow through a linear valve (constant sensitivity type characteristic) is given by

$$\frac{m}{M} = \frac{1}{R} \left[1 + (R - 1) \frac{x}{X} \right]$$

where m is the flow at any lift x, M is the maximum flow at maximum lift X, and R is the rangeability. If the valve passes 10 gpm at a maximum lift of 2.0 in. and the rangeability is 20, compute the valve sensitivity.

From the above equation

$$\frac{dm}{dx} = \left(\frac{R-1}{R} \right) \frac{M}{X} = \frac{19}{20} \times \frac{10 \text{ gpm}}{2 \text{ in.}} = 4.75 \text{ gpm/in.}$$

Example 7–8. Flow through an equal-percentage valve (increasing sensitivity type characteristic) is given by

$$\frac{m}{M} = R^{[(x/X)-1]}$$

where the symbols are the same as in Example 7–7. Derive an expression for valve sensitivity.

Differentiating the above expression

$$\frac{dm}{dx} = \left[\frac{M}{X}\ln R\right]\frac{m}{M}$$

Thus the valve sensitivity varies directly with flow rate m.

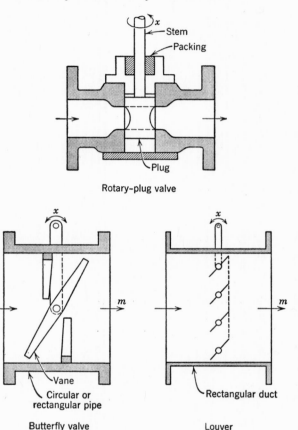

FIG. 7–28. Several rotating-shaft valves.

Rotating-Shaft Control Valves

Control valves in which the restriction is accomplished by the rotation of a plug or vane may be called rotating-shaft type. These are:

1. Rotating-plug valves
2. Butterfly valves
3. Louvers

The *rotating-plug valve* is illustrated in Fig. 7–28. The plug is a cylindrical or conical element with a transverse opening. It is rotated in the valve body by an external lever so that the opening on one side

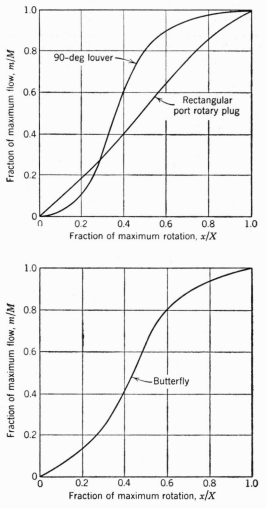

FIG. 7–29. Actual flow-angle characteristics of rotary-shaft control valves.

of the plug is gradually covered or uncovered. The shape of the opening or port may be circular, V-shape, rectangular, or any form that is desired to produce a given flow-angle characteristic. The flow-angle characteristic is shown in Fig. 7–29 for a near-rectangular port shape.

A rotating-plug valve having a conical plug can generally be closed tightly and has high rangeability. This type of valve is often employed for throttling the flow of oil to burner systems.

The *butterfly valve*, shown in Fig. 7–28, consists of a single vane rotating inside a circular or rectangular pipe or casing. The shaft projects through the casing and may be operated externally. The total rotation of the vane is usually restricted to about 60 degrees, because the additional 30 deg does not produce much further increase in flow. The V-port butterfly valve incorporates a V-slot in the body so that rotation of the vane opens a portion of the V-slot. The flow-angle characteristic is shown in Fig. 7–29 for a 60 deg butterfly valve. The rangeability may vary from 5 to 50 and tight shut-off may be obtained with special design. The butterfly valve is most often employed in sizes from 4 to 60 in. for the control of air and gas. It is also used for liquid flow if the pressure differential is not large.

The *louver*, Fig. 7–28, consists of two or more rectangular vanes mounted on shafts one above the other and interconnected so as to rotate together. The vanes are operated by an external lever. In the unirotational louver the vanes remain parallel at all positions. In a counterrotational louver alternate vanes rotate in an opposite direction. Flow guides are sometimes installed between adjacent vanes in order to improve the effectiveness of throttling. The flow-angle characteristic is shown in Fig. 7–29 for a 90 deg unirotational louver. It may be seen that the sensitivity is very high at midflow and that the last 30 deg of rotation is relatively ineffective. A louver cannot provide tight shut-off because of the long length of seating surfaces. Louvers are used exclusively for control of air flow (draft) at low pressure.

Control-Valve Sizing

The proper size of control valve is important because of the effect on the operation of the automatic controller. If the control valve is oversize, for example, the valve must operate at low lift and the minimum controllable flow is too large. In addition, the lower part of the flow-lift characteristic is most likely to be nonuniform in shape. On the other hand if the control valve is undersize, the maximum flow desired for operation of a process may not be provided.

The flow of a liquid through a fully open control valve is assumed to be given by

$$m = Ka \sqrt{\frac{2g\,\Delta P}{\gamma}} \qquad\qquad (7\text{--}25)$$

where m = flow rate, ft^3/sec

K = a flow coefficient

a = area of port opening, ft^2

g = acceleration due to gravity, ft/sec^2

ΔP = pressure differential, lb/ft^2

γ = fluid density, lb/ft^3

The flow coefficient K and port area a are different for every style or size of control valve. Consequently, it is standard practice to combine certain terms of the above equation into a single number C_v, termed the size coefficient:

$$m_L = C_v \sqrt{\frac{\Delta P}{G}} \tag{7-26}$$

where m_L = liquid flow rate in gallons per minute at the conditions for which specific gravity G is taken

C_v = size coefficient

ΔP = pressure drop, lb/in.^{2}

G = specific gravity of liquid (referred to water) at either flowing or standard conditions

The size coefficient C_v is defined as the flow rate of water in gallons per minute provided by a pressure differential of 1.0 lb per sq in. through a fully open control valve. The size coefficient for any control valve must be determined by actual test. The size coefficient for a control valve of the sliding stem and plug type is very approximately equal to the square of the nominal valve size multiplied by ten.

For the flow of gas or steam, the size coefficient with suitable conversion factors is also employed. The form of equation is an approximation to the complete isentropic flow equation, known as Fliegner's formula when used for air[1]

$$m_g = 760 \, C_v \sqrt{\frac{P_1(\Delta P)}{RT_1}} \tag{7-27}$$

where m_g = flow rate of gas, lb/hr

C_v = size coefficient (obtained for liquids)

P_1 = upstream absolute pressure, lb/in.^{2}

ΔP = pressure differential, lb/in.^{2}

R = gas constant for flowing gas

T_1 = upstream absolute temperature

[1] Kiefer, P. J., and M. C. Stuart, *Principles of Engineering Thermodynamics*, 2nd ed., John Wiley and Sons Inc., New York, 1954.

The calculation of flow rate of fluid through a control valve therefore depends directly upon the experimentally determined size coefficient C_v. As might be expected, the size coefficient is not a constant and depends upon both flow rate and fluid viscosity. In other words, the size coefficient is some function of a number corresponding to Reynolds number. The extent of this relation is not fully known.

The calculation procedure for flow of gas through a control valve must be modified when the pressure differential is greater than a critical value. When the downstream pressure at a control valve is sufficiently small, the flow rate does not depend upon downstream pressure. At the critical pressure ratio, or below, the gas attains the velocity of sound through the valve ports. The critical pressure ratio for air and steam are

	P_2/P_1
Air (70 F)	0.528
Steam (212 F)	0.539

The critical pressure ratio does not vary greatly for all common gases and a single flow formula may be employed with reasonable accuracy[1]

$$w = 158,000 \, C_v \sqrt{\frac{P_1}{V_1}} \qquad (7\text{--}28)$$

where w = flow rate, lb/hr

C_v = size coefficient

P_1 = upstream absolute pressure, lb/in.^{2}

V_1 = upstream specific volume, ft^3/lb

Determination of control-valve size, flow rate, or pressure differential is made in most industrial applications by the use of a nomograph or a slide rule. A typical nomograph is illustrated in Fig. 7–30. Generally, these nomographs or slide rules are based upon experimentally determined size coefficients and the equations given above, or upon experimentally determined empirical relations. It is important to note that control valves are not manufactured in an infinite number of sizes but are generally available in standard pipe sizes only.

The procedure for selection of control valve size may be as follows:

1. For the particular process under control, determine,

(a) The maximum value of flow rate required to sustain the controlled variable under any condition of process operation. This is the *normal maximum flow rate*.

(b) The value of flow rate that will be required most of the time. This is the *normal flow rate*.

[1] See Kent, R. T., *Mechanical Engineers' Handbook*, 12th ed., John Wiley and Sons Inc., New York, 1950.

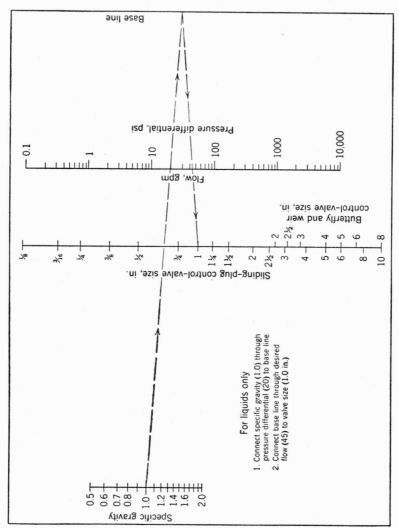

Fig. 7-30. Nomograph for sizing control valves. (For estimation only. Obtain actual data from manufacturer.).

(c) The minimum value of flow rate required to sustain the controlled variable under any conditions of process operation. This is the *normal minimum flow rate*.

2. Select the maximum flow rate which the control valve is to provide. This is generally based on the normal maximum flow rate of about 70 per cent of maximum flow rate. The additional flow is a factor of safety which allows for low estimation of pressure losses and high estimation of valve flow rate. The maximum flow rate usually selected is about 1.4 times the normal maximum flow.

3. Select the style and type of control valve to provide best operation for the fluid to be handled. Check the rangeability to insure that the minimum controllable flow is generously smaller than the normal minimum flow rate desired.

4. Calculate the pressure differential at the control valve at the maximum flow. This requires calculating line pressure losses, flow equipment pressure losses, and determining upstream head from pump or fan characteristic curves.

5. Determine the control-valve size from manufacturers nomographs, charts, or slide-rules. If the fluid viscosity is high, or line velocities are exceptionally low (Reynolds number in the pipe line less than about 10,000) the size coefficient C_v will be low, and the manufacturer should be asked to determine the valve size.

6. Calculate the characteristic coefficient:

$$\alpha = \frac{\text{Differential pressure with control valve wide open}}{\text{Differential pressure with control valve closed}} \quad (7\text{--}29)$$

If the number is relatively small (less than 0.10) or if

$$\alpha < \frac{1}{2500}\left(\frac{M}{M_{\min}}\right)^2 \quad (7\text{--}30)$$

where M = maximum flow rate
$M_{\min}$ = normal minimum flow rate

then the control valve will, at times, be required to operate at less than 2 per cent of total lift. If this occurs, the control valve would require accurate positioning by a powerful actuator, and the valve ports and plug must be precisely manufactured. Otherwise it is best to inspect the control-valve installation to determine whether the differential head can be increased by selecting larger pumps, larger line sizes, or minimizing losses in series flow equipment.

Example 7–9. A fully open 2-in. size valve passes 100 gpm of water at a pressure differential of 7.0 psi. Calculate the C_v coefficient.

From equation 7-26

$$C_v = m_L \sqrt{\frac{G}{\Delta P}} = 100 \sqrt{\frac{1.0}{7.0}} = 37.8$$

Note that the size squared (4) multiplied by 10 equals 40.

Example 7-10. A heating furnace requires a control valve passing 10 gpm preheated light fuel oil (sp. gr. = 0.8) at full load and only 0.2 gpm at the smallest heating load. The pressure differential at wide open is 20 psi. The source pressure is constant at 50 psi gage, but there is 10 psi drop in the oil preheater and 20 psi drop at the furnace burner nozzles. Determine the valve size.

1. Select a maximum flow rate of

$$\frac{10}{0.7} \cong 14 \text{ gpm}$$

2. The rangeability must be

$$\frac{14}{0.2} = 70$$

or the turndown is 50.

3. A rangeability of 70 is quite large and requires careful selection of valve plug style. Probably a rotating plug valve or possibly a single-seat plug valve would be satisfactory.

4. The pressure differential is 20 psi.

5. From Fig. 7-30,

$\frac{3}{8}$ in. size passes   6 gpm   (too small)
$\frac{1}{2}$ in. size passes   12 gpm
$\frac{3}{4}$ in. size passes   31 gpm   (too large)

The $\frac{1}{2}$-in. valve is selected because it is the nearest size passing the desired 14 gpm.

6. The characteristic coefficient is (equation 7-29)

$$\alpha = \frac{20}{50} = 0.4$$

so that the control-valve differential is 40 per cent of total differential and the characteristic is satisfactory.

Throttling Electrical Energy

Many heating processes employ electric energy instead of energy contained in fluids. In order to control such processes, electrical energy must be modulated in some way. There are two somewhat different methods of modulating electric energy:

1. Regulate the power on or off with varying periods of on and off times. This is accomplished by a two-position controller or by an average-position controller. The final control element is an electric power relay.

2. Regulate the voltage to the load by automatically adjusting the voltage. The final-control element may be an adjustable rheostat, variable transformer, controlled thyratron circuit, or a saturable-core reactor.

Electric relays for power loads must have appropriate contact life because they are required to be turned on and off frequently, especially in two-position control.

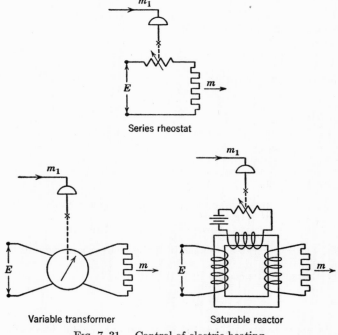

Series rheostat

Variable transformer   Saturable reactor
Fig. 7–31.   Control of electric heating.

A *series rheostat* as in Fig. 7–31 may be used for heating elements. If the voltage supply E is constant, then the load power is given by

$$\frac{m}{M} = \frac{R_L}{R_L + r} \tag{7-31}$$

where m = power to load, watts
  M = maximum power watts
  R_L = resistance of load, ohms
  r = series control resistance, ohms

The control resistance or rheostat is adjusted by a motor actuator, usually pneumatic or electric,

$$R_c - r = R_c m_1 \qquad (7\text{-}32)$$

where R_c = total resistance of series rheostat, ohms
m_1 = input signal to motor operator

Combining equations 7-31 and 7-32 to eliminate r, the relationship of heating energy m and operator input m_1 is

$$\frac{m}{M} = \frac{1}{1 + \dfrac{R_c}{R_L} - \dfrac{R_c}{R_L} m_1} \qquad (7\text{-}33)$$

This equation is plotted in Fig. 7-32. The rangeability of this method depends upon the value of resistance of the control rheostat,

$$R = 1 + \frac{R_c}{R_L} \qquad (7\text{-}34)$$

where R = rangeability. However, for rangeability greater than 6, the power characteristic becomes too steep. Consequently series rheostat control should be used only for low rangeability. In addition, a control rheostat of high resistance and high wattage is likely to be very bulky and expensive.

A *variable transformer* as in Fig. 7-31 is widely employed for control of electric heating. The power characteristic can be shown to be

$$\frac{m}{M} = m_1{}^2 \qquad (7\text{-}35)$$

if the output voltage of the transformer is directly proportional to motor operator position. The characteristic is plotted in Fig. 7-32 and is parabolic in form. A parabolic characteristic is almost identical to an equal-percentage or logarithmic characteristic.

The *saturable reactor* of Fig. 7-31 is another form of control for electric power. Alternating voltage E is supplied to the reactor, and the alternating voltage across the load depends upon the direct-current voltage on the control winding. The control voltage may be supplied or may be obtained directly as the output signal of an electric automatic controller. The reactor operates by regulation of the flux passing from the primary (input) winding to the secondary (output) winding. The flux regulation is accomplished by a controlled degree of saturation provided by the direct-current control winding.

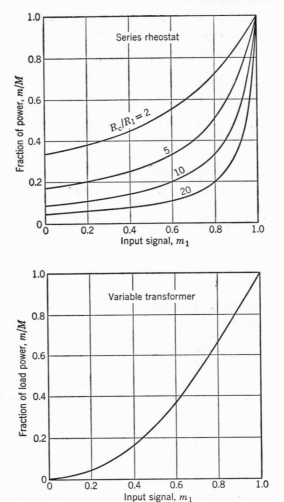

FIG. 7–32.   Characteristics of electric heating control.

Example 7–11.   A 1500-watt resistance heater for 110 volts is to be regulated by a series rheostat. For a rangeability of 5, calculate the resistance and power rating of the series rheostat.

The resistance of the heater is

$$R_L = \frac{E^2}{M} = \frac{12,100}{1500} = 8.1 \text{ ohms}$$

From equation 7–34

$$R_c = R_L(R - 1) = 8.1 \times (5 - 1) = 32.4 \text{ ohms}$$

It will probably be necessary to use a standard 35-ohm rheostat giving a range-ability of 5.32. At minimum setting the power absorbed in the control rheostat is

$$\frac{E^2 R_c}{(R_L + R_c)^2} = \frac{12,100 \times 35}{(35 + 8.1)^2} = 2300 \text{ watts}$$

PROBLEMS

7-1. Calculate the instantaneous horsepower required to oscillate a weight of one pound over 1-in. amplitude sine wave at 100 cps. Develop the general formula.

7-2. A pneumatic actuator requires Q cfm of free air at a pressure P psig. Calculate the horsepower required to run a motor-compressor of efficiency E.

7-3. A hydraulic actuator requires Q gpm at pressure P psig continuously. Calculate the horsepower of the pump-motor of efficiency E.

7-4. A valve actuator is to stroke once each minute, 24 hours per day, and must run five years. How many cycles represent minimum life?

7-5. A reversible electric motor has a stall torque of 30 oz-in. and a no-load speed of 3200 rpm. The torque-speed curve is a straight line. The output drives through a gear train. Calculate the maximum output force at a speed of 2 in. per sec if the gear train is 40 per cent efficient.

7-6. Calculate the time constant of a spring and diaphragm actuator operated through a pneumatic line of resistance R. (C = capacitance of top works, A = diaphragm area, K = spring constant).

7-7. If a control valve has a parabolic plug and has 50 per cent of the pressure differential across it at full flow, show that the flow versus position is nearly linear from 20 per cent flow up to maximum. (Hint: plot

$$y = \frac{1.41 x^2}{\sqrt{1 + x^4}} \Big)$$

7-8. The area of opening of a valve versus lift is given by $A = a + bx^2$. Derive the flow versus lift characteristic for this parabolic valve.

7-9. Liquid glycerin (density 78 lb/ft³) is required at a maximum flow of 18 gpm. The line drop is 40 psi and the valve pressure drop is 10 psi. What size plug valve is required?

7-10. Water flow is controlled by a 3.0-in. butterfly valve with a 10 psi differential. What is the maximum flow rate?

chapter 8

Process
Instrumentation

The results of automatic control must always be evaluated in terms of the quality of the finished product rather than in terms of accuracy or deviation of the controlled variable. The general purpose of automatic control is to obtain maximum efficiency of process operation.

Many processes are comparatively simple and possess a certain degree of inherent stability. On the other hand, some processes possess a confusing array of capacities, lags, and load changes. Between these two extremes lie a large number of processes, complex to a varying degree, and requiring careful analysis.

As a preliminary step, this analysis should include a separation of the variables to be controlled. Each controlled process can then be studied individually from the standpoint of capacity, lags, and load changes. Until this analysis has been made, there is little likelihood that the process can be successfully controlled.

The control system should be properly engineered, special care being taken in the selection of primary and final elements. In too many applications the controller is handicapped by being required to overcome such factors as a large measuring lag or a large dead zone in the control valve.

The general block diagram is seen in Fig. 8–1 which includes a feedback element as well as an input element. The operational equations for the system are

$$r = Av \qquad \text{input element} \qquad (8\text{–}1)$$

$$e = r - b \qquad \text{signal element} \qquad (8\text{–}2)$$

$$m = G_1 e \qquad \text{controller} \qquad (8\text{–}3)$$

$$c = G_2 m + Nu \qquad \text{process or system} \qquad (8\text{-}4)$$

$$b = Hc \qquad \text{feedback element} \qquad (8\text{-}5)$$

$$d = v - c \qquad \text{deviation} \qquad (8\text{-}6)$$

A new variable ($d =$ deviation) must be defined in order to distinguish the actual difference d between controlled variable and set point from the apparent difference or actuating signal e.

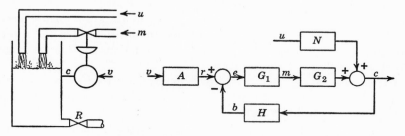

FIG. 8-1.   Automatic control with input and feedback elements.

The feedback variable b is the quantity indicated or recorded by the measuring element H. The controlled variable is never actually recorded anywhere and its magnitude must be inferred from the feedback variable b. Therefore it is of interest to compare the controlled variable in the general equations:

$$c = \frac{AG_1G_2}{1 + G_1G_2H} v + \frac{N}{1 + G_1G_2H} u \qquad (8\text{-}7)$$

to the feedback or measured variable given by the equation

$$b = \frac{AG_1G_2H}{1 + G_1G_2H} v + \frac{NH}{1 + G_1G_2H} u \qquad (8\text{-}8)$$

The actual deviation is given by

$$d = \frac{1 + G_1G_2(H - A)}{1 + G_1G_2H} v - \frac{N}{1 + G_1G_2H} u \qquad (8\text{-}9)$$

For load changes, the change of set point is taken as zero and the part of the deviation due to load may be calculated. For set point changes, the change of load is taken as zero and the part of the deviation due to the changing set point may be determined. Notice that these equations reduce to those of Chapter 4 when the input and feedback elements contain no time elements ($A = H = 1.0$).

Example 8–1. Derive the general equation for actuating signal.
From equations 8–1 through 8–9

$$e = \frac{A}{1 + G_1 G_2 H} v - \frac{NH}{1 + G_1 G_2 H} u$$

The actuating signal differs from deviation (see equation 8–9).

Effect of Measurement (Feedback) Lag

The effect of a lag in the measuring or feedback means is insidious; that is, the effect of the lag tends to become obscured by its own existence. The effect of a large measuring lag is to almost always cause large amplitude oscillations and slow return or stabilization. On the other hand a large measuring lag causes great attenuation, so that the large amplitude oscillations are not seen.

The process of Fig. 8–1 is typical of many industrial processes such as tank heaters, heat exchangers, and furnaces. For example, consider proportional control of a time-constant process:

$$G_1 = K_c \qquad \text{proportional control with negligible lag}$$

$$G_2 = \frac{R}{T_p s + 1} \qquad \text{process time constant } T_p$$

$$N = \frac{R}{T_p s + 1} \qquad \text{effect of load}$$

$$H = \frac{1}{T_m s + 1} \qquad \text{measuring time-element constant } T_m$$

The actual response of the controlled variable to a load change is given by

$$c = \frac{R(T_m s + 1)}{T_p T_m s^2 + (T_p + T_m)s + (RK_c + 1)} u \qquad (8\text{–}10)$$

The indicated response to a load change is given by

$$b = \frac{R}{T_p T_m s^2 + (T_p + T_m)s + (RK_c + 1)} u \qquad (8\text{–}11)$$

The damping ratio will be set to approximately one third by selecting a value of proportional sensitivity K_c. The solutions to each of these equations to a sudden change of load u are plotted in Fig. 8–2 for a process time constant (T_p) of 20 sec and two different measuring element time constants.

First compare the values of the feedback variable b and the controlled variable c. As the curves of Fig. 8–2 indicate, both have the same general characteristics, but the feedback variable shows less change and is retarded from the actual controlled variable. In fact, the feedback variable lags the controlled variable by about 45 degrees phase. It is well to remember that the controlled variable curve c is not usually indicated or recorded anywhere in the system. Therefore, changes of the actual controlled variable are always larger in magnitude than those indicated by the feedback variable.

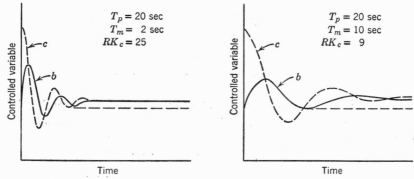

$T_p = 20$ sec
$T_m = 2$ sec
$RK_c = 25$

$T_p = 20$ sec
$T_m = 10$ sec
$RK_c = 9$

FIG. 8-2. Effect of measuring lag.

Second, compare the changes in controlled variable when the measuring lag is 2 sec to the case when the measuring lag is 10 sec. In the latter case the automatic controller is much less effective. This is indicated by the smaller value of proportional sensitivity when the measuring lag is larger. In consequence the offset is increased by about 170 per cent by the larger measuring lag, and in addition the control is made much slower acting. Therefore, an increased measuring lag may result in larger offset and slower recovery from a load change.

In temperature control, the measuring-element lag is likely to be the largest lag except for the process lag and it is desirable that the measuring lag be made as small as possible compared to the largest lag, a ratio of one tenth is a good figure to maintain.

In liquid-level control, the process is often of a single energy storage type, and the magnitude of measuring lag is generally not important. If any choice is possible, a measuring means should be selected that has the smallest measuring lag; that is, a measuring lag that is as small as possible compared to the largest time constant of the process.

In pressure control, the process is often of a single energy storage type. The magnitude of measuring lag is generally small except when long pressure connecting lines must be used. In this case also, the measuring lag should be maintained less than a small fraction of the largest time constant of the process.

In flow control, the lags of the measuring means and the controlling means are generally the only important lags in the system. For the flow-control system of Fig. 8–3 it is assumed that the measuring means

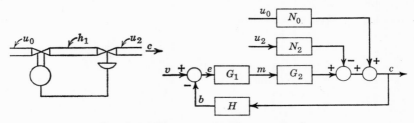

FIG. 8–3.   Flow control with measuring lag.

such as orifice head-meter, has a single time-constant measuring lag. The lag of the controlling means is neglected in this first example. The system functions are

$$G_2 = K_1 \qquad\qquad \text{control valve sensitivity}$$

$$N_2 = K_2 \qquad\qquad \text{downstream pressure sensitivity}$$

$$N_0 = K_0 \qquad\qquad \text{upstream pressure sensitivity}$$

$$G_1 = \frac{1}{Ts} \qquad\qquad \text{integral control}$$

$$H = \frac{1}{T_m s + 1} \qquad\qquad \text{measuring-element time constant } T_m$$

The system equation for a change of load u_2 with load u_0 and set point v fixed is

$$c = -\frac{K_2 T s (T_m s + 1)}{T T_m s^2 + T s + K_1} u_2 \tag{8–12}$$

The feedback variable is given by

$$b = \frac{-K_2 T s}{T T_m s^2 + T s + K_1} u_2 \tag{8–13}$$

For a sudden (step) change of load variable u_2, the solutions of each of these equations are plotted in Fig. 8–4. In each case the damping ratio is selected as one third (therefore $4 K_1 T_m = 9 T$).

Comparing the response with large measuring lag to the response with small measuring lag it is seen that the effect is to delay and attenuate the indication of changes in the controlled variable. However, a most serious consequence of the measuring lag in flow control is that an inspection of the indicated value of the controlled variable b might lead to the conclusion that the measuring lag of 20 sec produces a better control than if the measuring lag is 5 sec (compare the two solid curves of Fig. 8–4), whereas actually the measuring lag has made the control much less effective (compare the two dotted curves).

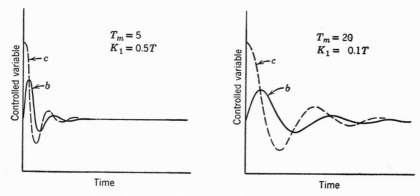

Fig. 8–4. Effect of measuring lag in flow control.

In flow control it often happens that the measuring lag and controller lag are of approximately the same magnitude, and both are larger than any other lags of the system. In this case, the system functions of Fig. 8–3 are

$G_2 = K_1$ valve-flow sensitivity

$N_2 = K_2$ downstream pressure sensitivity

$N_0 = K_0$ upstream pressure sensitivity

$G_1 = \dfrac{K_c}{T_c s + 1}$ proportional control with controller (or valve) time constant T_c

$H = \dfrac{1}{T_m s + 1}$ measuring element time constant T_m

The system operational equations, relating change of controlled variable to a change in load u_2, but with set point v and load u_0 fixed, is

$$c = \frac{-K_2(T_c s + 1)(T_m s + 1)}{T_c T_m s^2 + (T_m + T_c)s + (K_1 K_c + 1)} u_2 \qquad (8\text{–}14)$$

For the feedback variable

$$b = \frac{-K_2(T_c s + 1)}{T_c T_m s^2 + (T_m + T_c)s + (K_1 K_c + 1)} u_2 \qquad (8\text{–}15)$$

The solutions for a step change in load u_2 are given in Fig. 8–5 for three cases; measuring lag greater than $T_m = 10$, equal to $T_m = 5.5$, and less than $T_m = 3$, the controller lag. The damping ratio is maintained at one third, and in addition a ratio of lags has been selected that results in the same period of oscillation $(T_m T_c = 30)$. Thus in each of

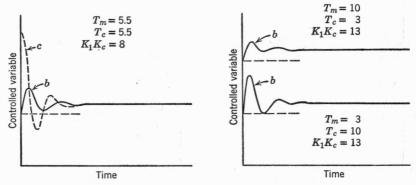

FIG. 8–5. Measuring lag and controller lag in flow control.

the three cases the actual controlled variable c has precisely the same behavior, i.e., the same damping ratio and same period of oscillation. The upper curve in the right-hand diagram has been displaced upward for better comparison.

It is apparent that, whereas the actual change of controlled variable is the same in all three cases, the indicated variable shows less change as the measuring lag T_m becomes larger. On the other hand, it is not valid to conclude that the controller lag should be large because if the controller lag is not the largest in the system, increasing it does not materially improve the control of the actual controlled variable.

Example 8–2. A flow-control system has a valve lag of 5 sec and a measuring time constant of 7 sec, and proportional control is used. Would doubling the measuring lag improve the flow control?

From equation 8–14, the damping ratio will be made 1.0 so

$$(T_m + T_c)^2 = 4(K_1 K_c + 1) T_c T_m$$

Old $K_1 K_c = 0.029$

New $K_1 K_c = 0.29$

The characteristic time is

$$T = \sqrt{\frac{T_c T_m}{K_1 K_c + 1}}$$

Old $T = 5.8$ sec

New $T = 7.4$ sec

No. The deviation is the same and the stabilization is slower. The record would look better, however.

Process Disturbances

A number of factors affect the quality of control, the most important of which is the behavior of the process load. The process load may be defined in terms of the setting of the final control element to maintain the controlled variable at the set point.

The location and source of process loads are illustrated in Fig. 8–6 by the gas-fired continuous heating furnace. The heat losses are made up by the stack u_4, radiation u_5, and work c. The heat supply is made up by work u_3 and fuel m.

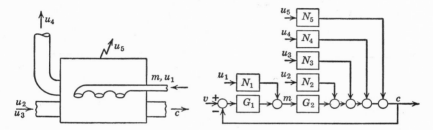

FIG. 8–6.   Origin of process load changes.

A load change is caused by variations in the rate of energy supply or loss due to causes other than controller action. For example, if the gas pressure u_1 changes, the flow of fuel will be altered. Another example is the clogging of the burners which decreases the flow of fuel for any one valve setting. For another example, the heat may be changed by varying the temperature of the work as it enters the furnace. The most common load change, however, is caused by variations in the rate at which the work flows through the process. Other load changes are those due to stack loss u_4, caused by changing draft pressure, and radiation or leakage loss u_5, due to varying ambient conditions. The effects of all these load changes must also be corrected by the controller.

The location of the load change has a great influence in the magnitude of the resulting change in the controlled variable. This is illustrated by the curves of Fig. 8–7. The curve on the left represents the result of a unit change of variable u_2 (temperature of the incoming work) in Fig. 8–6. When the load change occurs "close" to the controlled variable, the magnitude is large compared to the magnitude when the load change is located far from the controlled variable. The curve on the right shows the result of a unit change in variable u_1 (pressure of the fuel gas) in Fig. 8–6. Notice that the magnitude of the change is about two-thirds less.

The offset due to a step change of process load is easily calculated from the operational equation. Under steady-state conditions, all derivatives are zero, and the differential equation reduces to an algebraic

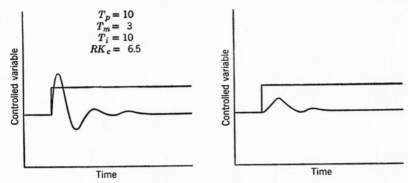

FIG. 8–7.   Location of load change.

equation.   Derivatives are zero when the operator s is zero, and the offset for a unit step change of load is given by

$$D_0 = \lim_{s \to 0} \left[\frac{-N}{1 + G_1 G_2 H} \right] \tag{8-16}$$

Substituting $G_1 = K_c(1 + Ts)/Ts$ for proportional-integral control in equation 8–16 there results

$$D_0 = \lim_{s \to 0} \frac{-NTsK_c}{Ts + G_2 H(Ts + 1)} \tag{8-17}$$

where T = integral time.   The limit is zero and the offset is therefore zero if the function $G_2 H/N$ does not contain any s^n factors where $n > 0$.

Elements of the capacitance type in the process function G_2 may make the use of integral control unnecessary.   Rewriting equation 8–16 for proportional control $G_1 = K_c$, and with $G_2 = 1/Cs$, the result is

$$D_0 = \lim_{s \to 0} \left[\frac{-NCs}{Cs + K_c H} \right] \tag{8-18}$$

Thus there is no offset when the function H/N does not contain any s^n factors.

Example 8–3.   For a process with two time lags,

$$G_2 = \frac{R}{(T_1 s + 1)T_2 s}, \qquad N = \frac{R}{T_1 s + 1}$$

and a controller time constant lag T_c, calculate the offset for proportional control.

From equation 8–16 and a change of load u,

$$D_0 = \lim_{s \to 0} \left[\frac{-R}{T_1 s + 1} \right] \left[\frac{1}{1 + \dfrac{K_c R}{(T_c s + 1)(T_1 s + 1)T_2 s}} \right]$$

$$D_0 = \underline{0}$$

A disturbance of the set point or input may be required in many process-control systems as when a process variable is required to follow a program, or when the system is a part of another system. The deviation resulting from a disturbance of the set point; i.e., when the set point is a function of time, is given by equation 8–9,

$$d = \frac{1 + G_1 G_2 (H - A)}{1 + G_1 G_2 H} v \qquad (8\text{–}19)$$

The character of the input element A affects the performance of the system. First it must be noted that the input element does not influence the stability, because this stability is governed by the closed-loop function $G_1 G_2 H$. Element A is not in this loop. The input element does, however, affect the overall response.

The effect of the input element may be seen more clearly by equation 8–7,

$$c = \frac{G_1 G_2}{1 + G_1 G_2 H} (A) v \qquad (8\text{–}20)$$

so that the system may be considered as two systems in series. When the input element is a simple lag like a time-constant element, the system response is appropriately delayed and attenuated in the normal fashion. If the input element contains a derivative term for example $(Ts + 1)$. it is possible to improve the performance of the system. Suppose

$$A = Ts + 1$$

$$G_1 = 1/T_i s$$

$$G_2 = 1/(T_1 s + 1)$$

$$H = 1.0$$

$$N = 0$$

The system function becomes

$$c = \frac{Ts + 1}{T_i T_1 s^2 + T_i s + 1} v \qquad (8\text{–}21)$$

Setting the integral time T_i to give critical damping $(T_i = 4T_1)$ there results

$$c = \frac{Ts + 1}{(T_2s + 1)^2} v \qquad (8\text{--}22)$$

where $T_2 = 2T_1$. Without input element lead $(T = 0)$, the system has second-order response. If the input element lead can be made equal to the process time constant $(T = 2T_1)$, a first order system results and the overall response could be made much faster.

Static error may result from a changing input or set point. For a unit step change of the set point, the static error is given by

$$D_S = \lim_{s \to 0} \frac{1 + G_1G_2(H - A)}{1 + G_1G_2H} \qquad (8\text{--}23)$$

This error is usually zero in process control.

Example 8–4. The static error caused by a unit step change of input may be written

$$D_S = \lim_{s \to 0} \left[1 - \frac{G_1G_2A}{1 + G_1G_2H} \right]$$

For the following functions calculate the static error:

$$G_1G_2 = \frac{K_c}{(Ts + 1)^2}, \qquad A = (T_a s + 1)$$

$$H = \frac{1}{T_Hs + 1}$$

$$D_S = \lim_{s \to 0} \left[1 - \frac{T_a s + 1}{\dfrac{(Ts + 1)^2}{K_c} + \dfrac{1}{T_Hs + 1}} \right]$$

$$D_S = 1 - \frac{1}{\dfrac{1}{K_c} + 1} = \frac{1}{K_c + 1}$$

Magnitude of Process Load

Often a controller is handicapped by being called upon to operate under conditions of large variations in process load. The resultant effect upon the quality of control may be such that a controller satisfactorily operating with high process load may produce entirely undesirable results at low process load. This effect is brought about by changing values of system parameters when the various parts of the system operate at different steady-state values of the pertinent variables. If these parameters are inside the loop, it may be possible to compensate the effect of the variations.

The steady-state sensitivities of the system are usually:

$$\text{Controller} \qquad K_c = \frac{\Delta x}{\Delta e}$$

$$\text{Control element} \qquad K_v = \frac{\Delta m}{\Delta x}$$

$$\text{Process} \qquad K_p = \frac{\Delta c}{\Delta m}$$

$$\text{Feedback} \qquad K_m = \frac{\Delta b}{\Delta c}$$

If it is assumed that under operating conditions the loop gain $K_c K_v K_p K_m$ is to be so proportioned that the control action has the same behavior at all loads, then it is possible to derive a control element function from

$$K_v = \frac{dm}{dx} = \frac{g(m)}{K_c K_p K_m} \tag{8–24}$$

or

$$x = \int_0^m \frac{K_c K_p K_m}{g(m)} \, dm \tag{8–25}$$

where $g(m)$ is the loop sensitivity as a function of load.

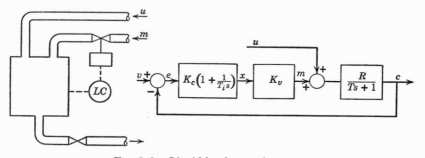

FIG. 8–8.   Liquid-level control system.

The effect of magnitude of process load will be illustrated by several examples of typical processes.   Consider the liquid-level control of Fig. 8–8.   Generally the measurement and controller lags are very small compared to the process lag.   The steady-state sensitivities (gains) are

$$\text{Controller} \qquad K_c = \frac{\Delta x}{\Delta e}$$

$$\text{Control valve} \quad K_v = \frac{\Delta m}{\Delta x}$$

$$\text{Process} \qquad R = \frac{\Delta c}{\Delta m}$$

as shown in the operational diagram of Fig. 8–8. The system operational equation is

$$c = \frac{K_c K_v R(T_i s + 1)}{T_i s(Ts + 1) + K_c K_v R(T_i s + 1)} v$$
$$+ \frac{RT_i s}{T_i s(Ts + 1) + K_c K_v R(T_i s + 1)} u \quad (8\text{–}26)$$

where T_i = integral time
T = process time constant = RC
C = process capacitance

For a damping ratio of one third, the relationship among the parameters is

$$\frac{(1 + K_c K_v R)^2}{K_c K_v R} = \frac{4T}{9T_i} \qquad (8\text{–}27)$$

Since the loop static gain $K_c K_v R$ is usually at least ten, we may write

$$K_c K_v R \cong \frac{4RC}{9T_i} \qquad (8\text{–}28)$$

or

$$K_c K_v \cong \frac{4C}{9T_i} \qquad (8\text{–}29)$$

The control-valve relation can now be derived:

$$K_v = \frac{dm}{dx} \cong \frac{4C}{9K_c T_i} = \alpha \qquad (8\text{–}30)$$

where K_c is a constant, providing the automatic controller has linear proportional action. Integrating gives

$$m = \int_0^x \alpha \, dx = \alpha x \qquad (8\text{–}31)$$

The latter requires a linear relation between flow and position at the control valve, as shown in Fig. 8–10. If equation 8–27 is solved exactly, the resulting flow-position characteristic does not vary more than a few per cent from a linear relation. It may be shown that controlling outlet flow instead of inlet flow, and, the use of proportional control instead of proportional-integral control provides the same result.

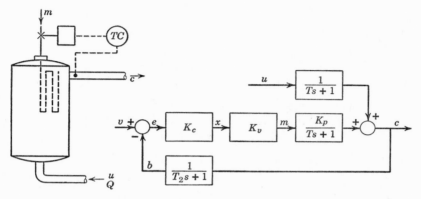

FIG. 8–9. Temperature-control system.

Consider the outlet temperature control of Fig. 8–9. Generally the measuring lag and the process lag are the largest lags in such systems. The steady-state sensitivities (gains) are:

$$\text{Controller} \qquad K_c = \frac{\Delta x}{\Delta e}$$

$$\text{Control element} \quad K_v = \frac{\Delta m}{\Delta x}$$

$$\text{Process} \qquad K_p = \frac{\Delta c}{\Delta m}$$

as shown in the operational diagram. The system operational equation is

$$c = \frac{K_c K_v K_p (T_2 s + 1)}{(Ts + 1)(T_2 s + 1) + K_c K_v K_p} v$$

$$+ \frac{T_2 s + 1}{(Ts + 1)(T_2 s + 1) + K_c K_v K_p} u \qquad (8\text{–}32)$$

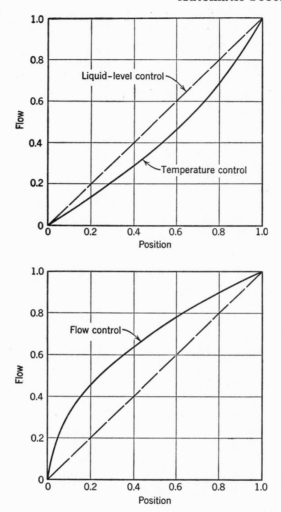

FIG. 8–10.   Desired characteristics of control elements.

where T_2 = measuring element lag
   T = process lag = W/Q
   W = weight of fluid in tank
   Q = flow rate of liquid through tank
   u = inlet temperature
   K_p = $1/QP$
   P = specific heat of fluid

For a given damping ratio ζ, the following relationship of the parameter is desired:

$$K_v K_c K_p = \frac{1}{4\zeta^2} \frac{(T + T_2)^2}{T T_2} - 1 \tag{8-33}$$

Substituting for the "variable" parameters, K_v, K_p, T

$$\frac{dm}{dx} = \frac{WP}{4\zeta^2 T_2 K_c} \left[\left(\frac{T_2 Q}{W} \right)^2 + (1 - 2\zeta^2) \frac{2 T_2 Q}{W} + 1 \right] \tag{8-34}$$

In this equation T_2, P, W, and K_c are constants. The throughput rate Q, however, affects the heat input m, because steady-state conservation of energy requires

$$m = QPD \tag{8-35}$$

where D = temperature difference inlet to outlet. Combining equations 8–34 and 8–35 to eliminate Q, and considering a damping ratio of 0.707,

$$\frac{dm}{dx} = \frac{WP}{2 K_c T_2} \left[\left(\frac{T_2 m}{WPD} \right)^2 + 1 \right] \tag{8-36}$$

The equation is now integrable and may be written,

$$\int \frac{dm_1}{m_1{}^2 + 1} = x_1 + K \tag{8-37}$$

where $m_1 = \dfrac{T_2 m}{WPD}$

$x_1 = \dfrac{x}{2 K_c D}$

K = constant

Integrating,

$$\tan^{-1} m_1 = x_1 + K \tag{8-38}$$

or

$$m_1 = \tan x_1 \tag{8-39}$$

This relation is plotted in Fig. 8–10. The particular temperature-control system of Fig. 8–9 would therefore require a control element of the increasing sensitivity type. Notice that the tangent function, parabolic function $(\pi x_1{}^2/2)$, and the exponential function $(e^{0.94 x_1} - 1)$ are all nearly identical. On the other hand, for small values these functions are all nearly linear.

Consider the flow-control system of Fig. 8–11. The measuring lag (at H) and the controller lag (at G_1) are usually the only lags of any

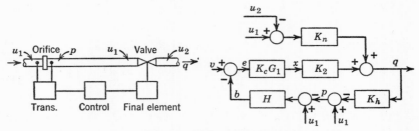

FIG. 8–11.   Flow-control system.

magnitude. These lags are also constants. The flow equation for the orifice or other restriction is

$$q = K_0 \sqrt{u_1 - p} \tag{8-40}$$

or regarding $p = f(u_1, q)$ and linearizing,

$$p = u_1 - K_h q \tag{8-41}$$

where

$$K_h = -\left(\frac{\partial p}{\partial q}\right)_{u_1} = \frac{2q}{K_0{}^2} \tag{8-42}$$

The flow equation for the valve is

$$q = K_v x \sqrt{u_1 - u_2} \tag{8-43}$$

where it is assumed that the permanent pressure loss of the measuring element is negligible (as for a Venturi). Regarding $q = f(x, u_1, u_2)$ and linearizing,

$$q = K_2 x + K_n (u_1 - u_2) \tag{8-44}$$

where

$$K_2 = \left[\frac{\partial q}{\partial x}\right]_{u_1, u_2} = K_v \sqrt{u_1 - u_2} \tag{8-45}$$

$$K_n = \left[\frac{\partial q}{\partial (u_1 - u_2)}\right]_x = \frac{K_v x}{2\sqrt{u_1 - u_2}} \tag{8-46}$$

These relations are shown in the operational diagram of Fig. 8–11.

The loop sensitivity (gain) must be constant (equal to A), regardless of the particular values of lags and loads (u_1, u_2), because the system loop gain depends only upon the time constants, and these do not depend upon pressure or flow.   The loop gain is therefore

$$K_c K_2 K_h = A \tag{8-47}$$

or

$$K_c \left[\frac{\partial q}{\partial x} \right]_{u_1, u_2} \left[\frac{\partial p}{\partial q} \right]_{u_1} = A \tag{8-48}$$

or

$$K_c K_v \sqrt{u_1 - u_2} \frac{2q}{K_0{}^2} = A \tag{8-49}$$

Eliminating the pressure differential by employing equation 8–43,

$$q = \sqrt{\alpha x} \tag{8-50}$$

where $A K_0{}^2 / 2 K_c = \alpha$.   This relation is plotted in Fig. 8–10.   Notice that the system calls for a control element of the decreasing sensitivity type when the set point is changed but pressure differential is constant.

Summarizing the effects of variable loop sensitivities, it can be shown for many process control systems that the effect of changing sensitivity caused by varying process load can be adequately compensated by "shaping" the final element characteristic.

Difficulty in analyzing every control application is caused by three important factors: first, changes in process system function with load are different for each disturbance; second, within each process the system function is different for each disturbance; and third, valve flow and area characteristics are not always identical.   Consequently, from a theoretical standpoint, different valve characteristics are required for different process arrangements.   It must be emphasized, however, that process loads do not often vary to any great extent, so that effects of process reaction and load are minimized.

Cascade Control Loops

Many processes are controlled by regulating the flow of a heating medium such as steam, gas, oil, or fuel for supplying heat to a process. Variations in flow not dictated by the controller are caused by changes in pressure differential at the valve, which, in turn, result from changes in pressure of the supply, changes in downstream pressure, and so on. These changes are difficult to counteract since they must carry through the process before they are detected in the controller.   Supply changes sometimes occur suddenly or over a wide range, and deviation may become excessive before a new balance of conditions can be established.

Consider the control system shown in Fig. 8–12. The temperature controller TC measures exit temperature of the process c and transmits a signal v_2 which becomes the set point of the flow controller FC. The flow controller measures and controls flow rate c_2 by adjusting a control-

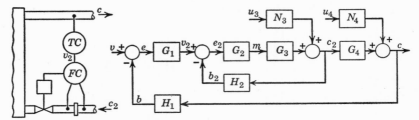

FIG. 8–12.   Control with metered flow.

valve setting m.   Load (u_3) at the inner loop is a variable upstream pressure at the control valve.   Load u_4 at the outer loop causes variation in controlled variable.   The operational equations are:

$$
\begin{aligned}
c_2 &= G_3 m + N_3 u_3 & c &= G_4 c_2 + N_4 u_4 \\
m &= G_2 e_2 & v_2 &= G_1 e \\
e_2 &= v_2 - b_2 & e &= v - b \\
b_2 &= H_2 c_2 & b &= H_1 c
\end{aligned}
\qquad (8\text{--}51)
$$

The controlled variable is given by

$$
c = \frac{(G_1 G_2 G_3 G_4)v + (G_4 N_3)u_3 + (N_4 + G_2 G_3 H_2 N_4)u_4}{1 + G_2 G_3 H_2 + G_1 G_2 G_3 G_4 H_1}
\qquad (8\text{--}52)
$$

The independent action of the inner loop is described by

$$
c_2 = \frac{G_2 G_3}{1 + G_2 G_3 H_2} v_2 + \frac{N_3}{1 + G_2 G_3 H_2} u_3
\qquad (8\text{--}53)
$$

The inner loop is generally a flow-control system and is considerably faster than the outer loop which is generally liquid-level or temperature control.   Consequently, the type of control employed in the inner loop (at G_2) is not as important as the type of control in the outer loop (G_1). The following observations are made, based upon a detailed study of the loop equations:

1. The control action of the inner loop should be the simplest.   Omit integral or derivative responses unless specifically desired.

2. Set the inner loop for tight control; i.e., high loop gain.

3. Measuring lag of inner loop (at H_2) provides a derivative action for outer loop. Consequently this measuring lag is not always harmful as long as it is not excessive.

Example 8-5. Control systems sometimes employ a pressure controller (regulator) to hold valve upstream pressure constant and it is often used in place of metered control. State an advantage and a disadvantage for this method as shown in the accompanying figure:

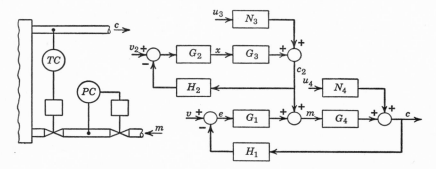

1. Advantage: Usually less expensive because a simple fluid regulator replaces expensive flow controller.
2. Disadvantage: Requires two valves in series with attendant pressure losses.

Cascade control is extensively applied in control of liquid level when a liquid-level controller regulates the set point of a flow controller. Pressure changes in the vessel and downstream from the control valve frequently make the control of liquid level in the tank difficult. By means of cascade control the effect of these pressure changes can be eliminated. Both liquid level and outflow can thereby be made more stable and consistent.

A pressure-balanced valve is another form of cascade control. The valve is so constructed that the output pressure of the controller is applied to one side of the diaphragm and the downstream gas pressure is applied to the other side of the diaphragm. The pressure-balanced valve is actually a self-operated pressure regulator whose set point is regulated by the master controller. Any change in gas pressure is counteracted by the pressure-balanced valve and is not allowed to pass into the process.

Ratio-flow control systems are arranged as shown in Fig. 8-13. The primary instrument here is not a controller but a transmitter. The set point of the controller is set in direct relation to the magnitude of the primary flow. As the magnitude of the primary variable changes, the

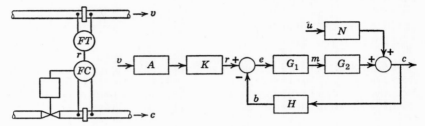

FIG. 8-13.   Ratio control.

set point of the controller is automatically moved to a new value so that an exact ratio is maintained between primary and secondary variables.

The controlled variable is given by

$$c = \frac{G_1 G_2 A K}{1 + G_1 G_2 H} v + \frac{N}{1 + G_1 G_2 H} u \tag{8-54}$$

Several important characteristics of ratio control may now be shown. Suppose, by way of example,

$$A = \left(\frac{1}{T_a s + 1}\right) \qquad G_1 G_2 = K_c\left(1 + \frac{1}{T_i s}\right)$$

$$K = k \qquad\qquad H = \left(\frac{1}{T_n s + 1}\right) \tag{8-55}$$

where T_a = primary measuring element lag
      k = desired ratio
      T_i = integral time of controller
      T_n = controller measuring element lag

Substituting in equation 8-54 and considering load u fixed,

$$\frac{c}{kv} = \left(\frac{T_n s + 1}{T_a s + 1}\right) \frac{T_i s + 1}{\dfrac{T_i T_n}{K_c} s^2 + T_i\left(\dfrac{1}{K_c} + 1\right) s + 1} \tag{8-56}$$

In order to obtain the best "following" of the controlled variable to the desired variable, the lags T_n, T_a and the integral time T_i should all be as small as possible. The proportional sensitivity K_c should be as large as possible and the control system requires careful adjustment.

Batch-Process Control

A process in which the materials or work are stationary at one physical location while being treated is termed a batch process. This type of process is distinguished from the continuous process in which the materials flow more or less continuously. Batch processes are most often of the thermal type where materials are placed in a vessel or furnace, and the system is brought up to temperature and pressure and controlled for a period of time. If the process reaction rate is slow, and lags and dead time are small, a two-position (on-off) controller is generally satisfactory.

If the process reaction rate is large or if lags are not small, it may be necessary to employ proportional control in order to avoid excessive cycling of the temperature. Suppose that we consider the action of the controller through one complete batch. Figure 8–14 shows the

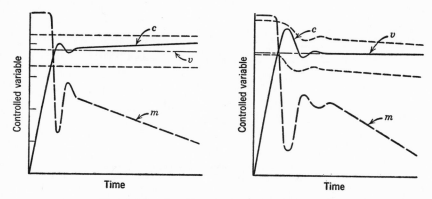

FIG. 8–14. Overshoot in batch-process control.

temperature and the corresponding valve action with proportional control. As the temperature rises when the processing begins, the valve is open. When the temperature reaches the lower edge of the proportional band the valve begins to close. The temperature then cycles about the set point before becoming stable.

With most processes a gradually decreasing valve setting is required in order to balance energy (offset).

The gradual closing of the valve can be accomplished only by a corresponding deviation of the variable from the set point. As long as proportional sensitivity is high, offset will also be small.

Offset may be eliminated by means of integral response. The action of the proportional-integral controller is shown in Fig. 8–14. The offset of temperature is nearly eliminated, and the temperature is maintained close to the set point after it has stabilized. Notice that the initial overshoot of temperature, when approaching the set point for the first time, is much larger than with only proportional control.

The large initial overshoot is due to the action of integral response. During the heating-up period the temperature is, of course, below the set point. The normal action of integral response is to shift the proportional band to urge the temperature toward the set point. Since the valve is already full open, integral response simply shifts the proportional band all the way.

Overshoot is prevented in one of several ways. First, many electric controllers with integral response incorporate a "rate of approach setter." This device limits the integral action until the first approach to the set point has been made. Second, a controller which incorporates a proportional-derivative unit followed by a proportional integral unit also may be adjusted to prevent overshoot. In the latter case the derivative response provides "anticipation" by making the integral controller think that the controlled variable has approached the set point

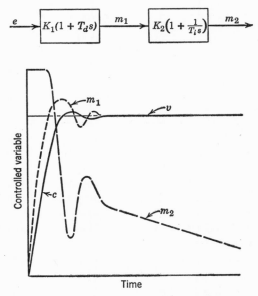

FIG. 8–15.   Series-control elements.

as illustrated in Fig. 8–15. The sensitivity of the first controller K_1 may be adjusted so that with a given setting of derivative time the overshoot is eliminated.

In the processing of metals and chemicals it is sometimes necessary to vary the controlled variable over a definite time schedule. For example, in annealing steel, a schedule may be required such that the furnace temperature is raised to 1500 F in 4 hr, held for 8 hr, and lowered to 500 F in 6 hr. This time schedule must be incorporated into the automatic control system.

Time-variable control is accomplished similarly to ratio control. All systems operate on the principle that the set point is moved through the desired time schedule. The control system functions to maintain the controlled variable, temperature in the example above, as close to the moving set point as required.

The time-variable control system is also illustrated by the general diagram of Fig. 8–13, where $v = f(t)$ is the desired time schedule. Very often it is required to change the controlled variable at a steady rate in such batch processes involving controlled rates of heating or cooling. In these applications the controlled variable lags behind the desired value. This may be calculated by employing the same technique as previously:

$$D_v = \lim_{s \to 0} \left[\frac{K}{s} \frac{1 + G_1 G_2 (H - A)}{1 + G_1 G_2 H} \right] \tag{8-57}$$

Usually, but not always, the velocity error is small.

Batch processes are nearly always defined by temperature, pressure, or associated conditions such as composition of environment. The degrees of freedom are usually well-defined. The purpose of such processes is to produce one or more products at (a) a given composition, (b) a maximum amount, and (c) best economy (employing least materials, energy, and time).

The product composition desired is that at the end of the processing period and thus cannot be measured. Consequently it is necessary to manipulate the variables of the process in such a manner that the behavior of the process insures obtaining the desired composition.

Maximum product and best economy result when the variables of the process are properly manipulated. Generally this is achieved by a time schedule for all variables of the system. A computing machine may be used to insure a relationship among variables providing best operation.

Continuous-Process Control

A process in which the materials or work flows more or less continuously through a plant apparatus while being treated is termed a continuous process. The problems of continuous-process control are caused by load changes.

Flow rate of the materials is almost always important in continuous processing, particularly where quantitative reactions are involved as in blending. On the other hand the supply of material is sometimes not constant and a flow control is necessary as shown in Fig. 8–16. The resulting flow of materials is nearly constant in spite of large changes of head in the tank. It is necessary to size the tank only large enough so that the longest charging period will not run the tank over, and the longest off-time of the inlet will not allow the tank to run dry. In order to keep load changes at a minimum, a short tank of large cross-section area (large capacitance) should be employed.

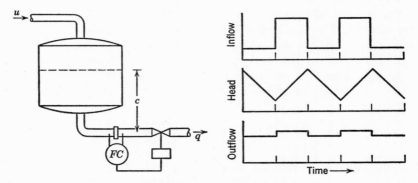

FIG. 8–16.   Storage-vessel control.

In many applications, particularly in continuous processing, the outflow of one unit becomes the feed to a succeeding unit. In order to obtain stability of operation in the plant, it is sometimes important that fluctuation of outflow and inflow be reduced to a minimum, thereby maintaining all feeds relatively constant. The storage capacity of the vessel may be utilized to proportion outflow against changes of inflow. The vessel thereby serves as a surge tank for absorbing fluctuations in flow rates. Averaging control gets its name since the outflow is "averaged" against level, and the level is controlled between upper and lower limits rather than at a single point.

For the vessel of Fig. 8–17 without control of outflow (outlet valve at a fixed setting),

$$A\dot{c} = u - q \qquad (8\text{–}58)$$

where A = cross-section area of tank. When the vessel is under controlled pressure, as is generally the case, the outflow is then constant if the pressure differential at the valve is constant. The inflow, head, and outflow are shown by the dotted curves in Fig. 8–17. Obviously if there is no control, the tank would ultimately fill or run dry. If control of level is added,

$$-q = K_c(v - c) \qquad (8\text{–}59)$$

where K_c is the proportional sensitivity of the proportional controller. Combining equations 8–58 and 8–59,

$$\frac{q}{u} = \frac{1}{Ts + 1} \tag{8–60}$$

and

$$\frac{c}{u} = \frac{1}{K_c}\frac{1}{Ts + 1} \tag{8–61}$$

where $T = A/K_c$. The inflow, head, and outflow are also shown in Fig. 8–17. The time constant T may be selected by adjusting the proportional sensitivity of the controller so as to "spread out" the inflow

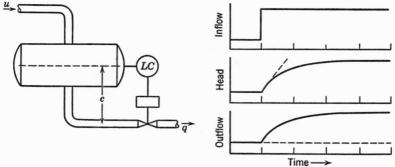

Fig. 8–17. Surge-vessel control.

change over a period of about four time constants. In order to absorb changes of inflow the time constant T should be made as large as possible (proportional sensitivity K_c as small as possible) without completely filling or emptying the tank. Sometimes a proportional-integral controller is used with integral time set to a large value so that the outflow is further increased and the head in the tank maintained near the set point.

Continuous processes possess a number of degrees of freedom given by the numbers of variables and defining relations for the system (refer to the first sections of Chapter 2). These variables are generally the temperature, pressure, flow-rate, and composition of each of the entering and leaving materials. Usually the purpose of the process is to produce one or more products at (a) a given composition, (b) a given or maximum flow-rate, and (c) best economy (employing least materials, energy, personnel time, and equipment).

Product composition is best insured by measuring product composition and controlling it by manipulating one of the degrees of freedom of the process.

Fixed product flow rate usually requires flow controllers at several points of entering and leaving materials. If the product flow rate is to be a maximum, the flow controllers should not be employed, or else they should be manipulated to achieve one of the purposes of the process.

Best economy is accomplished if at all by maintaining all process variables in a predetermined relation such that the highest efficiency, least waste, or some other criteria are satisfied. This practically precludes the complete use of automatic control because holding all variables constant does not allow variable inlet conditions or variable flow rate. Economy can be achieved by employing a computing machine and relating all variables, even in a transient state, so that the desired criteria are met.

Optimizing or Computing Machine Control

The objective of any process control system is to insure that the system under control produces the best product at maximum quantity and least cost. In order to achieve this objective the present approach is to use automatic controllers on each of the degrees of freedom of the system, thereby holding the system in a fixed state. A process operator (human) then manipulates each of the controllers until the objective stated above is accomplished.

Operation by a human overseer is rarely as effective as it might be for several reasons:

1. The processing relations are often so complex that a working grasp of the interrelations are beyond human abilities.

2. The process may operate in such a fast time scale that human action is always too late.

3. The process may operate in such a slow time scale that human attention is ineffective.

4. Safety may be of utmost concern.

5. Human operation is not possible in locations where human beings cannot go.

Optimizing (sometimes called optimalizing) control may be arranged by employing a computing machine to perform the operations normally provided by a human overseer. There are two general methods by which computer control can be accomplished:

A. A perturbation method whereby the various degrees of freedom of the system are changed incrementally and periodically until a selected function of performance is observed to be a maximum.

B. A continuous computing method wherein the relations defining optimum performance of the system are derived, and the control system is designed to manipulate the process variable in such a way that the optimum conditions are achieved.

The *perturbation method*[1] has recently been employed in the control of heat-engine performance, and a simple version of the method has been employed on heating furnaces. Suppose that it is desired to maintain best fuel–air ratio for maximum heat release in combustion in a furnace subject to whatever limitations may apply. This may be accomplished by changing the air flow at constant fuel flow by incremental amounts and on a fixed time period. The resulting change of heat release can be measured by combinations of flame temperature and stack losses, and, if the change of heat release is positive, another incremental step in air flow is made in the same direction as previously. All the while, fuel flow is controlled directly from work temperature. This incremental stepping is continued until a negative change in heat release results. The direction is then reversed and stepping is continued until again a negative change in heat release results. Thus the system will continue to oscillate about the maximum point.

The perturbation method is particularly applicable to systems having relatively simple optimum functions, and its great advantage is that little if any information about system behavior need be known. The disadvantages of this method are that it is difficult to apply to systems having more than one degree of freedom and to systems with long time lags. A further disadvantage is that this method will not locate an absolute maximum as shown in Fig. 8–18 but may stop at the lower maximum unless special features are built into the system.

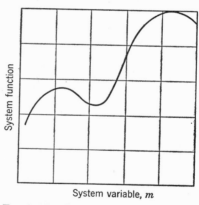

FIG. 8–18.   Optimum system function.

The *continuous computing method*[2] has been developed for use on either batch or continuous processing. The general method is illustrated in Fig. 8–19 for a batch process. Assume that the behavior of the process requires constant temperature, but, by properly manipulating process pressure, the batch may be taken from an initial point to the proper final point in least time.

[1] C. S. Draper, Y. T. Li, "Principles of Optimalizing Control Systems and an Application to an Internal Combustion Engine," *ASME* Publication, 1951.

[2] I. Lefkowitz, *Process Automation—Report I, 1954–1956*, Case Institute of Technology, Cleveland, Ohio.

The optimum behavior of the system is derived in general form. Euler–La Grange techniques and the calculus of variation are useful in this derivation. These equations are built into computer C_1. The final desired product quality c_f is set into servo S_1. The output of the servo is the pressure as a function of time. This function and the existing pressure P_1, temperature T_1, and coefficient K are fed into computer C_1 which then computes the predicted final value of product quality c_{fc}. This value is compared to the desired value, and the pressure is manipulated so as to "steer" the process to the proper final point, but always under the limitations imposed by minimum time.

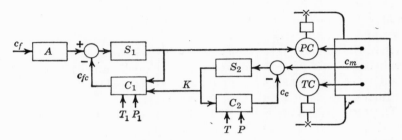

FIG. 8–19.   Computing-machine control.

There are two difficulties to be overcome with this method of control; first, the behavior of the system may not be known in general analytical form, and second, the system may have long time delays. In order to use the continuous computing method the system behavior must be known to some extent. The behavior can be tested experimentally and empirical relations found either by transient or sinusoidal response methods or by correlation methods.

Often it is sufficient to know only the general form of the behavior (as the general differential equations with unknown coefficients). In this case a self-checking method can be used. Referring to Fig. 8–19, system variable c_m is measured and is fed directly to servo S_2 which sets the unknown coefficient K of the reaction. Computer C_2 takes data on temperature, pressure, and coefficient and computes the value of the system variable that should exist, C_c. The computed value is fed back to the servo, and a new coefficient determined until computed and measured values match. The form of the system reaction must be assumed and fitted into computer C_2. The "self-checking" elements, S_2 and C_2, insure that the assumed equations fit process behavior in the region of actual operation. In a sense, the self-checking elements construct an analog of the process within the computer.

When long time delays (lags) are encountered, the continuous-computing method is also able to "predict" behavior during the period of the time delays and operate the process on schedule as though the time delay does not exist. This method works quite satisfactorily so long as the system behavior is not completely erratic.

PROBLEMS

8–1. The system block diagram can be redrawn with G_1G_2H in the forward loop when a feedback element H is present. What function is required at the input element?

8–2. A system (see Fig. 8–1) has the following elements:

$$A = 1 \qquad\qquad N = 1$$
$$G_1 = Ts + 1 \qquad H = 1/(T_2s + 1)$$
$$G_2 = (1/T_1s)^2$$

Calculate the values of derivative time T and measuring lag T_2 to give a transient response consisting of three equal time constants.

8–3. For the system of problem 8–2, calculate the values of (a) static error, (b) offset, (c) velocity error, (d) offset due to rate of change of load.

8–4. A furnace has a heating rate of 50 deg per min for full valve opening and a measuring element time constant of 60 sec. The measuring element time constant can be reduced to 20 sec. Would this change be worth while if proportional control is used?

8–5. A gas pressure vessel has pressure control by throttling the outlet which operates at acoustic velocity. The inlet is uncontrolled. Proportional control is used and the valve time constant is T_V. Prove that a linear valve provides constant loop gain at all loads and set points.

8–6. Considering cascade control as in Fig. 8–12 with

$$G_2 = K_c, \qquad G_3 = K, \qquad H_2 = \frac{1}{T_ms + 1}$$

show that the inner loop is a lead-lag network.

8–7. Considering cascade control as in Fig. 8–12 with

$$G_1 = K_1, \qquad G_2 = K_2, \qquad G_3 = \frac{K_3}{T_3s + 1}, \qquad H_2 = \frac{1}{T_2s + 1}$$

$$N_3 = K_3, \qquad G_4 = \frac{1}{T_4s + 1}, \qquad N_4 = 0$$

$$H_1 = \frac{1}{T_1s + 1}$$

show that the offset with load u_3 is greater when the inner loop is broken ($H_2 = 0$).

8–8. For the storage vessel in Fig. 8–16, sketch the outflow as a function of time with the inflow as shown if (a) integral control is used and (b) proportional control is used.

8-9.   For the storage vessel in Fig. 8-17 with a step inflow of U units, vessel area A, and proportional-integral control, calculate the offset in flow rate.

8-10.   For the surge vessel in Fig. 8-17 with integral control T_i, and no valve or measuring lags, calculate the integral time for critically damped performance.

8-11.   For the surge vessel in Fig. 8-17 with proportional control V_c, a valve lag T_V but no measuring lag, calculate the proportional sensitivity for critically damped performance.

Sinusoidal Analysis

The use of sinusoidal methods of analysis and test of dynamic systems has gained widespread popularity because of the simplicity in treating complex control systems. The transient analysis of the previous chapters is largely limited to second-order systems unless a specific system is considered. Sinusoidal analysis aids in qualitative considerations regarding stability of control systems and therefore is a convenient method for the engineer.

Sinusoidal Disturbance and Response

The response of a dynamic system may be found by imposing a disturbance at one point in the system, holding all variables but one constant, and noting the result upon the desired variable as indicated in Fig. 9–1. A sinusoidal change made in variable e while holding variable u constant results usually in the typical periodic curve at variable b.

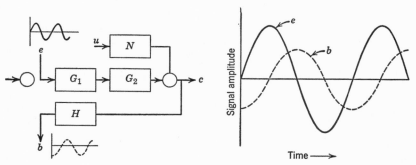

FIG. 9–1. Sinusoidal response.

269

It is not necessary that the response b of a system to a sinusoidal input be sinusoidal. If the performance of the system is described by a linear differential equation with constant coefficients then the response must be sinusoidal and, furthermore, the response will be of the same frequency as the disturbing function.

A nonsinusoidal response will result if the system is not linear; that is, if the system performance is not described by a linear differential equation with constant coefficients. In this case the principle of super-position does not apply, and there may be a great deal of difference if the order of elements in the system is changed. In addition, the response need not be of the same frequency as the input disturbance.

The steady-state sinusoidal response of linear systems is found by imposing a steady sinusoidal signal at variable m as indicated in Fig. 9–2,

$$m = \sin \omega t \tag{9–1}$$

The resulting periodic wave is recorded at variable c. The output c usually lags behind the input m and is usually smaller in amplitude.

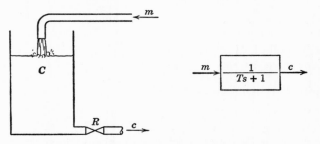

FIG. 9–2. A time-constant element.

It is important to note that the response or output is taken after the transient response has disappeared. For the purposes of illustration we will find the response of a time constant element to a sinusoidal input first, by classical differential equation solution, second, by complex solution, and third, by operational solution.

The *classical method* is to substitute the disturbing function:

$$T \frac{dc}{dt} + c = m = \sin \omega t \tag{9–2}$$

Next we construct the particular integral by the usual methods. Try the following solution:

$$c = A \sin \omega t + B \cos \omega t \tag{9–3}$$

where A and B are, as yet, unknown constants. Substituting in equation 9–2, there results

$$A\omega T \cos \omega t - B\omega T \sin \omega t + A \sin \omega t + B \cos \omega t = \sin \omega t \quad (9\text{--}4)$$

This must produce an identity so like-terms are compared to yield the following equations:

$$A\omega T + B = 0$$
$$A - B\omega T = 1 \tag{9--5}$$

Solving for unknowns A and B there results

$$A = \frac{1}{1 + \omega^2 T^2}$$
$$B = \frac{-\omega T}{1 + \omega^2 T^2} \tag{9--6}$$

The particular integral is, therefore,

$$c = \frac{1}{1 + \omega^2 T^2} (\sin \omega t - \omega T \cos \omega t) \tag{9--7}$$

Rewriting this result as a single function

$$c = \frac{1}{\sqrt{1 + \omega^2 T^2}} \sin (\omega t - \tan^{-1} \omega T) \tag{9--8}$$

Comparing the output c to the input m (equation 9–1), it is seen that the output sine wave has lesser amplitude. The ratio of the amplitudes is designated by the absolute value signs thus:

$$\left| \frac{c}{m} \right| = \frac{1}{\sqrt{1 + \omega^2 T^2}} \tag{9--9}$$

It is also seen that the output sine wave is delayed and the phase is indicated by the angle sign thus:

$$\underline{/\frac{c}{m}} = -\tan^{-1} \omega T \tag{9--10}$$

The magnitude and phase of the system can therefore be calculated.

The *complex solution* is found by writing the input of equation 9–1 in complex form:

$$m = \text{Im } e^{i\omega t} \tag{9--11}$$

where Im means "the imaginary part of." The function above is defined by Euler's relation,

$$e^{i\omega t} = \cos \omega t + i \sin \omega t \tag{9-12}$$

where $i = \sqrt{-1}$. The imaginary part of Euler's relation is the sine function.

Imposing the disturbing function on the time constant element,

$$T\frac{dc}{dt} + c = \text{Im } e^{i\omega t} \tag{9-13}$$

In order to find a particular integral for this equation, we rely upon a theorem of mathematics which, stated without proof, insures that for any linear differential equation with constant coefficients the real part of a solution is the solution to the real part of the disturbing function, and the imaginary part of a solution is the solution to the imaginary part of the disturbing function. Consequently the Im may be dropped,

$$T\frac{dc}{dt} + c = e^{i\omega t} \tag{9-14}$$

The solution to this equation is given by

$$c = B \, e^{i(\omega t + \Phi)} \tag{9-15}$$

Substituting in equation 9–14 gives

$$i\omega TB \, e^{i(\omega t + \Phi)} + B \, e^{i(\omega t + \Phi)} = e^{i\omega t} \tag{9-16}$$

Simplifying with the usual precaution that we do not divide by zero,

$$(i\omega T + 1)B \, e^{i\Phi} = 1 \tag{9-17}$$

Solving for B,

$$B = \frac{1}{(i\omega T + 1) \, e^{i\Phi}} \tag{9-18}$$

The solution is then, combining equations 9–15 and 18,

$$c = \left(\frac{1}{i\omega T + 1}\right) e^{i\omega t} \tag{9-19}$$

Next solve for the real part in the following series of manipulations:

$$c = \left(\frac{1}{i\omega T + 1}\right) (\cos \omega t + i \sin \omega t) \tag{9-20}$$

Clearing the denominator of i, we find

$$c = \left(\frac{1 - i\omega T}{1 + \omega^2 T^2}\right) (\cos \omega t + i \sin \omega i) \tag{9-21}$$

Breaking into real and imaginary parts, the solution is

$$c = \frac{\cos \omega t + \omega T \sin \omega t}{1 + \omega^2 T^2} + i \frac{\sin \omega t - \omega T \cos \omega t}{1 + \omega^2 T^2} \qquad (9\text{--}22)$$

It is recalled that we desire the imaginary part, therefore the desired solution is,

$$c = \frac{1}{1 + \omega^2 T^2} (\sin \omega t - \omega T \cos \omega t) \qquad (9\text{--}23)$$

or

$$c = \frac{1}{\sqrt{1 + \omega^2 T^2}} \sin (\omega t - \tan^{-1} \omega T) \qquad (9\text{--}24)$$

In this manner the response of systems described by linear differential equations with constant coefficients can be found by employing the procedures of the complex variable. This procedure is, however, lengthy and short-cut methods may be employed.

The *operational solution* for the response of the system may be found with operational mathematics. Stating the system equation in operational form for constant u,

$$\frac{c}{m} =' \frac{1}{Ts + 1} \qquad (9\text{--}25)$$

Replacing s by $i\omega$,

$$\frac{c}{m} = \frac{1}{i\omega T + 1} \qquad (9\text{--}26)$$

Compare this equation to equation 9–19. Clearing the denominator of equation 9–26 by multiplying both numerator and denominator by the complex conjugate $(1 - i\omega T)$

$$\frac{c}{m} = \frac{1 - i\omega T}{1 + \omega^2 T^2} \qquad (9\text{--}27)$$

Compare this equation to equation 9–21. The magnitude of this complex number is the square root of the sum of the squares of real and imaginary parts,

$$\left| \frac{c}{m} \right| = \sqrt{\frac{1}{1 + \omega^2 T^2}} \qquad (9\text{--}28)$$

The phase of a complex number is the arctangent of the imaginary part divided by the real part,

$$\angle \frac{c}{m} = \tan^{-1} (-\omega T) \qquad (9\text{--}29)$$

Compare these results to equations 9–9 and 9–10. Equations 9–28 and 9–29 show the amplitude and phase of sinusoidal response of the system to a sinusoidal disturbance of unit amplitude.

Example 9–1. Calculate the amplitude ratio and phase of the sinusoidal response of the system described by

$$T^2\ddot{c} + T\dot{c} = m$$

The system function is

$$\frac{c}{m} = \frac{1}{Ts(Ts + 1)}$$

Substituting $s = i\omega$,

$$\frac{c}{m} = \frac{1}{i\omega T(1 + i\omega T)}$$

Clearing,

$$\frac{c}{m} = \frac{-i(1 - i\omega T)}{\omega T(1 + \omega^2 T^2)} = \frac{-\omega T - i}{\omega T(1 + \omega^2 T^2)}$$

The amplitude is

$$\left|\frac{c}{m}\right| = \sqrt{\frac{1}{(1 + \omega^2 T^2)^2} + \frac{1}{\omega^2 T^2(1 + \omega^2 T^2)^2}}$$

or

$$\left|\frac{c}{m}\right| = \frac{1}{\omega T \sqrt{1 + \omega^2 T^2}}$$

The phase is

$$\angle \frac{c}{m} = \tan^{-1}\left(+\frac{1}{\omega T}\right)$$

The sign of the phase must be considered carefully because the inverse functions are multivalued.

Operations with Complex Numbers

Calculations of the steady-state sinusoidal behavior of systems is generally made by employing complex numbers. As described in the previous section, these calculations are considerably simplified if the rules of manipulation of complex numbers are used to the fullest.

A complex number can be written in rectangular form

$$\bar{z} = a + ib \tag{9–30}$$

and is sketched in Fig. 9–3 by marking off length a on the real number axis, and marking off the length b on the imaginary number axis. When a complex number is written in polar form, only the magnitude and the angle need be given.

The magnitude is calculated from Fig. 9–3:

$$|\bar{z}| = M = \sqrt{a^2 + b^2} \tag{9–31}$$

and the angle is given by

$$\underline{/\bar{z}} = \theta = \tan^{-1}\frac{b}{a} \tag{9-32}$$

Addition of complex numbers is made by adding real parts and imaginary parts respectively,

$$\bar{z}_1 + \bar{z}_2 = a + ib + c + id = (a + c) + i(b + d) \tag{9-33}$$

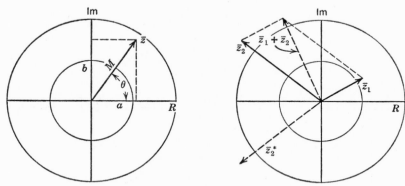

FIG. 9–3.   Vector complex numbers.

Addition is vector addition as shown in Fig. 9–3.   Multiplication of complex numbers is performed by algebraic manipulation:

$$(a + ib)(c + id) = (ac - bd) + i(bc + ad) \tag{9-34}$$

Multiplication is the most useful manipulation in dynamic systems studies.   By algebraic manipulation,

$$\bar{z}_1 \cdot \bar{z}_2 = (a + ib)(c + id) = (ac - bd) + i(bc + ad) \tag{9-35}$$

However, it may also be shown that

$$|\bar{z}_1 \cdot \bar{z}_2| = \sqrt{(a^2 + b^2)(c^2 + d^2)} \tag{9-36}$$

so that magnitudes are multiplied.   The phase is

$$\underline{/\bar{z}_1 \cdot \bar{z}_2} = \tan^{-1}\frac{b}{a} + \tan^{-1}\frac{d}{c} \tag{9-37}$$

so that the phases are added.   Therefore the product of two complex numbers is obtained when the magnitudes are multiplied and the phases are added.

The conjugate of a complex number is obtained by changing the sign of the imaginary part,

$$\bar{z} = a + ib, \quad \bar{z}^* = a - ib$$

as illustrated in Fig. 9–4. The conjugate is often used in clearing complex fractions because

$$\frac{\bar{z}_2}{\bar{z}_1} = \frac{\bar{z}_2 \cdot \bar{z}_1{}^*}{\bar{z}_1 \cdot \bar{z}_1{}^*} = \frac{\bar{z}_2 \cdot \bar{z}_1{}^*}{a^2 + b^2} \tag{9–38}$$

Multiplication of a complex number by i is equivalent to a rotation of the vector through 90 deg, because the real and imaginary parts are interchanged as indicated in Fig. 9–4.

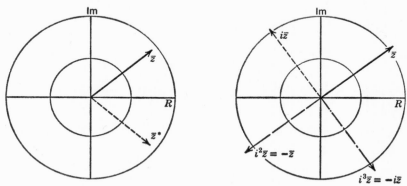

FIG. 9–4. Vector complex numbers.

Example 9–2. State the magnitude and phase of the following numbers:

Number	Magnitude	Phase Degrees	Radians
$4 - i3$	5.0	-36.8	-0.643
$+\sqrt{2} + \sqrt{-2}$	2.0	$+45.0$	$+0.785$
i	1.0	$+90.0$	$+1.57$
-10	10.0	180.0	3.14

Example 9–3. Multiply the number $3 + 4i$ by i and add its conjugate to $7 + 7i$.

$$(3 + 4i) \times i = -4 + 3i$$

$$(7 + 7i) + (-4 - 3i) = 3 + 4i$$

Plotting Sinusoidal or Frequency Response

The response of systems to a sinusoidal disturbance is, in general terms,

$$c = A \sin(\omega t + \Phi) \tag{9–39}$$

where A = amplitude and ϕ = phase. This function may be plotted as in Fig. 9–1, but the result is relatively uninformative. In order to visualize the response characteristics, it is much more descriptive to plot the amplitude and phase, since it is known that the function is sinusoidal. Furthermore the amplitude and phase are a function of frequency so that sinusoidal response may be considered in the frequency domain rather than the time domain.

Sinusoidal response may be plotted in three different ways: (1) The rectangular plot with amplitude ratio versus frequency, and phase versus frequency; (2) a polar plot with magnitude and phase shown in vector form with frequency as a parameter; (3) a phase margin plot with magnitude shown versus a function of phase with frequency as a parameter.

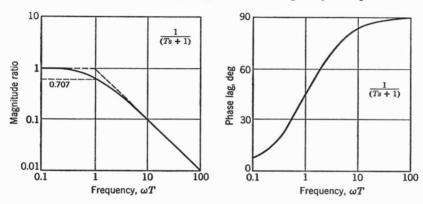

FIG. 9–5.   Magnitude- and phase-frequency plot.

The *rectangular* plots of magnitude vs frequency and phase (angle) versus frequency are by far the most common. This type of plot, often termed a Bode plot, is shown in Fig. 9–5 for the time-constant element:

$$G = \frac{1}{Ts + 1} \tag{9-40}$$

The magnitude ratio is

$$|G| = \frac{1}{\sqrt{1 + \omega^2 T^2}} \tag{9-41}$$

The magnitude ratio is plotted on log–log paper in order to gain the advantage of simple multiplication and in order to employ straight line asymptotes:

$$\text{Log } |G| = -\tfrac{1}{2} \log (1 + \omega^2 T^2) \tag{9-42}$$

At low frequencies, $\omega T \ll 1.0$, the magnitude ratio is a line horizontal at one since as $\omega T \to 0$,

$$\text{Log } |G| = 0 \quad \text{or} \quad |G| = 1.0 \tag{9-43}$$

At high frequencies, $\omega T \gg 1.0$, the magnitude ratio is a line from upper left to lower right with a slope of minus 45 deg because as $\omega T \to \infty$

$$\text{Log } |G| = -\log \omega T \quad \text{or} \quad |G| = \frac{1}{\omega T} \quad (9\text{-}44)$$

The phase is,

$$\underline{/G} = \tan^{-1} - \omega T \quad (9\text{-}45)$$

and is also plotted in Fig. 9–5. This graph is made on semi-log paper. Because of the arctangent function there is no linear approximation of the curve but, however, the function is symmetrical about the $\omega T = 1.0$ point.

The *polar* plot of real versus imaginary part is also used in stability studies. From the complex form of the system function,

$$G = \frac{1}{1 + i\omega T} = \frac{1 - i\omega T}{1 + \omega^2 T^2} \quad (9\text{-}46)$$

The real and imaginary parts may be calculated for different values of ωT and the locus of the end points of the vectors form a curve known as the system locus. The plot is as easily made by plotting magnitude and phase. The system locus is shown in Fig. 9–6 for a time-constant element. Note that the frequency ωT becomes a parameter marking out different points along the locus. The magnitude is the distance from a given point to the origin, and the phase is the angle taken counterclockwise from the positive real axis.

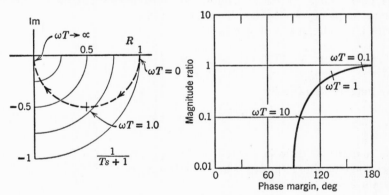

FIG. 9–6.   Polar plot.   FIG. 9–7.   Phase-margin plot.

The *magnitude* vs *phase* plot, Nichols chart or phase margin plot, is often used to define system performance. The magnitude is plotted vertically, and the phase is plotted horizontally, as shown in Fig. 9–7.

Instead of phase, the phase margin is plotted. The phase margin is 180 deg plus the phase. For a time-constant element, the plot for various frequencies begins at the right-hand center of the chart and proceeds downward and to the left. Frequently it is necessary to use extensions of the chart so as to provide for a gain greater than one and for negative phase margin.

Sinusoidal Response of Systems

The frequency response of systems containing a number of different dynamic elements may be calculated by suitably employing the magnitude and phase characteristics of each element separately. The calculation of magnitude is made from

$$|G_1 G_2| = |G_1| \times |G_2| \tag{9-47}$$

On the rectangular and phase margin plots, the magnitudes are set against a logarithmic scale, so that magnitudes are multiplied by adding vertical distances. The calculation of phase is made from

$$\underline{/G_1 G_2} = \underline{/G_1} + \underline{/G_2} \tag{9-48}$$

This amounts to the addition of phase. These points will be illustrated by examples at the end of this section.

Combinations of various dynamic elements may be investigated without conversion to frequency form. Any such combination can usually be described by the operational function

$$G(s) = K \frac{(a_m s^m + a_{m-1} s^{m-1} + \cdots + a_1 s + a_0)}{s^k (b_n s^n + b_{n-1} s^{n-1} + \cdots + b_1 s + b_0)} \tag{9-49}$$

where k, m, and n are positive integers. The total phase at sufficiently high frequencies approaches

$$\underline{/G}_{\omega \to \infty} = 90(m - n - k) \text{ deg} \tag{9-50}$$

Therefore the phase at infinite frequency corresponds to the net order of the denominator in units of $\pi/2$. The phase at low frequencies is given by

$$\underline{/G}_{\omega \to 0} = -90k \text{ deg} \tag{9-51}$$

or the phase at zero frequency corresponds to the net order of factorable s in the denominator.

The magnitude of system functions can similarly be investigated. The magnitude at infinite frequency is found from

$$\left|G\right|_{\omega \to \infty} = 0 \qquad \text{if } n + k > m$$

$$\left|G\right|_{\omega \to \infty} = \frac{a_m K}{b_n} \qquad \text{if } n + k = m \tag{9-52}$$

and

$$\left|G\right|_{\omega \to \infty} = \infty \qquad \text{if } n + k < m$$

The magnitude at zero frequency is found from

$$\left|G\right|_{\omega \to 0} = \infty \qquad \text{if } k > 0$$

$$\left|G\right|_{\omega \to 0} = \frac{a_0 K}{b_0} \qquad \text{if } k = 0 \tag{9-53}$$

$$\left|G\right|_{\omega \to 0} = 0 \qquad \text{if } k < 0$$

The rate of change of magnitude may also be determined since the rate corresponds to the units of phase lag. In terms of the slope when the system response is plotted on log-log coordinates,

$$\text{Slope of } \left|G\right|_{\omega \to \infty} = m - n - k \tag{9-54}$$

and

$$\text{Slope of } \left|G\right|_{\omega \to 0} = -k \tag{9-55}$$

By way of example suppose that it is desired to compute the frequency response of the system function:

$$G = \frac{1}{Ts(Ts + 1)} = \frac{1}{Ts} \times \frac{1}{Ts + 1} \tag{9-56}$$

The first element, $1/Ts$, is sketched on the magnitude-frequency plot of Fig. 9–8. The second element, $1/(Ts + 1)$, is next sketched. The magnitudes are multiplied (distances added by using dividers if necessary). The phases are added. From the form of the operational function 9–56 it is known that:

(a) Infinite frequency phase lag approaches 180 deg

$$(m - n - k = 0 - 1 - 1 = -2).$$

(b) Zero frequency phase lag approaches 90 deg $(k = -1)$.

(c) The magnitude at infinite frequency is zero.

(d) The magnitude at zero frequency is infinite.

(e) The infinite frequency rate of change of slope is −2.

(f) The zero frequency rate of change of slope is −1.

Asymptotic plots of magnitude versus frequency can be made because the value of the magnitude becomes asymptotic to straight-line functions at low and high frequency. Thus, asymptotic or straight-line plots may be made for many systems by combining the asymptotic plots for each individual component.

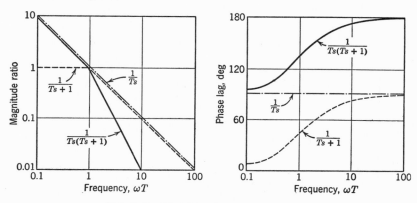

FIG. 9–8. Sketching frequency response.

Plotting of magnitude of functions is very often done in terms of decibels, abbreviated db. This unit of magnitude is defined as follows:

$$1.0 \text{ decibel} = 20 \log_{10} 1.1122 \qquad (9\text{–}57)$$

The magnitude of system functions are then calculated as follows

$$|G| \, db = 20 \log_{10} |G| \qquad (9\text{–}58)$$

The magnitude of functions may be plotted on semilog coordinates with frequency as abscissa. Phase margin diagrams are then plotted with rectangular paper.

Several significant magnitudes may be noted in the table:

Magnitude	Decibels
0.10	−20
0.50	−6.02
0.707	−3.01
1.0	0
2.0	6.02
10.0	20

Frequencies are often referred to as octaves (a factor of 2) or decades (a factor of 10). Slopes of magnitude functions are then given in the several terms

$$-1, \; -6 \; db/\text{octave}, \; -20 \; db/\text{decade}$$

and these are all equivalent.

Example 9–4. Sketch the phase margin of

$$\frac{1}{(s+1)^3}$$

The result is plotted in the figure shown below:

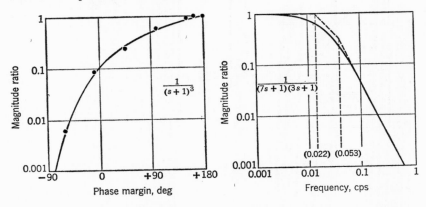

Example 9–5. Sketch the magnitude-frequency function for

$$\frac{1}{21s^2 + 10s + 1}$$

First, always factor the function if possible:

$$\frac{1}{(7s+1)(3s+1)}$$

The response may now be plotted as two time-constant elements. The result is plotted in the above figure.

Sinusoidal Response of Dynamic Elements

Frequency response of various process and controller elements may be calculated most easily by employing the notation of the complex variable. Frequency responses of various elements will be calculated and their magnitudes plotted in the magnitude-frequency phase, polar, and magnitude-phase diagrams.

The *capacitance element* has the operational function

$$G = \frac{1}{Ts} \rightarrow \frac{1}{i\omega T} = 0 + i\left(\frac{-1}{\omega T}\right) \tag{9-59}$$

The complex vector possesses an imaginary part only. The magnitude ratio, and phase are

$$|G| = \frac{1}{\omega T}, \qquad \underline{/G} = -90 \text{ deg} \tag{9-60}$$

These are plotted in Fig. 9–9. The magnitude versus frequency plot shows the magnitude to decrease inversely with frequency. Note that

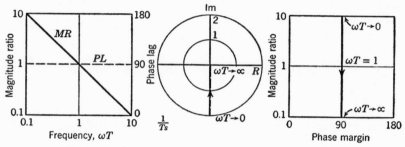

FIG. 9–9.   Frequency response of capacitance element.

the slope is -45 deg (1:1). The phase lag, PL is constant at 90 deg for any frequency. The polar plot is a vertical line along the negative end of the imaginary number axis. The magnitude-phase margin diagram is also a vertical line of infinite length.

The *time-constant element* has the operational function

$$G = \frac{1}{Ts + 1} \rightarrow \frac{1}{1 + i\omega T} = \frac{1 - i\omega T}{1 + \omega^2 T^2} \tag{9-61}$$

The magnitude ratio and phase are,

$$|G| = \frac{1}{\sqrt{1 + \omega^2 T^2}}, \qquad \underline{/G} = -\tan^{-1} \omega T \tag{9-62}$$

These are plotted in Fig. 9–10. The magnitude versus frequency relation approximates 1.0 at low frequencies and falls off at high frequencies. Again the slope is -45 deg (1:1) at high frequency. The phase lag is small at low frequencies and approaches 90 deg for high frequencies. At the frequency $\omega T = 1$,

$$|G| = 0.707, \qquad \underline{/G} = -45 \text{ deg}$$

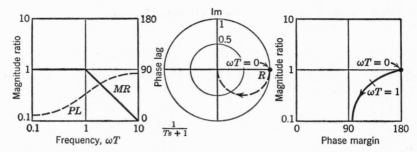

FIG. 9–10. Frequency response of time-constant element.

The polar plot is a semicircle as shown. The phase margin plot begins on the right and passes downward.

The *oscillatory element* has the operational equation

$$G = \frac{1}{T^2 s^2 + 2\zeta T s + 1} \rightarrow \frac{1}{(1 - \omega^2 T^2) + i(2\zeta\omega T)} \qquad (9\text{–}63)$$

The magnitude ratio and phase are

$$|G| = \frac{1}{\sqrt{(1 - \omega^2 T^2)^2 + (2\zeta\omega T)^2}}, \qquad \underline{/G} = -\tan^{-1}\left(\frac{2\zeta\omega T}{1 - \omega^2 T^2}\right)$$

$$(9\text{–}64)$$

These are plotted in Fig. 9–11 for several values of damping ratio ζ. The magnitude is greater than one for moderate frequencies and low

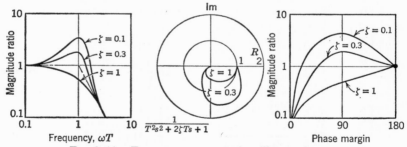

FIG. 9–11. Frequency response of oscillatory element.

damping. The phase lag is always small at low frequencies and approaches 180 deg at high frequencies. The damping ratio affects the phase slightly at frequencies just above and below resonance. The polar plot is a much distorted semicircle and is tangent from below to the negative real axis at high frequencies, because the phase lag is 180 deg in that region. The phase margin plot is tangent to the zero margin line at high frequencies. At the frequency $\omega T = 1$,

$$|G| = \frac{1}{2\zeta}, \qquad \underline{/G} = -90 \text{ deg}$$

Proportional-integral control has the operational equation

$$G = K_c\left(1 + \frac{1}{Ts}\right) \rightarrow K_c\frac{(1 + i\omega T)}{i\omega T} = K_c\frac{(-\omega T + i)}{\omega T} \qquad (9\text{-}65)$$

The magnitude ratio and phase are

$$|G| = K_c\sqrt{1 + \frac{1}{\omega^2 T^2}}, \qquad \underline{/G} = -\tan^{-1}\frac{1}{\omega T} \qquad (9\text{-}66)$$

These are plotted in Fig. 9–12 for a value of proportional sensitivity of one. The magnitude is greater than one at low frequencies, and the

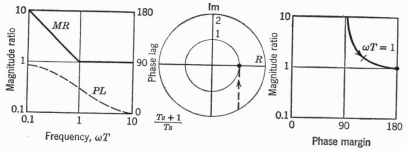

FIG. 9–12. Frequency response of proportional-integral controller.

characteristic of infinite magnitude at zero frequency is vital to the integral action of the controller. A change of value of proportional sensitivity K_c would simply move the plot bodily up and down on the left-hand and right-hand graphs. A change of proportional sensitivity expands the scale radially in the polar plot. Thus the change of proportional sensitivity does not alter the phase.

Proportional-derivative control has the operational equation:

$$G = K_c(1 + Ts) \rightarrow K_c(1 + i\omega T) \qquad (9\text{-}67)$$

The magnitude ratio and phase are

$$|G| = \sqrt{1 + \omega^2 T^2}, \qquad \underline{/G} = \tan^{-1}\omega T \qquad (9\text{-}68)$$

These are plotted in Fig. 9–13 for a value of proportional sensitivity of one. The magnitude is greater than one at high frequencies, and the characteristic of infinite gain at infinite frequencies is important in the derivative action. A change in proportional sensitivity moves the

Automatic Process Control

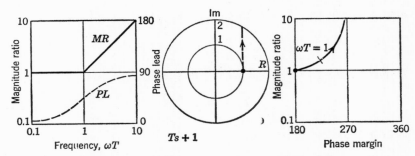

FIG. 9–13. Frequency response of proportional-derivative controller.

magnitude-phase and phase margin plots vertically. If we compare these results to those of Fig. 9–12 for proportional-integral control, the "opposite" characteristics of these two control actions are readily seen.

Proportional-integral-derivative control has the operational equation:

$$G = K_c \left(1 + \frac{1}{T_i s}\right)(1 + T_d s) \rightarrow K_c \left(1 + \frac{1}{i\omega T_i}\right)(1 + i\omega T_d) \quad (9\text{–}69)$$

The magnitude ratio and phase are

$$|G| = \frac{\sqrt{(1 + \omega^2 T_i^2)(1 + \omega^2 T_d^2)}}{\omega T_i} \quad (9\text{–}70)$$

$$\underline{/G} = -\frac{\pi}{2} + \tan^{-1} \omega T_i + \tan^{-1} \omega T_d \quad (9\text{–}71)$$

These are plotted in Fig. 9–14 for a proportional sensitivity of one. The magnitude is always greater than one and the phase passes from a lag to a lead at high frequency. The system has infinite gain at both zero and infinite frequencies. A change in proportional sensitivity moves the magnitude-phase curve and phase margin curve vertically.

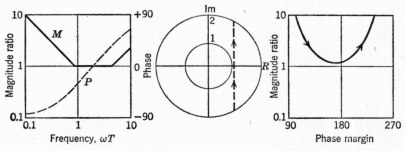

FIG. 9–14. Frequency response of proportional-integral-derivative control with $5T_d = T_i$.

Example 9–6. Sketch the polar plot for a system with the operational function Ts.

The vector complex number is calculated

$$G = Ts \rightarrow i\omega T$$

The amplitude and phase are

$$|G| = \omega T, \qquad \underline{/G} = +90 \text{ deg}$$

The polar plot is a vertical line out along the positive end of the imaginary axis.

Example 9–7. A thermocouple has a time constant of 5 sec. At what frequency will the element attenuate 50 per cent?

From equation 9–62,

$$f = \frac{1}{2\pi T} \sqrt{\frac{1}{(0.5)^2} - 1} = \underline{0.055 \text{ cps}}$$

Example 9–8. The test of a pressure gage shows a frequency response as shown in the diagram. What are the characteristics of the system?

The test points are clearly asymptotic to a line horizontal at one. At high frequencies the data lies on a line at negative 45 deg. Drawing these lines it is seen that the intersection is at 0.08 cps. As a check, the amplitude at this frequency is about 0.7 (should be 0.707). All factors point to a first-order system, and if there are other time constants they must be very small and can be ignored. The intersection point is always at $\omega T = 1$, so

$$T = \frac{1}{\omega} = \frac{1}{2\pi f} = \frac{100}{16\pi} = \underline{2.0 \text{ sec}}$$

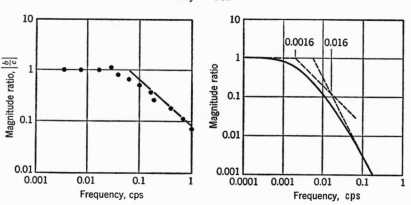

Example 9–9. A thermometer and thermal well have two time constants where $T_1 = 100$ sec, $T_2 = 10$ sec. Plot the amplitude-frequency response.

The plot of magnitude may be determined by using the approximate (asymptotic) method: making the graphs on log–log paper, the response due to each time constant may be added separately. The two responses are then combined additively to obtain the asymptotic response. The intersection frequencies are found from

$$f_1 = \frac{1}{2\pi T_1} = 0.0016 \text{ cps}$$

$$f_2 = \frac{1}{2\pi T_2} = 0.016 \text{ cps}$$

Example 9–10. A two-position controller maintains a temperature of a furnace oscillatory over 80 deg total amplitude with a period of one minute. A thermocouple and well having a first-order time constant of 96 sec is used to measure the same temperature. What amplitude would it indicate?

Referring to Fig. 9–10,

$$\omega T = \frac{2\pi}{60} \times 96 = 10$$

The amplitude is

$$\left| \frac{b}{c} \right| = \frac{1}{10} \times 80 = 8 \text{ deg}$$

Dead Time, Distributed-Parameter, and Exothermic Elements

The operational equation for dead time may be written

$$G = e^{-Ls} \tag{9–72}$$

where L is the dead time and e is the base of natural logarithms. This relation was derived in Chapter 2, by classical methods.

The frequency response of a dead-time element is calculated in the usual way. Replacing s by $i\omega$,

$$G = e^{-Ls} \rightarrow e^{-i\omega L} = \cos \omega L - i \sin \omega L \tag{9–73}$$

The magnitude ratio and phase are

$$|G| = 1.0, \qquad \underline{/G} = -\omega L \text{ (radians)} \tag{9–74}$$

These are plotted in Fig. 9–15. Dead time has the characteristic of a pure phase shift since the magnitude is always one. It is easily seen

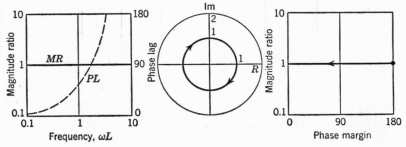

Fig. 9–15. Dead-time elements.

from the graphs that no other dynamic element builds up phase lag so much as dead time. In combination with other dynamic elements the phase lag of dead time is simply added to obtain the total phase lag.

A useful approximation for dead time L is the function from the Padé list,[1]

$$G = \frac{2 - Ls}{2 + Ls} \qquad (9\text{--}75)$$

The magnitude of this function is everywhere 1.0 and the phase lag corresponds very closely to dead time up to frequencies given by $\omega L = 0.5$. In addition, this function may be easier to incorporate into complex system analysis.

Thermal process control may involve elements having distributed parameters; that is, elements with distributed thermal resistance and distributed thermal capacitance. Pneumatic systems having long transmission lines may also be similar. As a typical example, consider the heat transfer through a solid material such as a thick wall or tube. The temperature distribution is governed by the equation,

$$\frac{\partial^2 c}{\partial x^2} = -\alpha^2 \frac{\partial c}{\partial t} \qquad (9\text{--}76)$$

where c = temperature at point x, time t, deg
  x = distance into material, ft
  α^2 = inverse of thermal diffusivity, sec/ft^2
  t = time, sec

Employing operational notation, a total differential equation results:

$$\frac{d^2 c}{dx^2} + (\alpha^2 s)c = 0 \qquad (9\text{--}77)$$

A solution to this equation is

$$c = Ae^{ax} \qquad (9\text{--}78)$$

Substituting in equation 9–77 and solving for a,

$$a = \pm \sqrt{-\alpha^2 s} \qquad (9\text{--}79)$$

The solution is therefore, with two independent constants,

$$c = Ae^{-ax} + Be^{+ax} \qquad (9\text{--}80)$$

[1] J. G. Truxal, *Automatic Feedback Control System Synthesis*, McGraw-Hill Book Company, Inc., New York, 1955, p. 550.

From boundary conditions,

$$c = c_1, \qquad x = 0$$

$$\frac{\partial c}{\partial x} = 0, \qquad x = L$$

The second condition results because it is assumed that no heat loss occurs at the inside (insulated on one face). The unknown coefficients A and B may be evaluated from the boundary conditions, and the resulting solution is

$$c = c_1 \left(\frac{e^{2aL}e^{-ax} + e^{+ax}}{e^{2aL} + 1} \right) \tag{9-81}$$

The temperature at the inside face can be calculated from

$$c_2 = c_1 \left(\frac{2}{e^{aL} + e^{-aL}} \right) \tag{9-82}$$

The system function is therefore

$$\frac{c_2}{c_1} = \frac{2}{e^{\sqrt{-\alpha^2 L^2 s}} + e^{-\sqrt{-\alpha^2 L^2 s}}} \tag{9-83}$$

or in hyperbolic form

$$\frac{c_2}{c_1} = \frac{1}{\cosh \sqrt{-\alpha^2 L^2 s}} \tag{9-84}$$

This is the system function for one particular distributed parameter system. Other boundary conditions yield a similar function, usually one multiplied by a complicated ratio of hyperbolic functions.

In order to expand the system function it is necessary to write the complex number a in a different form, employing the square root of i.

$$\sqrt{-\alpha^2 L^2 s} \rightarrow \sqrt{-\alpha^2 L^2 i\omega} = \sqrt{\alpha^2 L^2 \omega}\sqrt{-i} = \sqrt{\alpha^2 L^2 \omega} \left(\frac{1-i}{\sqrt{2}} \right) \tag{9-85}$$

The operational function is therefore

$$\frac{c_2}{c_1} = \frac{1}{\cosh \beta(1 - i)} \tag{9-86}$$

where $2\beta^2 = \alpha^2 L^2 \omega$. This function may be expanded and the magnitude and phase derived. The magnitude is

$$\left| \frac{c_2}{c_1} \right| = \frac{1}{(\cosh^2 \beta \cos^2 \beta + \sinh^2 \beta \sin^2 \beta)^{1/2}} \tag{9-87}$$

The phase may be calculated from

$$\angle \frac{c_2}{c_1} = \tan^{-1}\left(-\tanh \beta \tan \beta\right) \tag{9-88}$$

These are plotted in Fig. 9-16 where $\omega T = 2\beta^2$. The magnitude drops off exponentially with the square root of frequency, and the phase lag

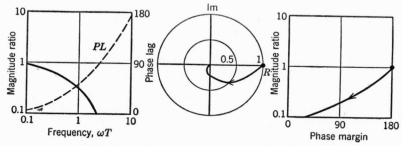

FIG. 9-16.   Distributed parameter elements.

builds up indefinitely with the square root of frequency. Notice the great similarity of the phase lag for dead time and the phase lag for distributed systems. This leads to the Ziegler–Nichols approximation for distributed systems.

$$G = \frac{e^{-L_0 s}}{T_0 s + 1} \tag{9-89}$$

In this approximation a dead time and a time-constant element are used to simulate the effect of distributed parameters. In most control problems this approximation is quite good.

Exothermic reactions are often encountered in process control. Such systems have a heat-generating source, generally chemical in nature, in which the amount of heat liberated is directly proportional to the temperature. This situation is described by

$$C \frac{dc}{dt} = -m + q \tag{9-90}$$

where C = capacitance of system
c = temperature
m = heat extracted by cooling
q = exothermic heat = $K_e c$

K_e is an exothermic coefficient. Combining these equations to eliminate the variable q, the system function results.

$$c = \frac{1}{K_e} \left(\frac{1}{-Ts + 1} \right) m \tag{9–91}$$

where $T = C/K_e$ is the time constant. The transient solution to this equation is, of course, an exponential with positive exponent. Thus, the system temperature grows without bound on a sudden increase in heat input.

The amplitude and phase of this function are easily computed:

$$|G| = \frac{K_e^{-1}}{\sqrt{1 + \omega^2 T^2}} \tag{9–92}$$

$$\underline{/G} = \tan^{-1} \omega T$$

The relations are plotted in Fig. 9–17. It is important to note that the phase begins at zero and increases positively. It must be remembered

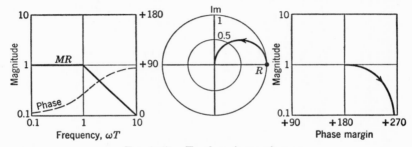

FIG. 9–17. Exothermic reactions.

that in exothermic systems it is generally necessary to add and extract heat at different times. Consequently proper attention must be paid to the sign of the function for heat addition $1/(Ts - 1)$ and for heat extraction $1/(1 - Ts)$. The magnitude ratios are the same but the phase differs by 180 degrees.

Example 9–11. A pneumatic transmission line probably has a dead time proportional to the length of line due to the time for transmission of pressure waves along the tube. Assuming a wave velocity of 1100 ft per sec, calculate the phase lag per unit length of line.

$$PL = \omega L \cong \frac{2\pi f l}{1100} \times \frac{360}{2\pi}$$

where l = length of line in feet. Therefore

$$PL \cong \frac{f}{3} l$$

The result is easy to remember: one-third deg per ft per cps.

Example 9–12. Calculate the characteristic time $\alpha^2 L^2$ for copper, aluminum, lead, steel, and glass walls of 0.1-in. thickness.

	Diffusivity ft²/hr	$\alpha^2 L^2$ sec
Copper	4.35	0.057
Aluminum	3.66	0.068
Lead	0.92	0.27
Steel	0.57	0.44
Glass	0.013	22

Limiting, Dead-Zone, and Hysteresis Elements

Many functions involved in automatic control are not describable by elementary techniques, and they must be described by graphical or other methods. This section is devoted to a description of three of these elements.

The output of a nonlinear element will not necessarily be sinusoidal even if the input is a pure sinusoid, but it will generally contain fundamental and harmonic waves. The frequency of the fundamental of the output will often be the same as the frequency of the input. In this case a *describing* function can be used and the element may be treated as a linear element.

The describing function is a transfer function for an element having slight nonlinearity and is expressed in terms of the amplitude and phase of the fundamental of the output signal related to the amplitude and phase of the input signal. The describing function can be obtained analytically or experimentally.

Describing functions are generally useful in automatic control analysis if the neglect of the harmonic in the output signal does not cause difficulties. They may be used with adequate results when the element in question is followed by one or more elements having appreciable attenuation.

Limiting (sometimes called saturation) occurs wherever one of the variables attains and cannot exceed maximum or minimum values. For example, a control valve cannot do more than go wide open or tight closed. This situation can be described by the frequency response of the element. Referring to Fig. 9–18, the output of the element y is plotted against input x providing a statical calibration. The limits are given at values $-X_l, +X_l$. The response of the system to a sinusoidal input is also shown in Fig. 9–18. The output y follows input x to the point at which limiting occurs. This point is given by

$$\theta_l = \sin^{-1} \frac{X_l}{X_a}, \qquad \text{if} \quad X_a \geq X_l \tag{9–93}$$

where θ_l = angle at which limiting occurs, radians

X_a = amplitude of input signal x

X_l = amplitude at which limiting occurs

The frequency response of such an element is defined somewhat differently; the magnitude ratio is the ratio of the magnitude of the fundamental of the output to the magnitude of the sinusoidal input, and the

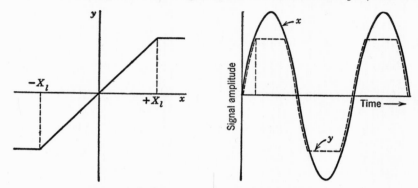

FIG. 9–18. Sinusoidal response during limiting.

phase is the angle of the fundamental of the output referred to the angle of the input.   It is not very difficult to write the Fourier series for the output y and to compute the amplitude and phase of the fundamental of this wave.[1] The phase is zero; that is, there is no phase lag between input and output.   The magnitude ratio is

$$|G| = \frac{1}{\pi} (2\theta_l + \sin 2\theta_l) \qquad (9\text{--}94)$$

The magnitude ratio is not a function of frequency but depends upon the amplitude of the input signal.   Essentially, the gain of the element decreases as the amplitude increases.   Limiting in automatic control therefore has the following effects:

1. If loop sensitivity is adjusted properly for large amplitude signals, the loop sensitivity increases when the amplitude signal decreases and insufficient stability may result.

2. If loop sensitivity is adjusted properly for small amplitude signals, the loop sensitivity decreases when the amplitude of signal increases and excessive stability may result.

[1] J. G. Truxal, *Automatic Feedback Control System Synthesis*, McGraw-Hill Book Company, New York, 1955, p. 568.

Dead zone, illustrated in Fig. 9–19, occurs in systems whenever there is a range of values of input signal to which the system does not respond. An example of "pure" dead zone is difficult to cite; however, some automatic controllers intentionally include a dead zone through mechanical or electronic means. In a certain sense, dead zone is the opposite of limiting as may be seen in Fig. 9–19 where dead zone cuts off the

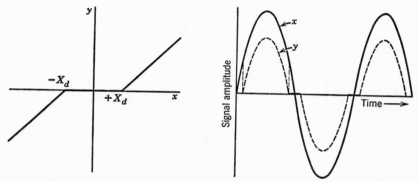

FIG. 9–19.   Sinusoidal response and dead zone.

"bottom" of the sinusoidal signal. Limiting cuts off the top of the signal. In dead-zone action, the output signal begins at an angle given by

$$\theta_d = \sin^{-1} \frac{X_d}{X_a}, \quad \text{if } X_a \geqq X_d \tag{9–95}$$

where θ_d = angle at which output signal begins,
$\quad X_a$ = amplitude of input signal x,
$\quad X_d$ = amplitude at which dead zone begins.

As before, the magnitude and phase may be calculated from the Fourier series. The phase is zero. The magnitude ratio is

$$|G| = \frac{1}{\pi} (\pi - 2\theta_d - \sin 2\theta_d) \tag{9–96}$$

The magnitude ratio is not a function of frequency but depends upon the amplitude of input signal. Dead zone in automatic control therefore has the following effects:

1. If loop sensitivity is adjusted properly for large amplitude signals, the loop sensitivity decreases when the amplitude of signal decreases, and excessive stability may result.

2. If loop sensitivity is adjusted properly for small amplitude signals, the loop sensitivity increases when the amplitude of signal increases and insufficient stability may result.

Hysteresis occurs most often because of dry (ideal) friction in mechanical systems, backlash and subsequent friction in gearing, electromagnetic effects, and so on. The action is described in Fig. 9–20. The

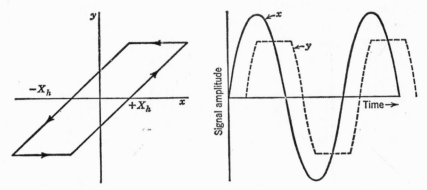

FIG. 9–20. Sinusoidal response with hysteresis.

static calibration produces the characteristic hysteresis loop. The output signal begins at an angle given by

$$\theta_h = \sin^{-1}\left(\frac{X_a - 2X_h}{X_a}\right) \tag{9–97}$$

where θ_h = angle at which hysteresis reversal occurs
X_a = amplitude of input signal x
X_h = amplitude of hysteresis reversal

The output signal continues until reversal of the velocity of input occurs. The output signal then holds its last value while crossing the hysteresis loop.   The magnitude ratio is

$$|G| = \frac{1}{2\pi} \sqrt{(1 + \cos 2\theta_h)^2 + (\pi + 2\theta_h + \sin 2\theta_h)^2} \tag{9–98}$$

The phase lag is

$$\underline{/G} = \tan^{-1} - \left(\frac{1 + \cos 2\theta_h}{\pi + 2\theta_h + \sin 2\theta_h}\right) \tag{9–99}$$

Thus hysteresis not only causes variable gain but also a phase lag. The gain decreases with smaller input signals. The phase lag increases for smaller signals. In automatic control these effects tend to cancel each other on changing amplitude of signal, but the overall effect of hysteresis is always to cause less effective control action.

Example 9–13.   A control valve has 2 per cent dead zone. The amplitude of signal generally occurring is 5 per cent. Estimate the gain.

From equation 9–95,

$$\theta_d = \sin^{-1} \tfrac{2}{5} = \underline{0.41 \text{ radian}}$$

The magnitude is

$$|G| = 1 - \frac{0.82}{\pi} - \frac{\sin 0.82}{\pi} = \underline{0.51}$$

Testing Sinusoidal Response

Obtaining a frequency response requires special equipment and careful testing. However, it is generally true that much information can be obtained from even a few very rough test values. The input sinusoidal signal should be reasonably free from harmonics (distortion), but it is not at all necessary that the input signal be purely sinusoidal. In fact, a rectangular or triangular wave can also be employed.

The sinusoidal signal may have to have mechanical, pneumatic, or electrical form. Thus a sine-wave generator is required. The frequency (cycles per second) of the signal may be very approximately as follows:

Thermal processes	0.001 to 1.0 cps
Fluid processes	0.005 to 10 cps
Process control mechanisms	0.01 to 100 cps
Fast control mechanisms	0.1 to 1000 cps

It is probable that a signal generator cannot cover the entire range of frequencies (10^6) required. Below about 0.01 cps, a mechanical generator is almost always employed. This consists of a variable speed drive, a sine–cosine mechanism (cam–push rod usually), and a suitable pneumatic or electrical amplifier if necessary. The variable speed drive may be mechanical or electrical. Above 0.01 cps a suitable electric generator such as an audio oscillator together with a suitable pneumatic amplifier is satisfactory.

The recording of input and output signals is best done on a two-pen electrical recording mechanism. For frequencies up to about 0.1 cps ordinary process-type fluid or electric potentiometric recorders may be used. Up to 100 cps frequency the recording oscillograph provides better accuracy. Above 100 cps frequency the oscilloscope or photoelectric oscillograph must be used. It is sometimes convenient to actuate the recording mechanism paper drive from the sine-wave generator in order that all periods of cycling occupy the same physical length on the chart. This makes calculation of phase lag much easier.

There are two methods of determining phase lag. First, simply record input and output and scale the difference. Second, provide a variable phasing of the recording of the input so that shifting phase of the input to match the input and output records enables reading phase lag directly.

In actually performing a frequency response test, it is always best to explore the response at a fixed frequency giving about 20 to 50 per cent attenuation but with several amplitudes of input signal. This is to insure that limiting, dead zone, or hysteresis will be recognized. It is best to record and plot test data as it is taken in order to save time by not taking unnecessary frequencies.

All physical systems have some nonlinearities. Therefore it is best to consider carefully the amplitude of input signal. A large signal will undoubtedly saturate a part of the equipment whereas a small signal may fall below frictional or dead-zone thresholds. It may be necessary to try several amplitude signals in order to select a representative result.

PROBLEMS

9–1. Calculate and plot the amplitude and phase of the following functions

    (a) $\dfrac{1}{Ts}$ (b) $(Ts+1)^2$ (c) $Ts-1$

    (d) $\dfrac{Ts}{Ts+1}$ (e) $\dfrac{Ts+1}{2Ts+1}$ (f) $\dfrac{1}{(Ts+1)(2Ts+1)}$

9–2. Sketch the phase of proportional-derivative-integral control for $Td = 0.1\,T_i$, $T_d = T_i$, and $T_d = 10\,T_i$. What effect does varying this ratio have in control behavior?

9–3. Plot $1/(Ts+1)^3$ in polar form.

9–4. Calculate the amplitude and phase of $1/(T^2s^2+1)$. What kind of system does this represent?

9–5. By plotting, compare the phase of e^{-Ls} and $(2-Ls)/(2+Ls)$.

9–6. A system with exothermic reaction and heat losses is described by the following equations:

$$Ccs = m + q - q_L$$

$$q = K_e c$$

$$q_L = \frac{1}{R}c$$

Describe the type of system for all values of RK_e.

9–7. A thermometer has an apparent time constant of 5 sec. The bulb has a $\frac{1}{16}$-in. thick bronze wall. Does the characteristic time of the wall seriously affect the response?

9–8. A system limits (saturates) at signal of 10 volts amplitude. A signal of 30 volts amplitude is passed to the system. Calculate the attenuation.

9–9. Because the angle and the sine function are nearly the same up to 45 deg, show that the magnitude with limiting is given by $|G| = \dfrac{4}{\pi}\dfrac{X_a}{X_i}$.

chapter 10

Stability Analysis

Stability of operation of the process and automatic control system is achieved when the deviation is maintained within predetermined limits. Stability is necessary because without it the system may execute wild oscillation leading to wear, failure, or destruction of parts of the system.

Good stability is difficult to define. Recovery with minimum area applies to the control of processes in which time of departure from the set point is of as great importance as magnitude of deviation. In order to stabilize the controlled variable in the shortest time, optimum stability must be obtained. In this way the smallest quantity of product is the least improperly processed.

Minimum deviation is a requirement for recovery of many controlled systems where ill effects are caused in the process equipment or in the product by momentarily excessive deviation. Here the magnitude of deviation is of greater importance than time of deviation. The limits of control are therefore generally narrow, and it is desired to remain as close as possible to the set point.

Minimum oscillation is sometimes required where periodic disturbances in the processing unit and plant must be avoided. If the output of one process is carried to a second process, as often occurs in continuous chemical processing, any cycling of the controlled variable becomes a cycling load change to the second process. Greater stability of control may be necessary in order to keep cycling at a minimum.

All the criteria for judging stability of control are derived from the purpose and requirement for which automatic control is used. *The quality of control is, therefore, always relative in the sense that it must necessarily depend upon factors of application.* A satisfactory recovery and stability in one controlled system may be entirely unsatisfactory in another.

The study of stability is greatly enhanced by the use of the La Place transform. The reader is referred to a number of texts on the subject and to a brief review in the appendix.

The Transfer Function

The analysis of a dynamic system provides a set of differential equations describing the performance of the system. For a simple system described by a single differential equation, for example,

$$A \frac{d^2y}{dt^2} + B \frac{dy}{dt} + Cy = x \tag{10-1}$$

the La Place transform of the equation is

$$A s^2 \mathcal{L}y - A s y_0 - A \dot{y}_0 + B s \mathcal{L}y - B y_0 + C \mathcal{L}y = \mathcal{L}x \tag{10-2}$$

where y_0 = value of y at $t \to 0$

$\dot{y}_0$ = value of dy/dt at $t \to 0$

This relation may be solved symbolically in order to find the response of the system,

$$\mathcal{L}y = \frac{1}{As^2 + Bs + C} \mathcal{L}x + \frac{1}{As^2 + Bs + C} (A y_0 s + A \dot{y}_0 + B y_0) \tag{10-3}$$

The response of the system, or rather the transform of system response, is characterized by the system function,

$$\frac{1}{As^2 + Bs + C}$$

regardless of any initial conditions $(y_0, \dot{y}_0)$. Suppose that the initial conditions are zero $(y_0 = 0, \dot{y}_0 = 0)$, and that the system is disturbed starting from "rest" condition:

$$\mathcal{L}y = \frac{1}{As^2 + Bs + C} \mathcal{L}x \tag{10-4}$$

The response of the system is therefore given by the product of system function and disturbing function.

The transfer function is therefore defined as the ratio of the La Place transform of the responding variable divided by the La Place transform of the disturbance variable, the transforms taken with zero initial conditions. From equation 10-4, the transfer function is

$$G(s) = \frac{\mathcal{L}y}{\mathcal{L}x} = \frac{1}{As^2 + Bs + C} \tag{10-5}$$

Thus there is no essential difference between the system operational function of Chapters 1 through 9 and the transfer function. An alternate definition for the transfer function is the La Place transform of the response of a system to a unit impulse disturbance starting with zero initial conditions. From equation 10–4, with a unit impulse disturbance,

$$\mathscr{L}x = 1 \tag{10–6}$$

the transfer function becomes

$$G(s) = \mathscr{L}(y) = \frac{1}{As^2 + Bs + C} \tag{10–7}$$

The transfer function concept is extremely important in dynamic systems analysis. In spite of seeming limitations imposed by initial conditions it is nevertheless true that *the transfer functions for a system completely define the performance of the system.* In any case, it is always possible to define the response and disturbance variables so that initial conditions are zero.

One serious limitation of the use of transfer functions is that for some kinds of systems the La Place transforms of the equations do not exist because the differential equations contain essential nonlinearities. However, even in such cases approximations may be made, and the transfer function ideas may be employed. Furthermore, a transfer function may often be determined experimentally even when they are difficult to deduce by analysis.

Fluid and thermal process systems exhibit many different dynamic characteristics, but all such systems may be described by employing combinations of the following transfer functions:

$$\frac{1}{Ts} \qquad \text{Capacitance element} \tag{10–8}$$

$$\frac{1}{Ts + 1} \qquad \text{Time-constant element} \tag{10–9}$$

$$\frac{1}{T^2s^2 + 2\zeta Ts + 1} \qquad \text{Oscillatory element,} \quad \zeta \gtrless 1.0 \tag{10–10}$$

$$\frac{1}{e^{Ls}} \qquad \text{Dead-time element} \tag{10–11}$$

The time-constant element (equation 10–9) and the oscillatory element (equation 10–10) are not necessarily fundamental but may be derived through closed-loop action as shown in Fig. 10–1.

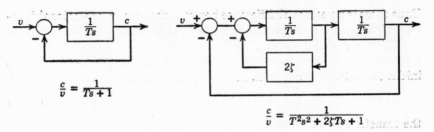

$$\frac{c}{v} = \frac{1}{Ts+1}$$

$$\frac{c}{v} = \frac{1}{T^2s^2 + 2\zeta Ts + 1}$$

FIG. 10–1.   Generation circuits for time-constant and oscillatory elements.

The transfer function for dead time (equation 10–11) may be derived by use of La Place transform.   Consider a dynamic action such that the disturbance (input) is

$$x = f(t) \tag{10–12}$$

The transform is

$$\mathcal{L}x = \mathcal{L}f(t) \tag{10–13}$$

The only action by the element is to delay the function in time without otherwise altering it.   Thus the response (output) can be given by

$$y = f(t - L) \tag{10–14}$$

The transform may be written

$$\mathcal{L}y = \int_0^\infty f(t - L)e^{-st}\, dt \tag{10–15}$$

Changing the variable under the integral sign, replace $(t - L)$ by t

$$\mathcal{L}y = \int_0^\infty f(t)e^{-s(t+L)}\, d(t + L) \tag{10–16}$$

or

$$\mathcal{L}y = e^{-Ls}\int_0^\infty f(t)e^{-st}\, dt \tag{10–17}$$

By definition of the La Place transform,

$$\mathcal{L}y = e^{-Ls}\mathcal{L}x \tag{10–18}$$

The transfer function for dead-time action is, therefore,

$$G(s) = e^{-Ls} \tag{10–19}$$

Note that this function was derived in Chapter 2 by expansion in Taylor's series.   Referring to Fig. 10–2, it is common to designate the transforms of a function of time by a capital letter, thus

$$C = C(s) = \mathcal{L}c(t) \tag{10-20}$$

and similarly for all other variables.

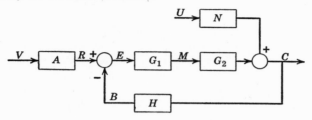

Fig. 10-2.   The closed loop.

The Transfer Function and Stability

The performance of the control system can be illustrated by the transfer functions of the system (see Fig. 10-2):

Open loop $B = (G_1G_2H)E + (NH)U$ $\tag{10-21}$

Closed loop $C = \dfrac{G_1G_2A}{1 + G_1G_2H} V + \dfrac{N}{1 + G_1G_2H} U$ $\tag{10-22}$

Closed loop $D = \dfrac{1 - G_1G_2A + G_1G_2H}{1 + G_1G_2H} V - \dfrac{N}{1 + G_1G_2H} U$ $\tag{10-23}$

The controlled variable or deviation may be calculated once the form of set-point function V or load function U are known.

The closed-loop transfer function for a system responding to a step change of load with set point fixed is, from equation 10-22,

$$C = \frac{N}{1 + G_1G_2H} U \tag{10-24}$$

In general, each term of the transfer function is a function of the complex variable s. Substituting for these functions, whatever they may be, would yield

$$C = \frac{a_m s^m + a_{m-1}s^{m-1} \cdots a_1s + a_0}{b_n s^n + b_{n-1}s^{n-1} \cdots b_1s + b_0} \tag{10-25}$$

where a_m and b_n are constants and m and n are integers. In any real physical system, furthermore, $n \geqq m$. The denominator of the transfer function may be factored.

$$C = \frac{a_m s^m + a_{m-1}s^{m-1} \cdots a_1s + a_0}{(s - r_1)(s - r_2) \cdots (s - r_n)} \tag{10-26}$$

where r_n are the roots of the denominator polynomial. Whether or not any roots are zero, or alike in value, the inversion of this transform can only yield terms like

$$C(t) = f(A, e^{+r_n t}, t^k e^{+r_n t}) \qquad (10\text{--}27)$$

where r_n are the roots of the denominator polynomial and may be real, imaginary, or complex numbers. The exponent k occurs wherever there are equal roots. The number A is a constant and may occur for zero roots. The time dependent terms, therefore, have the form

$$e^{+(\alpha + i\beta)t}$$

where $r_n = \alpha + i\beta$, a complex number. Now, if the real part of the root α is negative, the response of the controlled variable will be bounded because only exponentials with negative exponents will appear. On the other hand, if the real part of the root α is positive, the response of the controlled variable will ultimately increase to very large values and the system is said to be unstable.

The problem of stability in automatic control then reduces to the problem of determining whether the denominator of the closed-loop transfer function has any roots with positive real parts.

Example 10–1. As an illustration, consider the transfer function

$$G = \frac{s + 1}{s^3 + 3s^2 - 4}$$

Factoring the denominator,

$$G = \frac{s + 1}{(s + 2)^2 (s - 1)}$$

Since one of the factors has a positive root $(s - 1)$, the system represented by G is unstable. This is made evident by carrying out the following steps: Expanding into partial fractions,

$$G = \frac{C_1}{(s + 2)^2} + \frac{C_2}{s + 2} + \frac{C_3}{s - 1}$$

The unknown coefficients are determined and substituted into the partial fractions:

$$G = \frac{1}{9} \left(\frac{3}{(s + 2)^2} - \frac{2}{s + 2} + \frac{2}{s - 1} \right)$$

Using the La Place transform table to get the inverse transformations for a unit impulse input,

$$c = \tfrac{1}{9}(3\, t e^{-2t} - 2e^{-2t} + 2e^{t})$$

Since the third term has a positive exponent, c increases exponentially with time, i.e., the output has no steady-state value, and the system is unstable.

Routh–Hurwitz Condition for Stability

The Routh–Hurwitz condition for stability may be used to find whether the characteristic differential equation for the system has any roots with positive real parts.

The transient response to a change in load or in set point (see equation 10–25) is determined by the characteristic equation

$$b_n s^n + b_{n-1} s^{n-1} + \cdots b_1 s + b_0 = 0 \qquad (10\text{--}28)$$

Note that the left-hand side of this equation is determined by the denominator of the transfer function.

The response of the system is determined by the roots of the characteristic equation 10–28 because these roots determine the functions in the solution to the differential equation. The number of roots equals the degree of the characteristic equation. Instability can be determined at once if

1. All terms of the characteristic equation are not of the same sign.
2. All terms of the characteristic equation are not present in descending powers.

Either of these conditions may be detected by inspection and may be used to determine stability.

The procedure of Routh is as follows: Arrange the coefficients of the differential equation in rows and columns:

$$
\begin{array}{ccc}
b_n & b_{n-2} & b_{n-4} \\
b_{n-1} & b_{n-3} & b_{n-5}
\end{array}
$$

extending the rows until all b's are placed. The coefficients of the third row are found by cross-multiplication:

$$\frac{b_{n-1}b_{n-2} - b_n b_{n-3}}{b_{n-1}} \qquad \frac{b_{n-1}b_{n-4} - b_n b_{n-5}}{b_{n-1}}$$

Using rows two and three, the coefficients of the fourth row are found by cross-multiplying in the same manner, and new rows are formed in this way until no terms remain. In the course of development the coefficients in any row may be multiplied by a positive number without altering the result.

The system will be stable and non-oscillatory in the steady state if (1) all the coefficients of the characteristic equations are of the same sign, and (2) all the derived coefficients of the first column of the array are of one sign.

There are two exceptions to the process:

(a) If the first-column term in any row is zero, but the remaining terms are not zero, replace the zero by an arbitrarily small number ϵ and proceed.

(b) If all the coefficients in the second or any derived row are zero, there are roots of equal magnitude lying radially opposite on the real-imaginary plane. In this case form a polynomial with the coefficients of the last row, take the coefficients of the derivative of this polynomial for the next row and proceed.

The Routh–Hurwitz condition for stability is of limited usefulness in automatic control because no indication is given of the amount of instability and the direction to go to avoid it. On the other hand, it is often possible to explore the influence of one or two parameters of a system by considering values that may produce instability.

Example 10–2. Employ the Routh–Hurwitz condition for stability for

$$(s^2 + s + 2)(s + 2)(s + 1) = s^4 + 4s^3 + 7s^2 + 8s + 4 = 0$$

1	7	4
4	8	0
$\dfrac{4 \times 7 - 1 \times 8}{4} = 5$	$\dfrac{4 \times 4 - 1 \times 0}{4} = 4$	0
$\dfrac{5 \times 8 - 4 \times 4}{5} = \dfrac{24}{5}$	0	

The coefficients of the equation are all positive, and the left column is entirely positive, so the system is not unstable.

Example 10–3. Examine the stability and determine any limitations of parameter k for stability:

$$1 + (2s^2 - s + k)(s + 1)^2 = 2s^4 + 3s^3 + ks^2 + (2k - 1)s + (k + 1) = 0$$

It is immediately apparent that k must be greater than $+\frac{1}{2}$ to insure that all terms are present and non-negative. Next construct the array:

2	k	$k + 1$
3	$2k - 1$	
$\dfrac{2 - k}{3}$	$k + 1$	
$\dfrac{2k^2 + 4k + 11}{k - 2}$		

The third term of the first column requires that $k < 2$, and the last term requires that $k > 2$. Since these conditions cannot be fulfilled simultaneously, there is no value of k allowing stability.

The Transfer Locus

The stability of control systems may be determined from the closed-loop transfer function,

$$C = \frac{G_1 G_2 A}{1 + G_1 G_2 H} V + \frac{N}{1 + G_1 G_2 H} U$$

As stated before, a control system is unstable when the denominator of the closed-loop transfer function has roots with positive real parts. Study of this condition is made easier by considering the actuating signal rather than the controlled variable,

$$E = \frac{1}{1 + G_1 G_2 H} R - \frac{NH}{1 + G_1 G_2 H} U \qquad (10\text{--}29)$$

There is no loss of generality, because the stability of the input element A or the load-element N may be determined separately. The condition for stability now reduces to determining whether

$$1 + G_1 G_2 H$$

has any roots with positive real parts.

The transfer locus must be employed in order to determine whether the function $1 + G_1 G_2 H$ has roots with positive real parts. In general the function $1 + G_1 G_2 H$ is a function of the La Place transform complex variable s:

$$1 + G_1(s) G_2(s) H(s) \qquad (10\text{--}30)$$

A complex variable is defined by

$$s = \alpha + i\omega \qquad (10\text{--}31)$$

where α is the real part and ω is the imaginary part of the complex

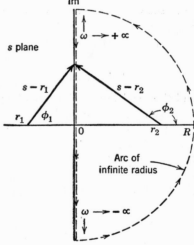

FIG. 10–3.   Roots in the complex plane.

number. Therefore, the function $1 + G_1 G_2 H$ is also a complex number and may be represented on the complex plane.

The roots of $(1 + G_1 G_2 H)$ are specific values of the complex variable s and may be located on the s plane in Fig. 10–3. The roots may be r_1 (a negative real number) and r_2 a positive real number by way of example. Suppose that we define a vector $(s - r_2)$ as in Fig. 10–3 by drawing a line from the root r_2 to a point on the imaginary axis. Suppose now that the tip of the vector follows the dotted line in a counterclockwise manner where the path of the end of the vector travels from positive infinity down the imaginary axis to negative infinity and around a circle of infinite radius back to the starting point. Thus, the value of complex variable s changes from

$$+i\omega \text{ as } \omega \rightarrow +\infty$$

to

$$-i\omega \text{ as } \omega \rightarrow -\infty$$

and back again. In this case it is desired that the real part of s be zero ($\alpha = 0$) so as to make this complete encirclement of the positive half of the s plane.

For a single positive root (as r_2) the vector $s - r_2$ makes one counterclockwise rotation, but for a negative root (as r_1) the vector $s - r_1$ makes no net revolutions. Therefore it is concluded that a root can be located by the simple scheme of determining the number of rotations of a test vector when $s = i\omega$ in the particular path encircling the right half plane. If there happens to be a root lying squarely in the imaginary axis or at zero, it is possible to alter the path of s ever so slightly around these points and proceed in the normal manner.

It is desired that s take on values given by $i\omega$, so

$$1 + G_1(s)G_2(s)H(s) \rightarrow 1 + G_1(i\omega)G_2(i\omega)H(i\omega) \qquad (10\text{--}32)$$

and the resulting function can be plotted on the function plane as shown in Fig. 10–4. The problem may be transferred from the s plane of Fig. 10–3 to the $G(s)$ plane in Fig. 10–4 by conformal mapping.

Suppose that the dotted line in Fig. 10–4 represents G_1G_2H for different values of $s = i\omega$. A line drawn from the origin 0 to the point P on the locus represents the vector G_1G_2H. The line from the origin to the $(-1, 0)$ point Q is the vector (-1). By subtraction the line joining QP is the vector $1 + G_1G_2H$. Thus it is concluded that we need only plot the locus of the open-loop function,

$$G_1(i\omega)G_2(i\omega)H(i\omega)$$

and a vector from the point $(-1, 0)$ represents the denominator of the transfer function. The transfer locus is a plot of a function of variable s for values of $s = i\omega$ from positive infinity to negative infinity. For convenience, only the values from positive infinity to zero need be plotted because values for negative $s = i\omega$ are a mirror reflection about the horizontal (real) axis.

The transfer locus is a closed curve and must be drawn with care if the function G_1G_2H contains an s^n in the denominator (n may be either a positive or a negative integer). If n is positive, then the transfer locus may pass to infinity as frequency ω approaches zero. The positive frequency end of the locus must then be connected by $n/2$ counterclockwise rotations at an infinite radius in order to connect to the negative frequency end of the locus and thereby form a closed curve.

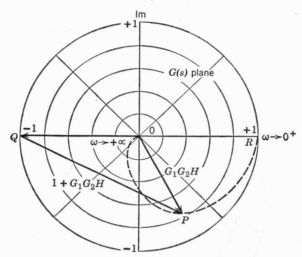

FIG. 10–4.   Open- and closed-loop functions.

Example 10–4.   Plot the transfer locus for

$$G_1 G_2 H = \frac{1}{s^2(Ts + 1)}$$

As shown in the figure, it is necessary to connect the ends of the locus by making

$$\frac{n}{2} = \frac{2}{2} = 1.0$$

complete counterclockwise rotation.

Example 10–5.   Plot the transfer locus for

$$G_1 G_2 H = \frac{1}{s(Ts + 1)}$$

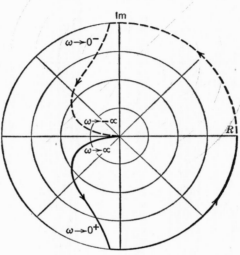

As shown in the figure, it is necessary to connect the ends of the locus by making

$$\frac{n}{2} = \frac{1}{2}$$

complete counterclockwise rotation.

Nyquist Stability Criterion

The Nyquist stability criterion follows directly from a consideration of the "poles" and "zeros" of the denominator of the closed-loop transfer function $(1 + G_1G_2H)$ and an inspection of the transfer locus of the open-loop transfer function (G_1G_2H).

A "pole" of $1 + G_1G_2H$ is said to occur at a value of $s = s_p$ when the value of $1 + G_1G_2H$ is infinite and if s_p has a *nonzero positive real part*. Thus the function

$$1 + G_1 G_2 H = \frac{1}{(3s - 1)(s + 1)}$$

has a pole at $s = +1/3$. It should be noted that the value of $s = -1$ is not counted as a pole because it has a negative real part. A pole of $1 + G_1G_2H$ is a pole of G_1G_2H, so that in counting poles only the open-loop transfer function G_1G_2H need be considered.

A "zero" of $1 + G_1G_2H$ is said to occur at a value of $s = s_0$ when the value of $1 + G_1G_2H$ is zero and if s_0 has a *nonzero positive real part*. For example, the function

$$1 + G_1G_2H = \frac{(s - 1)}{s(3s - 1)(s + 2)}$$

has a zero at $s_0 = +1$. Values of $s = \infty$ are not considered as being zeros.

The Nyquist criterion may be stated as follows: *A control system is stable only if the number of zeros of the function $1 + G_1G_2H$ is zero, and if the sum of the net number of counterclockwise rotations of the vector $1 + G_1G_2H$ and of the number of poles of the function G_1G_2H is zero.* The vector $1 + G_1G_2H$ is considered to follow the transfer locus G_1G_2H from $\omega = +\infty$ to 0 to $-\infty$. Thus

$$N + P = 0 \tag{10-33}$$

where N = number of net counterclockwise revolutions of vector QP in Fig. 10-4

P = number of poles of G_1G_2H (number of values of s with positive real parts that make this function infinite).

then there are no zeros of $1 + G_1G_2H$ and therefore no roots with positive real parts in the denominator of

$$\frac{1}{1 + G_1G_2H}$$

In many problems in automatic control it is interesting to note that the number of poles and zeros is zero so that the Nyquist criterion reduces to requiring no net rotations of the vector. The criterion then may simplify to the statement that the transfer locus does not encircle the $(-1, 0)$ point.

Example 10-6. Determine the stability of

$$G_1G_2H = \frac{1 - s}{s + 2}$$

G_1G_2H does not have a pole so $P = 0$. The transfer locus in the figure shows $+1.0$ counterclockwise rotations. Thus

$$N = +1.0$$
$$P = 0$$

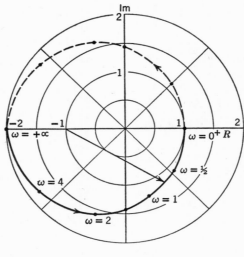

and

$$N + P \neq 0$$

Therefore, the system is unstable.

The Nyquist criterion may be applied whether $G_1 G_2 H$ is analytically determined or plotted from experimental results. The power of the method lies in the fact that the analytical form of $G_1 G_2 H$ need not be known and that it is not necessary to factor high order polynomials.

There are two limitations which we have implied in the development of the theory behind the Nyquist criterion:

1. The system is linear or can be represented by linear equations so that the La Place transforms may be applied.

2. The open-loop transfer function $G_1 G_2 H$ approaches zero as the frequency approaches infinity. This must be true in any real system with a finite source of power. If the transfer function does not go to zero for infinite frequencies, then it means only that we have left out some terms which are important at very high frequencies. It is correct in this situation to merely draw in the extension of $G_1 G_2 H$ so that it ends up at the origin.

The procedure for determining stability by application of the Nyquist criterion may be summarized as follows:

A. Plot the open-loop transfer locus $G_1 G_2 H$ on the complex plane for frequency varying from zero to infinity.

(a) If experimental data is used, plot the locus directly from the phase and magnitude data.

(b) If the transfer function G_1G_2H is given, make sure that the denominator is of order equal to or greater than that of the numerator. If this is not true it is necessary to go back to the analysis and pick up some of the higher order terms that have been neglected.

(c) If the locus does not terminate at the origin for infinite frequency, then draw an arbitrary line extending the locus to the origin.

(d) Plot the locus for positive frequencies. The plot for negative frequencies will always be the mirror image of the plot for positive frequencies, reflected about the real axis.

(e) If there are n factors of s in the denominator of G_1G_2H, then join the open ends of the locus of G_1G_2H with $n\pi$ radians of arc (at infinite radius), going counterclockwise.

B. Draw the vector from -1 to a point on the locus. Let the point vary from $\omega = +\infty$ to $\omega = -\infty$, and count the net number of counterclockwise rotations of the vector. This is N.

C. Determine the number of poles in the function G_1G_2H. These are the number of values of s having positive real parts (counting each repeated value) that make $1 + G_1G_2H$ infinite. This is P.

D. The system is stable if and only if

$$N + P = 0$$

The complex plane diagram can be used for more complete investigation of system performance short of solving for transient response. For example, it is often required to find the closed-loop performance knowing the open-loop performance. For any control system,

$$\frac{B}{E} = GH \quad \text{(open loop)} \tag{10–34}$$

and

$$\frac{C}{V} = \frac{A}{H}\left(\frac{GH}{1 + GH}\right) \quad \text{(closed loop)} \tag{10–35}$$

The analysis is made a great deal easier if the inverse functions are used. The inverse of a vector is obtained by inverting the amplitude and changing the sign of the phase. Let

$$\frac{E}{B} = Y = \frac{1}{GH} \tag{10–36}$$

Then

$$\frac{V}{C} = \frac{H}{A}(Y + 1) \tag{10–37}$$

Consequently, as shown in Fig. 10–5, all that is necessary is to plot the function Y and the function H/A. The output-input response C/V is easily obtained by inverting the final locus. Unfortunately this method is most useful if the feedback or measuring-element transfer function

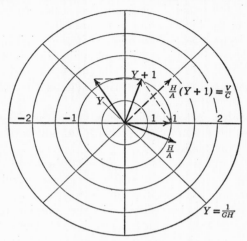

Fig. 10–5.   Inverse polar plot.

is 1.0. This situation occurs in automatic process control only when the measuring element (feedback) lag is zero.

Example 10–7.   Determine the stability of

$$\frac{B}{E} = \frac{K}{(10s + 1)^2}$$

This may represent proportional control of a process consisting of two time constants of 10 sec each. The open-loop function is plotted in Ex. Fig. 10–7 with $K = 1.0$ for all frequencies. The function for negative frequencies (the dotted portion of the curve) is the reflection about the real axis of the portion of the curve for positive frequencies. Thus only the portion for positive frequencies requires calculation.

The system is stable because for any value of K the net rotation of the test vector is zero and there are no poles. Notice that the only effect of an increase in the number K is to expand the plot radially, or conversely, to contract the radial coordinate markings. Thus, if the point $(-1, 0)$ is located at the first circle outward, the gain K is 10 and the system is still stable.

Example 10–8. Determine the stability of

$$\frac{B}{E} = \frac{10}{(16s + 1)^3}$$

This function may consist of proportional control (sensitivity 10) of a system with three equal time constants of 16 sec. The function is plotted in Ex. Fig. 10–8. The locus passes just beyond the point $(-1, 0)$. The net rotation

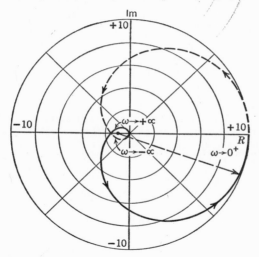

of the test vector is two $(N = 2)$ revolutions, and since there are no poles the system is unstable. If the proportional sensitivity is reduced to about 2.8, the system becomes marginally stable.

Example 10–9. Determine a maximum value of proportional sensitivity for stability of the function

$$\frac{B}{E} = \frac{K(60s + 1)}{60s(120s + 1)(30s + 1)}$$

This open-loop function may represent proportional plus integral control (integral time = 60 sec) for a system composed of two time constants (120 sec, 30 sec). The function is plotted in Ex. Fig. 10–9. For positive frequencies the locus begins at 90 deg lag and infinite magnitude. Thus at zero frequency the locus is tangent to the negative imaginary axis (this is due to the integral response $60s$ in the denominator). For negative frequencies the locus becomes tangent to the positive imaginary axis. The problem of joining the two loci at zero frequency is resolved as follows: *For each s term in the denominator, continue the locus one half revolution in the counterclockwise direction to*

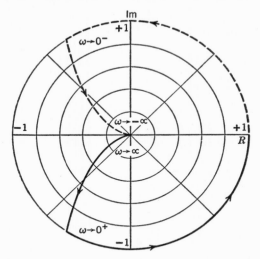

form the complete locus. (s^2 requires one complete circle, s^3 one and one-half circles, etc.) As shown in Fig. 10–8 the locus makes a half circle of infinite magnitude at $\omega = 0$. The test vector however makes no net rotations and the system is stable for any value of proportional sensitivity K.

Example 10–10. Determine the maximum value of proportional sensitivity for

$$\frac{B}{E} = \frac{K}{e^{5s}(20s + 1)}$$

This function may represent proportional control of a system having a dead time of 5 sec and a time constant of 20 sec. The open-loop function is plotted in Ex. Fig. 10–10 for a proportional sensitivity of $K = 1.0$. Notice that the dead time causes unlimited phase lag and as a result the locus spirals counterclockwise and outward as frequency decreases. The limit of proportional sensitivity is about 7.0 at a frequency of 0.007 radians per second as the locus passes through the Nyquist point $(-1, 0)$.

Example 10–11. Determine the stability of

$$\frac{B}{E} = \frac{-2}{(s - 1)(4s + 1)}$$

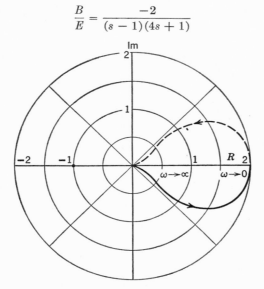

This function is plotted in Ex. Fig. 10–11. The net counterclockwise rotation of the test vector is zero and $N = 0$. Since there is a pole in the right half plane at $s = 1.0$, therefore $P = +1.0$. Thus

$$N + P \neq 0$$

The system is therefore unstable. In addition it should be noticed that the function $1 + G_1 G_2 H$ has a zero at $s = (3 \pm \sqrt{57})/2$ and this fact alone makes the system unstable.

Bode Magnitude–Phase Method of Analysis

The magnitude–phase method of analysis may be employed to determine the performance and stability of an automatic control system. It is undoubtedly the most widely used method of analysis and synthesis of control systems. It is also one of the simplest methods.

The Bode magnitude–phase method of analysis may be used for a wide range of problems, including the analysis of systems containing some nonlinear elements. Generally, however, it is more useful for systems having linear response.

In order to demonstrate the selection of stability by the magnitude–phase method consider the simple second-order closed-loop system for which the open-loop response is

$$G = \frac{1}{Ts(Ts + 2\zeta)}$$

The open-loop magnitude is

$$|G| = \frac{1}{\omega T \sqrt{(4\zeta^2 + \omega^2 T^2)}}$$

and the open-loop phase is

$$\underline{/G} = \tan^{-1} \frac{2\zeta}{\omega T}$$

Employing these relations it is possible to solve for the closed-loop damping ratio for any selected open-loop phase at a frequency ω for which the magnitude is one. The results are:

Open-Loop Phase, deg	Closed-Loop Damping Ratio, ζ	Closed-Loop Period of Oscillation
−105	0.95	20.0T
−120	0.61	7.9T
−135	0.42	6.9T
−150	0.27	6.5T
−165	0.13	6.2T

Therefore, a selection of open-loop phase will determine the closed-loop behavior for a second-order system. Generally it is desirable to select a damping ratio of about 0.3 to 0.5 and thus an open-loop phase lag of 135 deg seems appropriate.

The response of higher order systems may be investigated in a similar manner. It is usually found that here too the phase should be about 135 deg for a reasonable system response. If the system contains some nonlinearities, it is advisable to check stability by more than one method.

For closed-loop systems the analysis need only employ the open-loop response

$$B = G_1 G_2 HE + NU \tag{10–38}$$

For the action within the loop, the influence of the load variable is not important, so

$$\frac{B}{E} = G_1 G_2 H \tag{10–39}$$

The magnitude ratio and phase,

$$\left|\frac{B}{E}\right| = |G_1 G_2 H|, \qquad \underline{/\frac{B}{E}} = \underline{/G_1 G_2 H}$$

are plotted on log–log coordinates.

The amplitude plot is made on log–log coordinate paper, with frequency (ω radians per second or f cycles per second) as the abscissa and magnitude ratio as the ordinate. The amplitude function is obtained directly from the transfer function,

$$|G_1(s)\, G_2(s)\, H(s)|_{s \text{ by } i\omega} \tag{10-40}$$

or, since amplitudes must be multiplied,

$$|G_1(i\omega)| \times |G_2(i\omega)| \times |H(i\omega)| \tag{10-41}$$

On log coordinates, however, multiplying magnitudes means adding ordinates. Thus, the magnitude of several elements in series is obtained most easily by plotting each element and adding.

The phase function is plotted separately on semi-log coordinate paper with frequency on the log coordinate abscissa and phase in degrees as the ordinate. The phase function is obtained directly from the transfer function:

$$\underline{/G_1(s)\, G_2(s)\, H(s)}_{s \text{ by } i\omega} \tag{10-42}$$

or, since phases must be added,

$$\underline{/G_1(i\omega)} + \underline{/G_2(i\omega)} + \underline{/H(i\omega)} \tag{10-43}$$

The stability and performance may be determined from the graphs by the following rules:

1. If the phase lag is less than 180 deg at the highest frequency for which the magnitude is one, the closed loop is stable. Conversely if the phase lag is greater than 180 deg, then the system is unstable.

2. If the phase lag is approximately 135 deg at the highest frequency for which the magnitude is one, the closed-loop system is stable. Furthermore, the closed-loop response will be damped and slightly oscillatory in a "satisfactory" manner. Sometimes the analysis may be made by employing the magnitude–frequency diagram without reference to the phase lag. It is best however to use rule 3 as a check on the method listed above.

3. If the magnitude–frequency curve does not change slope appreciably over two octaves of frequency near the highest frequency at which the magnitude is one, and if the negative slope of the magnitude fre-

quency curve is less than 2.0 (plotted on log coordinates), the system is probably stable. Conversely if the negative slope is greater than 2.0 then the system is probably unstable.

4. If the magnitude–frequency curve does not change slope appreciably over two octaves of frequency near the highest frequency at which the magnitude is one, and if the negative slope is 1.5, the closed-loop system is probably stable. Furthermore, the closed-loop response will be damped and slightly oscillatory in a "satisfactory" manner.

As an example consider the following system function:

$$\frac{C}{E} = \frac{10}{(16s + 1)^3} \tag{10–44}$$

This function could represent proportional control of a three-time-constant process. The proportional sensitivity of the controller is 10 and the process time constants are each 16.0 sec. The magnitude is

$$\left|\frac{C}{E}\right| = \frac{10}{(1 + \omega^2 T^2)^{3/2}} \tag{10–45}$$

The phase is

$$\underline{/\frac{C}{E}} = -3 \tan^{-1} \omega T \tag{10–46}$$

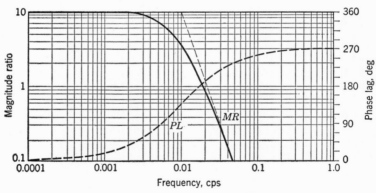

FIG. 10–6.   Bode plot of $\dfrac{10}{(16s + 1)^3}$.

The magnitude and phase are plotted in Fig. 10–6. Stability checks 1, 2, 3, 4 above are as follows:

1. The system is just unstable because the phase is slightly more than 180 deg when the magnitude is one (190 deg at 0.0191 cps).

2. Satisfactory stability is achieved if the proportional sensitivity is made equal to 2.83. This is easily checked by sliding the magnitude curve vertically downward until it passes through the $MR = 1.0$, $f = 0.01$ point. The magnitude is then 1.0 when the phase lag is 135 deg.

3. The magnitude–frequency curve is reasonably flat near a frequency of 0.01 cps and the slope is 2.36 at that point consequently the system is probably unstable.

4. Satisfactory stability is obtained if the proportional sensitivity is made about 2.6. This is found by sliding the magnitude curve downward until the slope is 1.5 at the point at which the magnitude is 1.0.

For a proportional sensitivity of 10 the transient response has an exponential factor and a slowly growing oscillatory factor. The solution of the differential equation for closed-loop behavior is

$$c = 18e^{-0.20t} + 35e^{0.006t} \sin (0.116t - 31°) \qquad (10\text{–}47)$$

A unit impulse disturbance was assumed and the roots of the characteristic equation found by trial division:

$$(5s + 1)(820s^2 - 10s + 11) \qquad (10\text{–}48)$$

As the solution in equation 10–47 shows, the response is definitely unstable because of the positive exponent of the second exponential term. This produces an ever increasing amplitude of oscillation.

For a proportional sensitivity K of 2.83 the solution of the differential equation for the same conditions becomes

$$c = 170e^{-0.15t} + 170e^{-0.019t} \sin (0.077t - 90°) \qquad (10\text{–}49)$$

The roots of the characteristic equation were found by trial division:

$$(6.7s + 1)(610s^2 + 23s + 3.83) \qquad (10\text{–}50)$$

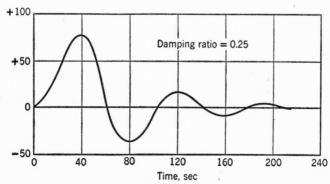

FIG. 10–7. Transient response of system of Fig. 10–6.

This solution is a stable one, as shown in Fig. 10–7. The damping ratio of the oscillatory component is 0.25 and is generally considered satisfactory.

Example 10–12.   Determine the integral time for integral control with two time constants of 2.5 sec and 0.625 sec.   The open-loop function is

$$\frac{C}{E} = \frac{1}{Ts(2.5s + 1)(0.625s + 1)}$$

The magnitude and phase are

$$\left|\frac{C}{E}\right| = \frac{1}{\omega T} \sqrt{\frac{1}{(1 + 6.25\omega^2)(1 + 0.39\omega^2)}}$$

$$\underline{/\frac{C}{E}} = -90° - \tan^{-1} 2.5\omega - \tan^{-1} 0.625\omega$$

First, the phase angle does not depend upon the integral time T. The frequency for 135 deg phase lag is easily calculated:

$$\omega = 0.28$$

For a magnitude of 1.0,

$$\omega T = \frac{1}{\sqrt{(1 + 0.49)(1 + 0.0306)}}$$

and

$$T = \frac{1}{0.28 \times 1.24} = \underline{2.9 \text{ sec}}$$

The integral time should therefore be about 2.9 sec.

Example 10–13.   Determine the proportional sensitivity for a control system having a dead time of 5 sec and a single time constant of 20 sec.
  The open-loop function is

$$\frac{C}{E} = \frac{K}{e^{5s}(20s + 1)}$$

The magnitude and phase are

$$\left|\frac{C}{E}\right| = \frac{K}{\sqrt{1 + 400\omega^2}}$$

$$\underline{/\frac{C}{E}} = -(\tan^{-1} 20\omega) - \left(5\omega \times \frac{180}{\pi}\right)$$

For 135 deg phase lag, the frequency ω must be about 0.20 radians per sec. The amplitude must be one, so

$$K = \sqrt{1 + 400 \times 0.2^2} = \sqrt{17} = \underline{4.12}$$

PROBLEMS

10–1. Check the following systems for stability. The function given is $1 + G_1 G_2 H$.

(a) $6s^3 + 11s^2 + 6s + 1$ (c) $100s^4 + 210s^3 + 121s^2 + 22s + 1$
(b) $s^3 + s^2 + s + 21$ (d) $T^2 s^3 + T s^2 + s$

10–2. The Ziegler–Nichols approximation for a process is

$$\frac{1}{e^{Ls} T s}$$

The proportional-derivative control equation is,

$$K_c (T_d s + 1)$$

Show that the best settings are nearly

$$K_c = \frac{T}{L} \left(\frac{5}{4} \right), \ T_d = \frac{3L}{11}$$

as given in Chapter 4.

10–3. A proportional controller is used for a system having n equal time constants. Calculate the open-loop gain K_c for 135 deg phase lag with

$$G_1 G_2 H = \frac{K_c}{(T s + 1)^n}$$

and the loop closed. Does the open-loop gain depend upon the value of the time constant?

10–4. A controller and process function are

$$\frac{K_c}{e^{+Ts} T s (T s + 1)}$$

Calculate the open-loop gain K_c for best estimated response.

Automatic Control Definitions

Actuating signal, e, is the reference input minus the primary feedback.

Automatic controller is a mechanism which measures the value of a variable quantity or condition and operates to correct or limit deviation of the measured value from a selected reference.

Capacitance, C, is the amount of energy or material which must be added to a closed system to cause unit change in potential.

Control elements, G_1, comprise the portion of the control system which includes control action relating the manipulated variable to the actuating signal.

Control ratio, c/r, is the response of the controlled variable to a change of reference input.

Controlled system, G_2, is the body, process, or machine, a particular quantity or condition of which is to be controlled.

Controlled variable, c, is that quantity or condition of the controlled system which is directly measured and controlled.

Controlling means are the elements of an automatic controller which are involved in producing a corrective action.

Corner frequency of a transfer function is the frequency at which lines asymptotic to its log-magnitude vs. log-frequency curve intersect.

Dead time, L, is a fixed interval of time between the change of an input to an element and the beginning of response to the input.

Dead zone, X_d, is the largest range of values of the input variable to which an element does not respond.

Derivative action is a controller action in which there is a continuous linear relation between the derivative of the actuating signal and output signal of the controller.

Derivative time is the time difference by which the output of a proportional-derivative controller leads (is ahead of) the input when the input changes linearly with time.

Deviation, d, is the difference at any instant between the value of the controlled variable and the set point.

Differential gap is the two-position controller adjustment: the smallest range of values through which the controlled variable must pass in order to change the output signal of the controller from maximum to minimum.

Disturbance, u, is a signal (other than the reference input) which tends to affect the value of the controlled variable.

Error ratio, e/r, is the response of the closed-loop system actuating signal to a change of the reference input.

Feedback elements, H, comprise the portion of the controller which establishes the relationship between the primary feedback and the controlled variable.

Final control element is a portion of controlling means which directly determines the value of manipulated variable.

Frequency response of a system or element is the steady-state magnitude ratio and the difference in phase of the output with respect to a sinusoidal input.

Gain of a system or element is the ratio of magnitude of the output with respect to the magnitude of sinusoidal input.

Input elements, A, comprise the portion of the controller which provides the reference input in response to the set point.

Integral action is a controller action in which there is a continuous linear relation between value of controlled variable and rate of change of controller output signal.

Integral time, T_i, is the time required for the output of a proportional-integral controller to change an amount equal to the amount of proportional response provided by a step change of actuating signal.

Lag is the retardation or delay of one physical condition with respect to some other condition to which it is closely related.

Load change is the change in process conditions which requires a change in the average value of manipulated variable to maintain the controlled variable at the desired value.

Load error. See *Offset.*

Manipulated variable, m, is the quantity or condition which is varied by the automatic controller so as to affect the value of controlled variable.

Offset, E_o, is the steady-state deviation resulting from a change in value of the load variable.

On–off action. See *Two-position action.*

Open-loop gain, b/e, is the ratio of the change in the feedback variable and the change in actuating signal.

Phase margin is the angle by which the phase of the open-loop response of an element or system differs from 180 deg.

Primary feedback, b, is a signal which is a function of the controlled variable and which is compared with the reference input to obtain the actuating signal.

Proportional action is a controller action in which there is a continuous linear relation between value of the controlled variable and the value of the output signal of the controller.

Proportional sensitivity, K_c, is a proportional action adjustment. It is the steady-state ratio of the change of controller output variable and the change in actuating signal.

Rangeability is the ratio of maximum flow to minimum controllable flow through a final-control element.

Rate time. See *Derivative time.*

Reset rate is the inverse of integral time.

Reference input, r, is a signal established as a standard of comparison for a feedback control system by virtue of its relation to the command.

Response time of a system or element is the time required for the output to first reach a specified value after the application of a step input or disturbance.

Rise time of a system or element is the time required for the output to increase from one specified percentage of the final value to another, following the application of a step input.

Servomechanism is a feedback control system in which the controlled variable is mechanical position.

Set point is the selected reference value of controlled variable which it is desired to maintain.

Settling time is the time required for the absolute value of the difference between the output and its final value to become and remain less than a specified amount, following the application of a step input or disturbance.

Static error, E_s, is the steady-state deviation resulting from a change in value of the set point.

Time constant is the time required for the output of a first-order system to change from a given value to within 36.8 per cent of the final value (or 63.2 per cent of the amount of total change) when a step change of input is made.

Transfer locus is a plot of magnitude and phase angle of sinusoidal response of a system.

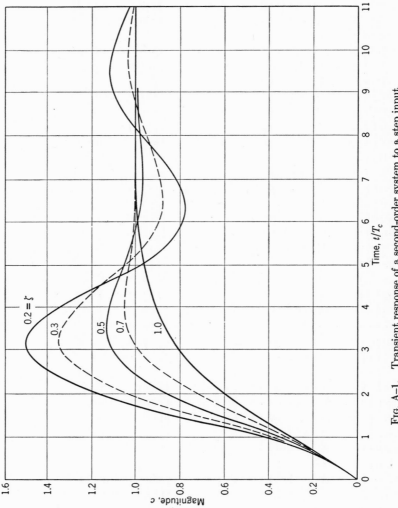

FIG. A–1.   Transient response of a second-order system to a step input.
$T_c^2 \ddot{c} + 2\zeta T_c \dot{c} + c = 1$ with $c_0 = \dot{c}_0 = 0$

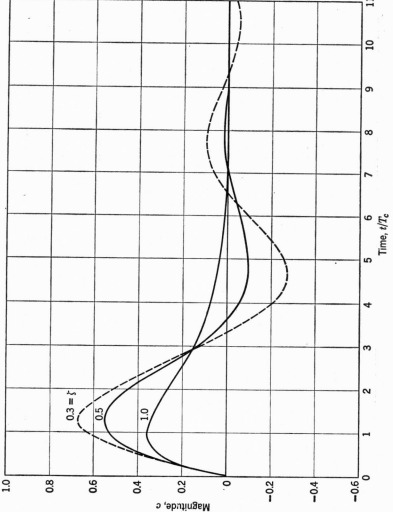

Fig. A–2.   Transient response of a second-order system to a unit impulse input.
$T_c{}^2\ddot{c} + 2\zeta T_c\dot{c} + c = 0$ with $c_0 = 0,\ \dot{c}_0 = 1/T_c$

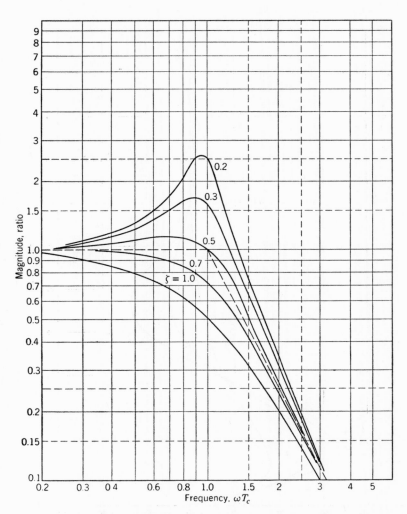

FIG. A–3.   Sinusoidal response of a second-order system, amplitude.
$$T_c^2 \ddot{c} + 2\zeta T_c \dot{c} + c = \sin \omega t$$

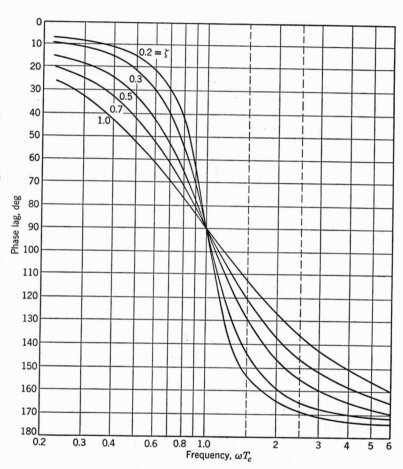

Fig. A–4.   Sinusoidal response of a second-order system, phase.

La Place Transformation

The solution of linear integro-differential equations by ordinary methods requires obtaining (*a*) a characteristic equation, (*b*) the roots of the characteristic equation, (*c*) the complimentary solution, (*d*) particular integral, and (*e*) the known initial or boundary conditions in order to evaluate the undetermined coefficients of the final equation.

The La Place transformation permits a change of variable from the time domain to the complex variable or "*s*" domain. The resulting functional expression can then be manipulated by the laws governing ordinary algebra even though "*s*" is a complex variable. After the desired manipulations are performed an inverse transformation returns the original function expressed in the *s* domain back to its original domain in a more useful form.

The "direct" transformation is made using the integral

$$X(s) = \int_0^\infty x(t)\, e^{-st}\, dt \tag{A-1}$$

where the function $x(t)$ is in the time domain *before transformation* and $X(s)$ is in the *s* domain *after transformation*. Symbolically this transformation is written

$$X(s) = \mathcal{L}x(t) \tag{A-2}$$

Equation A–2 is read "$X(s)$ equals the La Place transform of $x(t)$."

The La Place transform of a function $x(t)$ may be obtained by substituting in equation A–1 and integrating. For example, if

$$x(t) = t$$

then the La Place transform is obtained from

$$X(s) = \int_0^\infty t e^{-st}\, dt$$

Performing the integration by parts,

$$X(s) = e^{-st}\left|\frac{t}{s} - \frac{1}{s^2}\right|_0^\infty = \frac{1}{s^2}$$

Thus, it is possible to evaluate the transform by direct integration. In order to save time a table of transforms, such as Table A–1 or Table A–2 may be used. The table of direct transforms is a set of functions that may be transformed by direct integration as may be seen in Table A–1. The inverse transform table is simply a set of solutions with arbitrary coefficients for a corresponding set of simple differential equations.

The transforms for all the terms appearing in the differential equation

$$a_2 \ddot{x}(t) + a_1 \dot{x}(t) + a_0 x(t) = y_0 u(t)$$

can be found using the theorems of Table A–1. The disturbance $u(t)$ is the step function

$$u(t) = 0, \qquad t < 0$$
$$u(t) = 1, \qquad t \geq 0$$

The transformed result is an equation in the variable "s" which may be solved algebraically for $X(s)$.

$$(a_2 s^2 + a_1 s + a_0) X(s) = y_0 \frac{1}{s} + a_2 s x(0+) + a_2 \dot{x}(0+) + a_1 x(0+)$$

Two quantities appear in the transformed equation which are values of the variable x and its derivatives at $t = 0+$. These quantities are the initial conditions of the problem and should be evaluated immediately in terms of given information before a solution is found by an inverse transformation. This is one of the important properties of the La Place transformation in that all of the terminal conditions of the problem are accounted for during subsequent manipulation.

By solving for the variable $X(s)$ there results

$$X(s) = \frac{y_0 + (a_2 s^2 + a_1 s) x(0+) + a_2 s x(0+)}{s(a_2 s^2 + a_1 s + a_0)}$$

This function represents the La Place transform of the variable $x(t)$. The La Place transform may now be inverted by evaluating the integral,

$$x(t) = \frac{1}{2\pi i} \int_{\alpha - i\infty}^{\alpha + i\infty} X(s) e^{st} \, ds \qquad (A\text{–}3)$$

This requires integration with respect to the complex variable s. This step is usually somewhat more difficult than direct transformation and can be made unnecessary by employing a different procedure. If the function $X(s)$ can be expanded in a series, the inverse transforms may be found from the relatively simple polynomial of each term of the expansion. The transform

$$X(s) = \frac{b_m s^m + b_{m-1} s^{m-1} + \cdots b_1 s + b_0}{a_n s^n + a_{n-1} s^{n-1} + \cdots a_1 s + a_0} \qquad (A\text{–}4)$$

can be expanded by factoring the denominator

$$X(s) = \frac{b'_m s^m + b'_{m-1} s^{m-1} + \cdots b'_1 s + b'_0}{(s - r_1)(s - r_2)(s - r_3) \cdots (s - r_n)} \qquad (A\text{–}5)$$

Table A-1.   Operation and Function Transforms

Operation or Function	Function $f(t)$	Transform $F(s)$
Derivative	$\dfrac{d}{dt}f(t)$	$sF(s) - f(0)$
	$\dfrac{d^2}{dt^2}f(t)$	$s^2F(s) - sf(0) - f'(0)$
	$\dfrac{d^3}{dt^3}f(t)$	$s^3F(s) - s^2f(0) - sf'(0) - f''(0)$
Integral	$\int f(t)\,dt$	$\dfrac{1}{s}F(s) + \dfrac{1}{s}f^{-1}(0)$
Translation	$f(t - a)$	$e^{-as}F(s)$
Unit impulse	(Dirac or delta function)	1
Unit step	$u(t)$	$\dfrac{1}{s}$
Ramp	t	$\dfrac{1}{s^2}$
	t^n	$\dfrac{n!}{s^{n+1}}$
Sinusoid	$\sin \omega t$	$\dfrac{\omega}{s^2 + \omega^2}$
	$\cos \omega t$	$\dfrac{s}{s^2 + \omega^2}$
Exponential	e^{-at}	$\dfrac{1}{s + a}$
Initial value	$\lim\limits_{t \to 0} f(t)$	$\lim\limits_{s \to \infty} sF(s)$
Final value	$\lim\limits_{t \to \infty} f(t)$	$\lim\limits_{s \to 0} sF(s)$

where the roots (r_n) of the denominator are found, including zero and repeated roots. The transform can now be expanded in a series of terms,

$$X(s) = \frac{f_1(s)}{(s - r_1)} + \frac{f_2(s)}{(s - r_2)} + \cdots \frac{f_n(s)}{(s - r_n)} \qquad \text{(A-6)}$$

Considering the terms one at a time, the inversion may be made by recognizing a series of relatively simple inversions. These are compiled in a table of transforms as in Tables A-1 and A-2.

Table A-2. Inverse Transforms

$F(s)$	$f(t)$
1	Unit impulse, $\Delta(t) = \lim\limits_{a \to 0} \dfrac{u(t) - u(t-a)}{a}$
$\dfrac{1}{s}$	Unit step, $u(t)$
$\dfrac{1}{(Ts+1)^n}$	$\dfrac{1}{T^n(n-1)!}\, t^{n-1} e^{-t/T}$
$\dfrac{1}{T^2 s^2 + 2\zeta T s + 1}$	$\dfrac{1}{T\sqrt{1-\zeta^2}}\, e^{-\zeta t/T} \sin \sqrt{1-\zeta^2}(t/T)$
$\dfrac{1}{s(T^2 s^2 + 2\zeta T s + 1)}$	$1 + \dfrac{e^{-\zeta t/T} \sin[\sqrt{1-\zeta^2}(t/T) - \Phi]}{\sqrt{1-\zeta^2}}$ where $\Phi = \tan^{-1}\dfrac{\sqrt{1-\zeta^2}}{-\zeta}$
$\dfrac{1}{(T_1 s+1)(T^2 s^2 + 2\zeta T s + 1)}$	$\dfrac{(T_1/T^2)e^{-t/T_1}}{1 - 2\zeta(T_1/T) + (T_1/T)^2}$ $+ \dfrac{(T)^{-1}e^{-t/T} \sin[\sqrt{1-\zeta^2}(t/T) - \Phi]}{(1-\zeta^2)[1 - 2\zeta(T/T_1) + (T/T_1)^2]^{1/2}}$ where $\Phi = \tan^{-1}\dfrac{(T_1/T_2)\sqrt{1-\zeta^2}}{1 - \zeta(T_1/T_2)}$
$\dfrac{T_2 s + 1}{(T^2 s^2 + 2\zeta T s + 1)}$	$\dfrac{1}{T}\left[\dfrac{1 - 2\zeta(T_2/T) + (T_2/T)^2}{1 - \zeta^2}\right]^{1/2} e^{-\zeta t/T}$ $\sin[\sqrt{1-\zeta^2}(t/T) + \Phi]$ where $\Phi = \tan^{-1}\dfrac{(T_2/T)\sqrt{1-\zeta^2}}{1 - \zeta(T_2/T)}$
$\dfrac{T_2 s + 1}{s(T^2 s^2 + 2\zeta T s + 1)}$	$1 + (1-\zeta^2)^{-1/2}$ $[1 - 2\zeta(T_2/T) + (T_2/T)^2]^{1/2} e^{-\zeta t/T}$ $\sin[\sqrt{1-\zeta^2}(t/T) + \Phi]$ where $\Phi = \tan^{-1}\dfrac{(T_2/T)\sqrt{1-\zeta^2}}{1 - \zeta(T_2/T)} - \tan^{-1}\dfrac{\sqrt{1-\zeta^2}}{-\zeta}$

The partial expansion fraction may be made as follows:

1. For a number of distinct roots (no repeated roots), factor the polynomial and write

$$\frac{A(s)}{B(s)} = \frac{A_1}{s - s_1} + \frac{A_2}{s - s_2} + \cdots \frac{A_n}{s - s_n} \tag{A-7}$$

Note that a zero root may be treated exactly like a nonzero root. In order to solve for the A's, multiply the transform by the denominator factor and set s equal to that particular root. Thus,

$$A_3 = \frac{A(s)}{(s - s_1)(s - s_2)(s - s_4) \cdots (s - s_n)}\bigg|s = s_3$$

Example A-1. Find the inversion for

$$\frac{A(s)}{B(s)} = \frac{s + 1}{(s + 4)(s + 3)(s + 2)}$$

$$= \frac{A_2}{s + 2} + \frac{A_3}{s + 3} + \frac{A_4}{s + 4}$$

$$A_2 = \frac{s + 1}{(s + 4)(s + 3)}\bigg|_{s=-2} = \frac{-1}{2 \times 1} = -\frac{1}{2}$$

$$A_3 = \frac{s + 1}{(s + 2)(s + 4)}\bigg|_{s=-3} = \frac{-2}{-1 \times 1} = +2$$

$$A_4 = \frac{s + 1}{(s + 3)(s + 2)}\bigg|_{s=-4} = \frac{-3}{-1 \times -2} = -\frac{3}{2}$$

The desired expansion is

$$\frac{A(s)}{B(s)} = -\frac{1}{2} \frac{1}{(s + 2)} + \frac{2}{(s + 3)} - \frac{3}{2} \frac{1}{(s + 4)}$$

The inversion is (Table A–1 or Table A–2)

$$f(t) = \frac{-e^{-2t}}{2} + 2e^{-3t} - \frac{3e^{-4t}}{2} \qquad (Ans.)$$

2. For m repeated roots with $(n - m)$ distinct roots, write the repeated root to each power:

$$\frac{A(s)}{B(s)} = \frac{A_1}{s - s_1} + \cdots \frac{A_{n-m}}{s - s_{n-m}} + \frac{B_m}{(s - s_m)^m}$$

$$+ \frac{B_{m-1}}{(s - s_m)^{m-1}} + \cdots \frac{B_1}{(s - s_m)}$$

$$(A-8)$$

In order to solve for the A's, multiply by the denominator factor and set s equal to that particular root as in the previous case. In order to solve for the B's, a derivative is necessary,

$$B_m = \frac{A(s)}{(s - s_1) \cdots (s - s_{n-m})}\bigg|_{s=s_m}$$

$$B_{m-1} = \frac{d}{ds} \frac{A(s)}{(s - s_1) \cdots (s - s_{n-m})}\bigg|_{s=s_m}$$

Example A–2. Find the inversion for

$$\frac{A(s)}{B(s)} = \frac{s+3}{s(s+2)(s+1)^2}$$

$$= \frac{A_1}{s} + \frac{A_2}{s+2} + \frac{B_1}{(s+1)^2} + \frac{B_2}{(s+1)}$$

$$A_1 = \frac{(s+3)}{(s+2)(s+1)^2}\bigg|_{s=0} = \frac{3}{2}$$

$$A_2 = \frac{s+3}{s(s+1)^2}\bigg|_{s=-2} = -\frac{1}{2}$$

$$B_1 = \frac{s+3}{s(s+2)}\bigg|_{s=-1} = -2$$

$$B_2 = \left|\frac{d}{ds}\frac{s+3}{s(s+2)}\right|_{s=-1} = -1$$

The desired expansion is

$$\frac{A(s)}{B(s)} = \frac{3}{2s} - \frac{1}{2(s+2)} - \frac{2}{(s+1)^2} - \frac{1}{(s+1)}$$

The inversion is

$$f(t) = \frac{3}{2} - \frac{e^{-2t}}{2} - 2te^{-2t} - e^{-t} \qquad (Ans.)$$

Use of Differential Analyzers

The differential analyzer in one of its forms, mechanical, electronic analog, or electronic digital, has become a common engineering tool for the analysis of automatic control systems. By employing the differential analyzer the various portions of a control system may be studied and the results obtained in either the sinusoidal or transient response form. Discussion in this text will be directed mainly toward use of electronic analog computers, but the general discussion and results apply equally to all forms of computers.

The electronic analog computer employs feedback d-c amplifiers and capacitors and resistor networks to accomplish mathematical manipulation. These elements are shown in Fig. A–5. The d-c amplifier consists

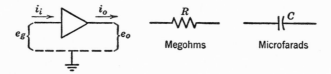

FIG. A–5. Analog computer elements.

usually of ordinary triode tubes with resistance coupling. The input direct voltage is applied to the grid of the first stage, and the output voltage is generally taken from a cathode-follower output section. The operation of the amplifier is such that

$$e_o = -Ke_g \qquad \text{(A–9)}$$

where e_o = output direct voltage with respect to ground
   K = amplifier gain (usually from 10^3 to 10^9)
   e_g = input voltage with respect to ground

The output voltage must be negative relative to the positive input voltage. The capacitors and resistors are high quality components having small leakage and small temperature coefficient.

The *coefficient circuit* is shown in Fig. A–6. All direct current passing

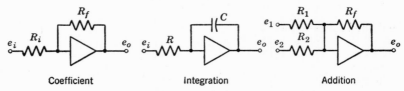

Coefficient   Integration   Addition

FIG. A–6.   Basic computer circuits.

through resistor R_i passes through resistor R_f because the grid current to the input of the amplifier is negligible. Then

$$e_i - e_g = iR_i \qquad \text{(A–10)}$$

and

$$e_g - e_o = iR_f \qquad \text{(A–11)}$$

Combining equations A–9, –10, –11 to eliminate current i and grid voltage e_g,

$$e_o\left[\frac{1}{K}\left(\frac{R_f}{R_i}+1\right)+1\right] = -\frac{R_f}{R_i}e_i \qquad \text{(A–12)}$$

If amplifier gain K is greater than about 1000, and if the resistance ratio R_f/R_i is not greater than about 10, then the equation above reduces to, with small error,

$$e_o = -\left[\frac{R_f}{R_i}\right]e_i \qquad \text{(A–13)}$$

Actually the amplifier gain is usually much higher than 1000, so that the error is less than a small fraction of one per cent. As the last equation shows, this circuit may be used for multiplying by a fixed coefficient. The coefficient is set by selecting the ratio of resistances.

The *integrating circuit* is also shown in Fig. A–6. For the resistor and capacitor

$$e_i - e_g = iR \qquad (A\text{--}14)$$

$$C \frac{d}{dt}(e_g - e_o) = i \qquad (A\text{--}15)$$

Eliminating current i and grid voltage e_g by employing equation A–9, there results

$$RC\left(\frac{1}{K} + 1\right)\frac{de_o}{dt} + \left(\frac{1}{K}\right)e_o = -e_i \qquad (A\text{--}16)$$

Again if amplifier gain is high enough we may write with little error,

$$e_o = -\int \frac{e_i}{RC}\,dt + K' \qquad (A\text{--}17)$$

Thus this circuit provides integration. The initial value of the output is the constant K' and is represented by the initial voltage charge across the capacitor. Integration is always accompanied by a "scale coefficient" of $1/RC$. By selecting values of the time constant RC a change of time scale may be made. Scaling is discussed in a later section.

The *adding circuit* of Fig. A–6 may be analyzed in a manner similar to the coefficient and integrating circuits. With current i_1 in the resistor R_1 and current i_2 through resistor R_2, the equation becomes

$$e_o\left[1 + \frac{1}{K}\left(1 + \frac{R_f}{R_2} + \frac{R_f}{R_1}\right)\right] = -\left(\frac{R_f}{R_1}\right)e_1 - \left(\frac{R_f}{R_2}\right)e_2 \qquad (A\text{--}18)$$

Again if the amplifier gain K is large and if all resistances are equal,

$$e_o = -e_1 - e_2 \qquad (A\text{--}19)$$

Thus the summing circuit simply adds voltages while changing their algebraic signs.

The combinations of coefficient, addition, and integration now allow solution of ordinary linear differential equations with constant coefficients. A voltage input function corresponding to the desired disturbance function is required. A means of indicating or recording direct voltage is also necessary in order to display the solution. The solution of equation proceeds as follows:

1. Solve for the highest derivative term of the equation.
2. Set up the analog circuit for all terms on the right of the equation.
3. Close the loop to compel agreement of left and right sides of the equation.

4. Check to see that the number of amplifiers in each and every closed loop is odd.

5 Check to see if circuits can be simplified.

Example A–3.   Given the equation

$$5\frac{dx}{dt} + x = y(t)$$

Solve for the highest derivative:

$$\frac{dx}{dt} = \frac{1}{5}[y(t) - x]$$

The circuit is displayed in Fig. A–7 in sequence of drawing. First start with a line in which the voltage represents the velocity (highest derivative). Passing through an integrating circuit provides minus x (ignore initial conditions for the present). Next add y(t) and minux x by using the adding

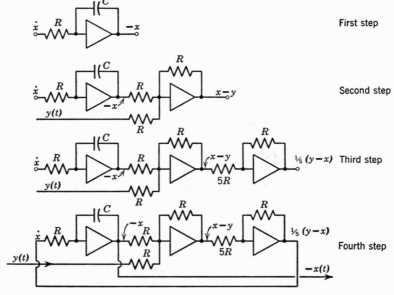

First step

Second step

Third step

Fourth step

FIG. A–7.   Deriving analog circuits.

circuit.   Then multiply by $\frac{1}{5}$ using the coefficient circuit.   This yields the right-hand side of the equation.   Close the loop by connecting the output back to the input, thereby compelling agreement.   Note that there are three amplifiers in the loop.

The disturbance voltage is introduced at y(t) and may be a 20-volt change in voltage representing a step change.   The output (minus x) is recorded or indicated and is the solution to the equation.   As will be shown later this circuit may be simplified.

Example A–4.   Given the simultaneous equations

$$x = z(t) + \dot{y}$$

$$2\dot{y} + 2y = x + \dot{x}$$

The equations are solved for the highest derivatives:

$$\dot{y} = z(t) - x$$

$$-\dot{x} = x - 2\dot{y} - 2y$$

Next draw the circuits for each equation and interconnect the circuits. The result is shown in Fig. A–8. Notice that the amplifier 6 in the lower row is used merely to change signs. This is often necessary in computer problems. Note that each of the three loops contains an odd number of amplifiers.

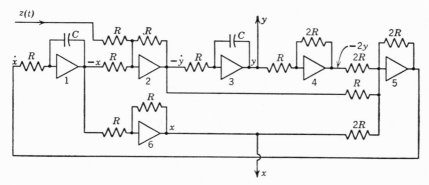

Fig. A–8.   Computer circuit for simultaneous equations.

When the actual analog circuits are drawn out, a short study often indicates that certain combination functions could be employed and some amplifiers eliminated. For example, the circuit in the upper row in Fig. A–9 could be simplified to one circuit as shown. The circuit employing fewer components is always more accurate.

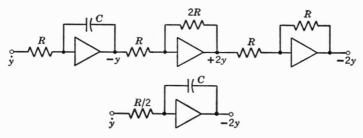

Fig. A–9.   Example of circuit simplification.

Time scaling is the alteration of the time scale of the actual problem. Consider a differential equation,

$$M \frac{d^2x}{dt^2} + B \frac{dx}{dt} + Kx = y(t) \qquad \text{(A-20)}$$

Select a change of time variable so that

$$\tau = \alpha t \qquad \text{(A-21)}$$

where τ = "machine" time
α = time coefficient
t = "real" time

Substituting equation A–21 in equation A–20,

$$\alpha^2 M \frac{d^2x}{d\tau^2} + \alpha B \frac{dx}{d\tau} + Kx = y\left(\frac{\tau}{\alpha}\right)$$

Thus a time scaling requires alteration of the coefficients of the differential equation and is employed for several reasons:

1. The actual problem solution may require so much time that speeding up is necessary to save time.

2. The actual problem solution occurs so quickly that a slowing down is necessary to "see" what is going on.

3. Better accuracy is obtained by operating a computer in the best ranges of time events, neither too fast nor too slow.

The coefficients set into the computer ($\alpha^2 M$, αB) must take into account the fact that every integration is accompanied by the multiplication of the solution by the inverse of the integrator time constant RC. This is handled most easily by labelling every point on the computer diagram with the proper values of variables, including the scaling.

Example A–5. Set up the computer diagram for

$$10 \frac{dx}{dt} + x = y(t)$$

where t is in minutes. Scaling,

$$\frac{dx}{d\tau} = \frac{1}{10\alpha} (y - x)$$

The circuit shown in Fig. A–10 is simplified from that of Fig. A–7. If the computer is to speed up the problem by a factor of 60, then

$$\alpha = \frac{\tau}{t} = \frac{\text{machine time}}{\text{real time}} = \frac{1}{60}$$

The capacitor and resistance values that may be selected are shown in the table below.

R_2	R_1	C
1 megohm	1 megohm	10 mfd
5 megohms	5 megohms	2 mfd
10 megohms	10 megohms	1 mfd

All these combinations provide the same scaling and the selections of one or the other is dictated by the particular kind of computer employed.

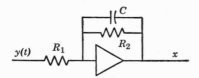

FIG. A–10.   Example of time scaling.

Magnitude scaling may be necessary in automatic control problems when a specific physical problem is being solved or when nonlinear effects are present. Let

$$X = \beta x \tag{A-22}$$

where X = machine volts
β = magnitude coefficient
x = real variable

Substituting in equation as used for time scaling,

$$\alpha^2 M \frac{d^2X}{d\tau^2} + \alpha B \frac{dX}{d\tau} + KX = \beta y\left(\frac{\tau}{\alpha}\right)$$

Thus the only effect of magnitude scaling is to alter the magnitude of the disturbance signal $y(t)$ when solving linear equations.

Example A–6.   Scale the equation

$$\frac{d^2x}{dt^2} + 2\frac{dx}{dt} + x = t$$

The scaled equation is

$$\alpha^2 \frac{d^2X}{d\tau^2} + 2\alpha \frac{dX}{d\tau} + X = \frac{\beta}{\alpha}\tau$$

Suppose that a time-scale factor of $\frac{1}{60}$ is employed so that $\alpha = \frac{1}{60}$ in order to speed up the problem. Suppose also that 50 volts equals 10 in. so that $\beta = 5$ volts per in. The disturbing function originally proceeded at the rate of 1 in. per sec. The disturbing function must be a direct voltage changing at the rate of

$$\frac{\beta}{\alpha} = \frac{1 \text{ in.}}{\text{sec}}\left(\frac{60}{1}\right)\frac{5 \text{ volts}}{\text{in.}} = 300 \text{ volts/sec}$$

If this rate of change of voltage is too high for the available function generating equipment then new values of time and magnitude scaling must be selected until all parts of the problem satisfactorily fit the computing equipment.

Analog computers may be used with a repetitive or nonrepetitive method of operation. In nonrepetitive operation the problem is scaled in time to take place in approximately 1–10 min, the disturbance or input signal actuated once, and the solution plotted on paper by an oscillographic recorder. In repetitive operation the problem is scaled in time to take place in approximately 0.010 to 1.0 sec and the disturbance or input is inserted as a repetitive wave of frequency 100 cps to 1 cps. The solution is, in this case, usually displayed on an oscilloscope, sometimes photographically recorded. In repetitive operation, the integrators must usually be returned to zero voltage and initial conditions inserted in the form of repetitive pulses. This action is termed "clamping."

Initial conditions correspond in every case to the initial charge on the capacitors. Since there are a number of integrators equal to the order of the differential equation, there will be a like number of initial conditions to be set. For such purposes a d-c power supply with a number of outlets must be available. Each capacitor is connected by a switch to the voltage to which it is to be initially charged. After all capacitors are charged the switch is turned to the proper connection. The solution may then begin by introducing the disturbance function. Fortunately in automatic control zero initial conditions are very often used.

The *input* or *disturbance* must be introduced as a voltage at some function of time after time scaling,

$$y(t) = y\left(\frac{\tau}{\alpha}\right)$$

The input signals most commonly used in automatic control are:

1. Step change which can be provided by a simple switch with a battery or a square-wave generator set for long period.

2. Impulse can be simulated by a rectangular wave or pulse generator.

3. Ramp function $y = t$ can be generated with a triangular wave generator or by integrating a step function.

4. Parabolic function $y = t^2$ can be generated by a twice-integrated step function or by squaring techniques.

5. Sinusoidal functions are best generated by an oscillator but are sometimes generated in the computer using two integrators in series.

The *output* of the computer must be displayed in order to obtain the solution to the problem. This is usually done on an oscillograph recorder but the solution may also be displayed on an oscilloscope. Either method is satisfactory when it is recalled that specific and accurate solutions to automatic control problems is usually not necessary. The computer is more often employed for system studies than for particular problem solution.

Nonlinear operations are often encountered in process control and must be accommodated in the analog computer. In fact, some nonlinear problems can only be solved by a computer. Multiplication and division can be accomplished with most analog computers by means of specialized electronic circuits, the details of which may be found in many reference books.[1]

1. Multiplication: Multipliers can be used to multiply two functions of time:

$$x(t)y(t) = z(t)$$

These have two input points (accepting voltages) and one output voltage. Whereas the product of two large numbers is even larger, it is common to reduce the output by a factor, as

$$z = \tfrac{1}{25}yx$$

most multipliers will multiply either positive or negative values.

2. Division may sometimes be obtained by the feedback circuit given by

$$\frac{y}{x} = (1 - x)\frac{y}{x} + y$$

as shown in Fig. A–11. In this circuit extreme caution should be used in handling negative values so that the feedback loop is stable. Other

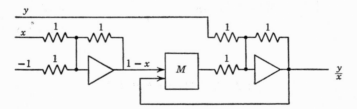

Fig. A–11.   Division by multiplication.

nonlinear effects such as hysteresis, dead zone, and limiting may be accurately simulated by employing diode circuits. A function generator may also be employed to introduce nonlinear functions.

[1] G. A. Korn and T. M. Korn, *Electronic Analog Computers*, McGraw-Hill Book Company, New York, 1952.

EXPERIMENT 1. PROCESS TIME CONSTANT

Preparation: Chapter 2

The object of this experiment is to determine the transient response to a step change of a first-order fluid process.

The process, shown in Fig. A–12, consists of a fluid storage vessel with an inlet flow set by a control valve and with the outflow through a valve, orifice,

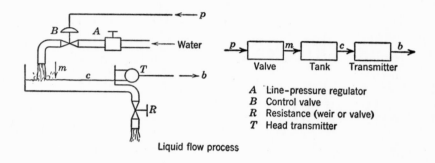

Liquid flow process

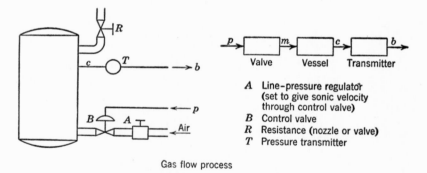

Gas flow process

FIG. A–12. Time-constant study.

nozzle or other restricting device. With the inflow set to a midvalue, and after waiting a short time for steady-state conditions to be achieved, the pressure or head in the vessel is constant, and outflow equals inflow. A quick change of inflow of about 10 per cent magnitude will cause a pressure or head change in the vessel. This change should be recorded on an instrument. This is the transient response of the process. The time constant can be determined from the experiment and compared to the calculated value.

The following procedure is suggested:

1. Measure the outflow resistance by plotting pressure or head versus flow for several values near the operating point. The resistance is calculated from the slope of the curve:

$$R = \frac{dh}{dq} \quad \text{(liquid) sec/ft}^2$$

$$R = \frac{dp}{dq} \quad \text{(gas) sec/ft}^2$$

2. Measure the capacitance of the vessel:

$$C = A \quad \text{(liquid) ft}^2$$

$$C = \frac{V}{R_g T} \quad \text{(isothermal gas) ft}^2$$

where R_g = ideal gas constant (53.3 ft/R, air).

3. Calculate the time constant $T = RC$.

4. Record the process transient response on a suitable pressure or head recorder. Use the same operating points as in previous steps.

5. Measure the time constant as the time for 63.2 per cent of the total change. This value should check the calculated value within 10 per cent.

6. Sketch the block diagram of the apparatus and show the system function in terms of its actual numbers, R and T:

$$\frac{R}{Ts + 1}$$

EXPERIMENT 2. PROPORTIONAL-INTEGRAL CONTROLLERS

Preparation: Chapter 3 required, Chapter 6 suggested

The object of this experiment is to investigate the operation of a pneumatic or electronic controller with proportional-integral action and to determine the calibration of the proportional and integral adjustments.

The controller to be tested should be inspected carefully and its general operation understood through the manufacturers' catalogs and instruction books. In particular the controller should be connected to supply air of the correct pressure or a line of proper voltage and frequency. The output of the controller should be connected to a large indicating instrument and to a control element in accordance with the usual method of installation.

Either the measuring element c or the set point v of the controller should be fixed, preferably the measuring element, so that the set point can be varied manually to test the action. The measuring element input (or pointer) should be positioned at a midvalue. The integral action should be turned off (integral time to infinity) or as near to off as possible. The proportional sensitivity should be set to a middle value; 50 per cent band or 0.5 gain is satisfactory.

The set point may then be varied in small steps and the output of the controller noted for each value of the input, thereby calibrating the proportional action.

The integral action may be tested by measuring the time required for the output signal to change a specified amount. With the proportional sensitivity set to midvalue and the integral time adjustment set to the smallest value (fastest reset rate), move the set point up or down until the output remains constant and is at a midvalue. The integral adjustment should now be turned to the largest value (off) and the set point moved to give a change in output of about 10 per cent.

The time required to repeat the original change (10 per cent) may be measured with a stop or wrist watch and is the integral time of the controller.

The following procedure is suggested:

1. Fix measuring element or input at midvalue. Turn integral adjustment to as near off as possible and set proportional sensitivity to desired value.

2. Calibrate output variable against values of set point and plot on linear coordinate paper. Repeat for a number of values of proportional sensitivity. The results should be a set of straight lines. Calculate the slope

$$\frac{dm}{dv} = \text{proportional sensitivity}$$

3. Turn integral adjustment full on and set proportional sensitivity to midvalue. Move set point until output is stationary at a midvalue. This is zero actuating signal. Turn integral adjustment off.

4. Move set point to give a change of output of some definite amount, such as 1 psi or 10 per cent or 0.2 milliamperes. Turn integral adjustment quickly to the desired value.

5. Measure the time required to repeat this definite change of output set above. This is the integral time or inverse of reset rate.

6. Sketch the block diagram of the apparatus and show the system function in terms of its actual numbers (adjustments at midvalue).

$$K_c \left(1 + \frac{1}{T_i s}\right)$$

EXPERIMENT 3. INTEGRAL CONTROLLERS

Preparation: Chapter 3 required, Chapter 6 suggested

The object of this experiment is to determine the action of an integral or proportional-speed floating controller.

The controller to be tested should be inspected carefully and its operation understood through the manufacturers' catalogs and instruction books. In particular, the controller should be connected in accordance with the usual method of installation. The output of the controller should be connected to a large indicating instrument. Either the measuring element c or the set point v of the controller should be fixed, preferably the measuring element, so that the set point can be varied manually. A given change of set point will result in the controller output having a rate of change (dm/dt) directly proportional to the magnitude and sense of the change in set point.

The following procedure is suggested:

1. Fix measuring element or input at midvalue.

2. Change set-point value until output is stationary and at a midvalue. This is zero actuating signal.

3. Change set-point value a small but definite amount, and measure the rate of change of the controller output. Repeat for several values of set point change.

4. Plot rate of change of output versus values of set point on linear co-ordinate paper. Calculate the integral time from

$$T_i = \frac{e}{\dfrac{dm}{dt}}$$

5. Explain why the upper and lower limits of velocity of output exist.

6. Sketch the block diagram of the apparatus and show the system function in terms of its actual numbers.

$$\frac{1}{T_i s}$$

EXPERIMENT 4. PROPORTIONAL-DERIVATIVE CONTROLLERS

Preparation: Chapter 3, Chapter 6, and La Place transform

The object of this experiment is to determine the effect on the controller output of the derivative action provided by a proportional-derivative controller.

The controller to be tested should be inspected carefully and its general operation understood through the manufacturers' catalogs and instruction books. In particular, the controller should be connected to supply air of the correct pressure or a line of proper voltage and frequency. The output of the controller should be connected to a recording instrument and to a control element in accordance with the usual method of installation.

The measuring-element input c of the controller should be fixed so that the set point can be manually varied in order to test the action. The input should be set to a midvalue. The proportional sensitivity should be set to a large value; 100 per cent band or 1.0 gain.

The set point may then be changed quickly from one value to another value about 5 per cent higher or lower, thereby simulating a step change. The change of output signal should be recorded and from this record it is possible to obtain the derivative time and the controller lag as will be explained in the following section.

The transfer function of the controller is given by

$$m = K_c \frac{T_D s + 1}{T_L s + 1} e_i$$

where m = controller output
 T_D = derivative time
 T_L = time constant
 e_i = input signal
 K_c = proportional sensitivity

The response to a step change of magnitude E is given by

$$M(s) = K_c \frac{T_D s + 1}{T_L s + 1} \frac{E}{s}$$

This transform can be written as

$$M(s) = \frac{T_D E K_c}{T_L s + 1} + \frac{E K_c}{s(T_L s + 1)}$$

and inverted

$$m(t) = \left[1 + \left(\frac{T_D - T_L}{T_L}\right) e^{-t/T_L}\right] K_c E$$

This curve is plotted in Fig. A–13 for $T_D = 5T_L$ and $K_c = 0.5$. The ratio of the maximum to the final value of m is the time constant ratio T_D/T_L. The 63.2 per cent time of the decay is T_L.

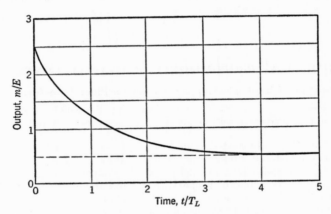

FIG. A–13. Proportional-derivative response.

The following procedure is suggested:

1. Fix measuring element at midvalue. Set proportional sensitivity to 100 per cent or 1.0 gain. Set derivative time to moderate value (approximately 30 sec). Move set point slowly until controller output is at midvalue.

2. Make a step change of set point of some definite amount, say 5 per cent, and record the resulting change in controller output.

3. From a record of the controller output, measure the highest output obtained (see Fig. A–13). The ratio of time constants is the ratio of the highest value to the final value of output:

$$\frac{T_D}{T_L} = \frac{m_{\max} - m_i}{m_\infty - m_i}$$

where m_i = the initial output before set point was changed.

$m_{\max}$ = maximum value at time of change (it may be necessary to extrapolate the curve backward to find this point).

m_∞ = final value of output.

4. From the record measure the lag time constant T_L and calculate T_D.

5. Repeat for several magnitudes of changes and in both directions.

6. Sketch the block diagram of the apparatus and show the system function in terms of its actual numbers (adjustments at midvalue).

$$\frac{K_c(1 + T_D s)}{1 + T_L s}$$

EXPERIMENT 5. PROPORTIONAL CONTROL OF A PROCESS

Preparation: Chapters 2 and 3, or 6 and 4

The object of this experiment is to measure and calculate the open-loop gain for a proportional automatic process control system.

The control system is shown in block diagram form in Fig. A–14. A recording instrument should be connected at feedback variable b in order to

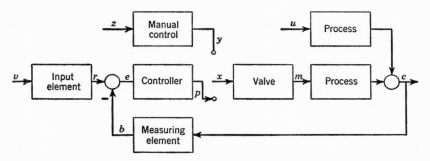

FIG. A–14.   Process control loop.

record the transient response of the process under control. The automatic controller should have manual control means by which manual control of the process ($y \rightarrow x$ connection) can be obtained. Automatic control is achieved by switching in the controller ($p \rightarrow x$ connection).

The open-loop response, b output to x input, should be second-order, otherwise loop gain is not easily calculated. The response is generally

$$b = \frac{R}{(T_1 s + 1)(T_2 s + 1)} x$$

where R = process or system sensitivity (units of b/units of x) and the two time constants may be (a) valve and process, (b) valve and measuring element, (c) process (two), (d) process and measuring element. Other combinations are not likely to occur. It is assumed that all other lags are negligible.

The two time constants (T_1 and T_2) may be either calculated or measured. The loop gain (RK_c) can then be calculated for proportional control:

$$RK_c = \frac{1}{4\zeta^2}\left(\frac{T_1}{T_2} + \frac{T_2}{T_1} + 2\right) - 1$$

where ζ = damping ratio of closed-loop response.

The process can be placed on automatic control and the proportional sensitivity of the controller adjusted until a transient response to a set-point change (or load change) exhibits the desired damping ratio (compare to curves in the appendix). The loop gain is measured by switching to manual control and making a steady-state test of the ratio p/x. The test value should be compared to the calculated value.

Two difficulties are often encountered in this experiment. First, make sure that all variables are operating in the same range of values during all tests. Fluid processes are usually nonlinear and values of resistance change with operating point. Second, use a sufficiently small amplitude of signal so that none of the apparatus is caused to go to limits.

The following procedure is suggested:

1. Select operating set point v for system and check to see that all variables p, m, c, and b are in middle of respective ranges.

2. Determine the system time constants (use previous data if possible).

3. Calculate the loop gain RK_c for one-third damping ratio.

4. Experimentally determine the value of proportional sensitivity K_c to give one-third damping ratio on control record.

5. Use manual control to check loop gain. Set Δz to give a Δx and measure Δp divided by Δx. Check with calculated value.

6. Calculate the static error and offset.

7. Test the static error due to a change in set point, and compare to the calculated value.

8. Test the offset due to a change in load (if a load change can be made), and compare to the calculated value.

9. Sketch the block diagram of the apparatus and show the system function in terms of actual numbers.

EXPERIMENT 6. PROPORTIONAL-INTEGRAL-DERIVATIVE CONTROL OF A PROCESS

Preparation: Chapters 2 and 3, or 6 and 4

The object of this experiment is to determine the "best" setting of a proportional-integral-derivative controller when controlling an actual process.

The control system is shown in the block diagram of Fig. A–14. A recording instrument should be connected at feedback variable b in order to record the response of the process to various changes of parameter. The open-loop response, b output to r input, may be of any order, but the number and size of all lags should be known. It is preferable to have two time constants so that the response is

$$b = \frac{R}{(T_1 s + 1)(T_2 s + 1)} x$$

The time constants may be determined by calculation or measurement and the open-loop gain (RK_c) for a given damping ratio may thereby be calculated.

There are three methods of determining the proper value for proportional-sensitivity:

1. Analytical method wherein the proper damping is determined from solution of the differential equation. For processes with only two time constants, T_1, T_2,

$$RK_c = \text{open-loop gain} = \frac{1}{4\zeta^2}\left(\frac{T_2}{T_1} + \frac{T_1}{T_2} + 2\right) - 1$$

where ζ = damping ratio (0.33 is a good value). This value of loop gain may be tried, and the period of oscillation noted (P_p). The apparent lag of the process is

$$L = 0.2P_p$$

The settings of integral and derivative time may now be determined by the Ziegler–Nichols equations.

2. Reaction curve method wherein the response of the open-loop system (minus the controller) is obtained from a step disturbance, as detailed in Chapter 4. The parameters R, L, N, K are then scaled from the curve and the desired settings computed.

3. Stability limit method wherein the response of the closed-loop system is observed for gradually increased settings of proportional sensitivity. Note the value of proportional sensitivity K_u which just causes continuous oscillation. Note also the period of oscillation P_u. Then

$$K_c = 0.6K_u$$

and

$$L = 0.25P_u$$

The settings of integral and derivative time may now be determined by the Ziegler–Nichols equations.

The procedure is as follows:

1. Select operating set point v for system and check to see that all variables p, m, c, and b are in middle of respective ranges.

2. Turn off integral effect and derivative effect.

3. Gradually increase proportional sensitivity so that a steady oscillation begins. Make sure that none of the variables p, m, c, or b is allowed to limit during this operation. Move set point to see that marginal stability is definite and sustained. Note proportional sensitivity K_u and period of oscillation P_u.

4. Set proportional sensitivity to 60 per cent of the value causing marginal stability. Check now by moving the set point slightly to see that the transient response is satisfactory; one-ninth ratio of succeeding amplitudes is suggested. Trim setting if necessary. This setting will be denoted as K_{co}.

5. Calculate the "apparent lag" L of the process as one quarter of the observed period of oscillation.

6. The settings of the proportional, integral and derivative effects should now be calculated for a *nonseries-type* controller:

$$K_c = \frac{5}{3}K_{co}$$

$$T_d = \frac{1}{3}L$$

$$T_i = 2.5L$$

For a *series-type* controller:

$$K_i' = \frac{4}{3}K_{co}$$

$$K_d' = 0.4L$$

$$T_i' = 2L$$

With the selected settings check the stability by moving the set point slightly to see that the transient repsonse is satisfactory. Trim the settings if necessary, maintaining a one-ninth ratio of amplitudes, good return, and small period of oscillation.

7. Check the settings obtained above by employing the reaction-curve method.

8. Compare the various values of parameters K_c, T_i, and T_d obtained in the tests and discuss any significant differences.

EXPERIMENT 7. ANALOG COMPUTER ANALYSIS OF CONTROL

Preparation: Chapters 2, 3, and 4, and Appendix

The object of this experiment is to set up a process with proportional-integral-derivative control on an analog computer and determine the transient performance with proper controller adjustments.

For illustration a system consisting of two time constant elements in series under proportional-integral-derivative control, with the control element having a significant time constant of its own, will be considered. The analog computer circuit is shown in Fig. A–15. The control-element (valve) time constant is represented by amplifier 5.

The transfer function of this part of the analog is

$$\frac{m}{x} = \frac{1}{R_5 C_5 s + 1}$$

where $R_5 C_5$ is the valve time constant (usually 1 to 10 sec). The first process time constant is represented at amplifier 6,

$$\frac{h}{m} = \frac{1}{R_6 C_6 s + 1}$$

so that the process time constant is set by $R_6 C_6$. The second process time constant is represented at amplifier 7,

$$\frac{c}{h} = \frac{1}{R_7 C_7 s + 1}$$

and this process time constant is set by $R_7 C_7$.

The controller is represented by amplifiers 1, 2, 3, and 4. The set-point voltage v and the controlled variable c feed into the amplifier 1. The amplifier is set for a maximum gain of 10 with the potentiometer R_3 at maximum. The proportional sensitivity is therefore set by R_3 and so is the loop gain. The open-loop gain may therefore be read directly at potentiometer R_3. The second amplifier provides proportional-derivative action, and the third amplifier is necessary for sign changing. The transfer function of amplifiers 2 and 3 is

$$\frac{y}{z} = [S_2(1 - S_2)R_2 C_2]s + 1$$

so that an adjustment S_2 of potentiometer R_2 will vary the derivative time from 0 to 0.25 $R_2 C_2$. The input resistor R_2 to amplifier 2 is fixed but has the same resistance value as potentiometer R_2. Only potentiometer R_2 in the

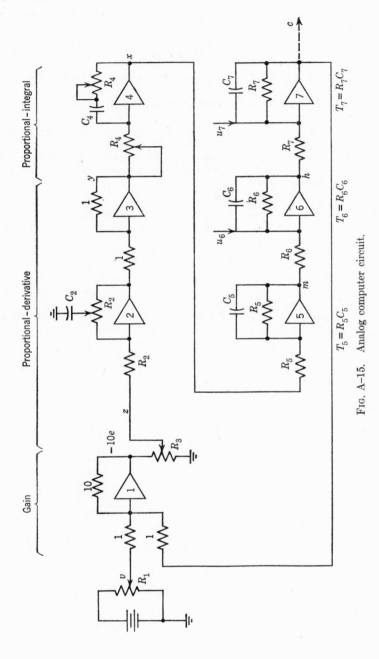

Fig. A–15.   Analog computer circuit.

feedback is adjusted. Amplifier 4 provides proportional-integral action and its transfer function is

$$\frac{x}{y} = 1 + \frac{1}{S_4 R_4 C_4 s}$$

so that an adjustment S_4 of potentiometer R_4 will vary the integral time from 0 to $R_4 C_4$.

Load changes may be introduced at u_6 and u_7 if their effects are to be observed.

The entire circuit should next be time and amplitude scaled thereby selecting values of all resistors and capacitors, R_1 through R_7, and C_2 through C_7.

When the computer is set up and ready for operation the open-loop gain may be determined. The derivative and integral time can then be set and the effect of load changes observed.

The following procedure is suggested:

1. Measure the time constants T_5, T_6, and T_7 for the process to be investigated. If one of the time constants is zero, simply remove the corresponding capacitor in the computer circuit.

2. Time scale the computer circuit. The time scaling will depend upon the make of computer in use. In general, since this is an exploratory problem and accuracy is not important, the fastest scaling should be used. For the Philbrick computer a scale factor of $\alpha = 4 \times 10^{-4}$ is suggested. Set the computed values of resistors and capacitors in the circuit.

3. Set the derivative time to zero and the integral time to infinity (as large as possible). Try a loop gain of 5.0 (set potentiometer R_3 to 50 per cent) and test the stability by moving the set point. Select a value of gain that gives a desirable transient response.

4. Turn in derivative time (potentiometer R_2) and increase loop gain about 25 per cent. Try several related values of derivative time and loop gain until a transient response with good stability and minimum period of oscillation is obtained.

5. Turn off the derivative action and decrease loop gain by 35 per cent from the last step (90 per cent of original value). Set the integral time to give a good return *on a load change.*

6. Turn in derivative time to 30 per cent more than the value set in step 4. Set integral time to double that value found in step 5. Set proportional sensitivity to about 20 per cent higher than in step 5. Try several values near these settings to see if a better response can be obtained. Use the highest derivative time possible because this will improve loop gain and provide smaller period of oscillation.

7. Leave all settings at their best values and turn out derivative action to show its effect. Next turn out integral action and with a load change at u_6 or u_7 determine whether the offset is

$$\frac{1}{1 + \text{loop gain}}$$

as a fraction.

8. Eliminate the control-element lag by removing capacitor C_5. Find new control settings to determine whether there is a significant improvement when the control-element lag is removed.

EXPERIMENT 8. TWO-POSITION CONTROL

Preparation: Chapters 2, 3, and 4

The object of this experiment is to observe the action of a two-position controller with differential gap.

The process should consist of one large capacitance (or time constant) together with a minimum number of small time constants. A small dead time may also be present. The two-position controller should have a differential gap, preferably adjustable. The controlled variable should be recorded so that various features of the behavior can be studied.

The following procedure is suggested:

1. Move the set point with the measured (feedback) variable maintained at a fixed value and determine the value of the differential gap G.

2. Start the system in operation and maintain the control element open. The maximum value attained by the controlled variable may be called K above that obtained when the control element is off.

3. Set the set point at the value $K/2$ and let the system control about this point for a short time. Note the amplitude of oscillation A and the period of oscillation P. (Note: always measure amplitude as double amplitudes and divide by 2 to obtain G and A.)

4. From the Ziegler–Nichols equations, calculate the lag ratio (see Chapter 4)

$$R = \frac{L}{T} = \ln \frac{K - G}{K - A}$$

where L = apparent dead time and T is an apparent process time constant.

5. Calculate the apparent dead time from

$$L = \frac{P}{\dfrac{4}{R} \tanh^{-1} \dfrac{2A}{K}}$$

The apparent process time constant T may now be calculated.

6. Estimate the amplitude and period of oscillation if differential gap G is zero. The following equations are used:

$$A = V(1 - e^{-R})$$

$$P = 4L \frac{1}{R} \tanh^{-1} \frac{A}{V}$$

where V = value of set point. Verify by actual test.

7. Move the set point to a new value not equal to $K/2$. With a given differential gap, the amplitude and period of oscillation should not change significantly when an unsymmetrical cycle is observed.

8. Move the set point to the opposite direction as in step 7 and observe that the saw-tooth-like wave reverses its symmetry.

9. Explain how the magnitude of "load" on a system can be determined by inspection of the shape of the saw-tooth wave.

EXPERIMENT 9. CONTROL VALVE CHARACTERISTICS

Preparation: Chapters 2, 3, 4, 7, and 8

The object of this experiment is to synthesize a flow-position characteristic for a fluid control valve used for process control.

There are sometimes encountered problems in automatic process control in which the maintenance of controller stability under all conditions is difficult even if the pressure differential across the control valve is constant. In that case a specified control characteristic may be selected to keep loop gain at its best level. However, nothing is usually done about maintaining integral time or derivative time at their best values.

The process should be a fluid process (as in Fig. A–12) with a nonlinear resistance at the outlet, the usual case. The controller should be set for two responses such as proportional-derivative. Although the industrial problem usually involves control for various load changes, it is easier in the laboratory to move the controller set point. Consequently, a valve characteristic will be synthesized for various set points. A different valve characteristic would be required for variable load but it would be obtained through the same procedure.

The suggested procedure is

1. Set the controller in operation and check all operating values of variables to insure correct operation.

2. Beginning with the set point at a midvalue (50 per cent) determine the best loop gain and integral or derivative time to give a certain transient response. Record the value of flow through the control valve required to maintain the set point, and record the value of controller output x at each of these points. Note these values.

3. Repeat operation 2 for as many set-point values as are desired, at least 20, 35, 50, 65, 80 per cent. The loop gain is

$$\frac{dx}{de}\frac{dm}{dx}\frac{dc}{dm} = K$$

where $\dfrac{dx}{de}$ = controller sensitivity = K_c

$\dfrac{dm}{dx}$ = valve sensitivity = K_v

$\dfrac{dc}{dm}$ = process sensitivity = K_p

The set point (or controlled variable) should be plotted against valve flow. The slope of this curve is K_p.

4. The required valve characteristic may now be synthesized by calculating

$$K_v = \frac{dm}{dx} = \frac{K}{\dfrac{dc}{dm}\cdot\dfrac{dx}{de}}$$

5. The controller proportional sensitivity is to remain constant, so

$$K_v = \frac{dm}{dx} = \frac{K}{K_c K_p}$$

Use the values of K and K_p, and calculate the slope of the curve K_v at each value of flow m.

6. By cut and try, parabolic curve fitting and integration, or other methods, find the curve $m = f(x)$. Compare this curve to the actual plot of m versus x for the valve in use, and indicate whether it has the desired characteristic.

7. If the process is of second order and the constants are known, use the analytical method given in Chapter 8 to verify these results.

Answers to Problems

1–2. Furnace thermostat, hot water heater control, water-pressure regulator, toilet tank water-level control, electric iron thermostat, refrigeration control.

1–3. Wattmeter, water meter, gas meter, thermometer, pressure gage.

2–1. Inflow, outflow, inlet temperature, outlet temperature, electric current.

2–2. Inflow behind dam, outflow, head, weir setting.

2–3. Air temperature, stack loss, air infiltration, air inlet temperature, heat loss, gas flow.

2–4. $2H/5Q$

2–5. H/nQ

2–6. $C = \pi(Dh - h^2)$ for $O \leqq h \leqq D$

2–7. Area proportional to square root of head.

2–8. Area proportional to inverse of square root of head.

2–9.

$e = Ri$	electrical	Ohm's law
$e = Ri$	fluid	Poisseuille–Hagen law
$\sqrt{e} = Ri$	fluid	Bernoulli's law
$e^4 = Ri$	heat	Stefan–Boltzmann law
$e = Ri$	heat	Fourier law

2–10. 0.05 in.^{2} isothermal **2–11.** 2900.0 sec F/Btu

2–12. 8.3 Btu per F **2–13.** 0.028 Btu/F

2–14. Hydrogen smallest (least molecular weight), carbon dioxide largest.

2–15. 77.0 sec

2–16. 300 min

2–18. Horizontal if $4L > \pi D$

2–19. AB, AL, BL, $\sqrt{A^2 + B^2}L$, $\sqrt{A^2 + L^2}B$, $\sqrt{B^2 + L^2}A$

2–20. $K = 0.057$ lb/in.; $D = 6.5$ lb sec/ft

2–21. $R = \dfrac{1}{2\pi KL} \ln \dfrac{D_o}{D_i}$

2–22. $[T_{21}T_{22}s^2 + (T_{21} + T_{22})s]c = R_2 m - (T_{22}s + 1)R_2 u_2$

2–23. $[RCR_1C_1s^2 + (RC + R_1C + R_1C_1)s + 1]c = R_1 m$

2–24. $(RCs + 1)c = -RK_v m + Ru$

2–25. $(Ms^2 + Bs + K)x = f + Ky + Bsz$

2–26. $(Ms^2 + Bs)x = f$

2–27. $f = Bsx$

2–28. $m_2(R + R_1 + RR_1Cs) = m_1(R_1 + RR_1Cs)$

2–29. $[(R_1 + R)Cs + 1]m_2 = (RCs + 1)m_1$

2–30. $(T^2s^2 + 3Ts + 1)m_2 = m_1$

2–31. $[(L/g)s^2 + (B/A\gamma)s + 1]c = m/\gamma$, where γ = fluid density, A = tube area

2–32. $(Ms^2 + Bs + K)c = Am$, $K = WRA^2T/V^2$

V = volume under piston, R = gas constant, T = temperature

2–33. $(Ts + 1)c = m$, $T = \rho DC/4H$

ρ = density, D = diameter, C = sp. ht., H = conv. coeff.

3–4. $T_1T_2/T_1 + T_2$; $T/(T_1 + T_2)$; $(T_1 + T_2)$

3–5. Prop. K; integral KT

3–6. Prop. T_2/T_1; integral T_2

3–7. Prop. $(T_1 + T_2)/T_2$; integral $(T_1 + T_2)$; derivative $T_1T_2/(T_1 + T_2)$

3–8. Prop. K; derivative $(T_1 + T_2)/K$

3–9. Prop. T_1/T_2; derivative T_2

3–10. Prop. 1; derivative $2T$; second derivative T^2.

4–6. 25%   **4–7.** 10%

4–8. Yes   **4–9.** $4C = K_cT_i$

4–10. $T_d + C/K_c$ **4–11.** $U/(1 + RK_c)$

4–12. $2K_iRT = (1 + RK_c)^2$ **4–13.** $K_c = T_1/4R_1T_2$; zero

4–14. $(T_1 + R_1K_cT_d)^2 9 = 4R_1K_cT_1T_2$; $P = 2\pi \sqrt{(T_1T_2)/(R_1K_c)}$

4–15. $P = 2\pi \sqrt{T_1T_2/(R_1K_c + 1)}$; $E_o = U/(R_1K_c + 1)$

5–1. 5 deg   **5–2.** About 7 sec

5–3. 0.54 sec   **5–4.** $R = 12,000$ sec/ft²; $T = 0.06$ sec

5–5. 1.6 sec   **5–6.** Lag = $T_1 + T_2$

6–1. $Le = Kv + (L - K)c$

6–2. $m = \dfrac{1}{1 + \dfrac{K_DK_s}{K_eA}} e$ where K_D = diaphragm stiffness

K_s = supply orifice coeff. $\partial w/\partial m$, K_e = control nozzle coeff. $\partial w/\partial x$, A = diaphragm area

6–3. $m = \left(1 - \dfrac{A_2}{A_1}\right) e$

6–4. $q = \dfrac{K\pi D}{\sqrt{T}} [P_{av}.e + E_{av}.p]$

6–5. $(Ts + 1)m = K_ce$, $T = \dfrac{A^2}{K(K_2 + K_3)}$, $K_c = \dfrac{AK_1}{K(K_2 + K_3)}$

6–6. $\Delta P/\Delta w = K/AC$ where K = spring gradient, A = diaphragm area, C = nozzle coefficient $\partial w/\partial x$

6–7. $m = -\left(\dfrac{1}{Ts} + 1\right) e$; $T = RC$, prop. integral

6–8. $m = -\left(\dfrac{1}{Ts} + 1\right) e$; $T = RC$, prop. integral

6–9. $m = -(1 + Ts)e$, $T = RC$, prop. derivative

6–11. Fraction "on" $= \dfrac{P}{2}\left[1 - \dfrac{2}{\pi}\sin^{-1}\left(1 - \dfrac{e}{E}\right)\right]$,

where E = radius of circle.

6–12. $H = Ts/(Ts + 1)$

7–1. $HP = \dfrac{MA^2\omega^3}{1100}\sin 2\omega t$; 48 hp   **7–3.** hp $= PQ/1720E$

7–4. 2,628,000   **7–5.** 10π lb

7–6. $R(C + A^2/K)$ **7–8.** $\dfrac{m}{M} = \dfrac{1}{R}\left[1 + (R - 1)\left(\dfrac{x}{X}\right)^2\right]$

7–9. 1.0 in.   **7–10.** 420 gpm

8–1. A/H from $C = \dfrac{A}{H}\left(\dfrac{G_1G_2H}{1 + G_1G_2H}\right)v$

8–2. $T = \sqrt{3}\,T_1$, $T_2 = T_1/\sqrt{27}$

8–3. (a) Zero (b) Zero (c) Zero (d) Zero

8–4. Probably yes.   Period is reduced by 67%.

8–6. $C_2 = \alpha KK_c\dfrac{T_m s + 1}{\alpha Ts + 1}$, $\alpha = (KK_c + 1)^{-1}$

8–7. With $E_o = \dfrac{K_3}{1 + K_2K_3 + K_1K_2K_3}$

Without $E_o = \dfrac{K_3}{1 + K_1K_2K_3}$

8–8. (a) Square wave as shown.   (b) Triangular wave.

8–9. Zero

8–10. $T_i = 4K_1A/K_2{}^2$, A = vessel area, $K_1 = \partial q/\partial x$ valve, $K_2 = \partial q/\partial c$ valve.

8–11. $K_1K_c = \dfrac{A}{4T_v} + \dfrac{T_vK_2{}^2}{4A} - \dfrac{K_2}{2}$,

where A = vessel area,
$K_1 = \partial q/\partial x$ valve,
$K_2 = \partial q/\partial c$ valve

9–1. (a) $1/\omega T$, $-90°$, (b) $(1 + \omega^2T^2)$, $2\tan^{-1}\omega T$

(c) $\sqrt{1 + \omega^2T^2}$, $\tan^{-1} - \omega T$ (2nd quadrant)

(d) $\omega T/\sqrt{1 + \omega^2T^2}$, $90° - \tan^{-1}\omega T$

(e) $\sqrt{\dfrac{1 + \omega^2T^2}{1 + 4\omega^2T^2}}$, $\tan^{-1}\omega T - \tan^{-1}2\omega T$

(f) $1/\sqrt{(1 + \omega^2T^2)(1 + 4\omega^2T^2)}$; $-\tan^{-1}\omega T - \tan^{-1}2\omega T$

9–4. $\dfrac{1}{1 - \omega^2T^2}$, $\tan^{-1}0$ (2nd quadrant)

9–5. $-\omega L$ and $\tan^{-1}\dfrac{-4\omega L}{4 - \omega^2L^2}$

9–6. $RK_e < 1$ time constant element
$RK_e = 1$ capacitance element
$RK_e > 1$ exothermic

9-7. $\alpha^2 L^2 = 0.29$ sec; Probably not.

9-8. 60%.

10-1. (a) $s = -1, -0.5, -0.33$ stable

      (b) $s = -3, 1 \pm i\sqrt{6}$ unstable

      (c) $s = -1,\quad -1,\quad 0.05\ (-1 \pm i\sqrt{3})$ stable

      (d) $s = 0, (-1 + i\sqrt{3})/2T$ unstable

10-3. $K_c = \left[1 + \left(\tan \dfrac{135}{n} \right)^2 \right]^{n/2}$

10-4. at $\omega T = 0.40$, $\phi = 135°$ (open loop), $K_c = 0.42$

Index